OFFICIAL SQA PAST PAPERS WITH ANSWERS

ADVANCED HIGHER

ENGLISH
2008-2011

Publisher's Note

We are delighted to bring you the 2011 Past Papers and you will see that we have changed the format from previous editions. As part of our environmental awareness strategy, we have attempted to make these new editions as sustainable as possible.

To do this, we have printed on white paper and bound the answer sections into the book. This not only allows us to use significantly less paper but we are also, for the first time, able to source all the materials from sustainable sources.

We hope you like the new editions and by purchasing this product, you are not only supporting an independent Scottish publishing company but you are also, in the International Year of Forests, not contributing to the destruction of the world's forests.

Thank you for your support and please see the following websites for more information to support the above statement –

www.fsc-uk.org

www.loveforests.com

© Scottish Qualifications Authority
All rights reserved. Copying prohibited. No part of this publication may be reproduced, stored in a retrieval system, or transmitted in any form or by any means, electronic, mechanical, photocopying, recording or otherwise.

First exam published in 2008.
Published by Bright Red Publishing Ltd, 6 Stafford Street, Edinburgh EH3 7AU
tel: 0131 220 5804 fax: 0131 220 6710 info@brightredpublishing.co.uk www.brightredpublishing.co.uk

ISBN 978-1-84948-230-1

A CIP Catalogue record for this book is available from the British Library.

Bright Red Publishing is grateful to the copyright holders, as credited on the final page of the Question Section, for permission to use their material. Every effort has been made to trace the copyright holders and to obtain their permission for the use of copyright material. Bright Red Publishing will be happy to receive information allowing us to rectify any error or omission in future editions.

ADVANCED HIGHER SQP

2008

[BLANK PAGE]

[C115/SQP308]

English Advanced Higher Specimen Question Paper for use in and after **2008**	Time: 1 hour 30 minutes **or** 3 hours	NATIONAL QUALIFICATIONS

> **Note:**   The questions in the Literary Study and Language Study sections of this paper reflect the new specified lists for use in and after session 2007–2008 and in and after the 2008 examination.

There are four sections in this paper.

Section 1—Literary Study	pages	2–10
Section 2—Language Study	pages	11–16
Section 3—Textual Analysis	pages	17–28
Section 4—Reading the Media	pages	29–31

Depending on the options you have chosen, you must answer **one** or **two** questions.

If you have submitted a Creative Writing folio, you must answer only **one** question.

Otherwise you must answer **two** questions.

If you are required to answer only **one question**

- it must be taken from **Section 1—Literary Study**
- you must leave the examination room **after 1 hour 30 minutes**.

If you are required to answer **two questions**

- your first must be taken from **Section 1—Literary Study**
- your second must be taken from **a different section**
- each answer must be written in **a separate answer booklet**
- the maximum time allowed for any question is **1 hour 30 minutes**.

You must identify each question you attempt by indicating clearly

- **the title of the section** from which the question has been taken
- **the number of the question** within that section.

You must also write inside the front cover of your Literary Study answer booklet

- **the topic** of your Specialist Study (Dissertation)
- **the texts** used in your Specialist Study (Dissertation).

SCOTTISH
QUALIFICATIONS
AUTHORITY
©

Section 1—Literary Study

This section is **mandatory** for all candidates.

You must answer **one question only** in this section.

DRAMA

1. Beckett

"The basic questions posed in Beckett's plays seem to be these: Who are we? What is the true nature of self? What does a human being mean when he says 'I?'."

How effectively, in your view, does Beckett address such questions in *Waiting for Godot* and in *Endgame*?

2. Byrne

"... brilliant social commentary ..."
"... biting satire ..."
"... a powerful blend of comedy and pathos ..."

Taking into account **one** or **more than one** of the above critical comments, outline your own response to *The Slab Boys Trilogy*.

3. Chekhov

"Chekhov knows what it is for people to yearn for self-realisation and self-fulfilment ... and knows the negative side of these ideals, where yearning produces only continuing frustration and pain."

What indications are there in the plays that Chekhov sees **more** in human life than yearning, frustration and pain?

4. Friel

"Friel's later plays deal with the inadequacy of language and move towards an exchange beyond rational thought, beyond language ..."

How far, in your view, does this assertion apply to *Translations* **and** to *Dancing at Lughnasa*?

5. Lindsay

Discuss the contribution of pageantry to *Ane Satyre of The Thrie Estaitis*.

6. Lochhead

"Liz Lochhead's principal dramatic talent is to find the ordinary in the apparently grand."

Discuss.

7. **Pinter**

Speaking of his plays, Pinter has said, "*We cannot understand other people; we cannot even understand ourselves; the truth of any situation is almost always beyond our grasp.*"

Discuss the relevance of this statement to Pinter's treatment of character and situation in **each** of the specified plays.

8. **Shakespeare**

EITHER

(a) ***Othello* and *Antony and Cleopatra***

"***Othello*** *is a simple domestic tragedy with a black male protagonist; the tragedy of **Antony and Cleopatra** derives from the clash of opposing worlds at a key moment of world history.*"

Discuss the nature of the tragedy of both plays in the light of this assertion.

OR

(b) ***The Winter's Tale* and *The Tempest***

Analyse the principal means by which Shakespeare dramatises the struggle between good and evil **either** in ***The Winter's Tale* or** in ***The Tempest* or** in **both** plays.

9. **Stoppard**

Read the following extract from ***Rosencrantz and Guildenstern are Dead*** and then answer the question that follows it:

	ROS:	[*At footlights*] How very intriguing! [*Turns*] I feel like a spectator—an appalling prospect. The only thing that makes it bearable is the irrational belief that somebody interesting will come on in a minute . . .
	GUIL:	See anyone?
5	ROS:	No. You?
	GUIL:	No. [*At footlights*] What a fine persecution—to be kept intrigued without ever quite being enlightened . . . [*Pause.*] We've had no practice.
	ROS:	We could play at questions.
	GUIL:	What good would that do?
10	ROS:	Practice!
	GUIL:	Statement! One-love.
	ROS:	Cheating!
	GUIL:	How?
	ROS:	I hadn't started yet.
15	GUIL:	Statement. Two-love.
	ROS:	Are you counting that?
	GUIL:	What?
	ROS:	Are you counting that?

	GUIL:	Foul! No repetitions. Three-love. First game to . . .
20	ROS:	I'm not going to play if you're going to be like that.
	GUIL:	Whose serve?
	ROS:	Hah?
	GUIL:	Foul! No grunts. Love-one.
	ROS:	Whose go?
25	GUIL:	Why?
	ROS:	Why not?
	GUIL:	What for?
	ROS:	Foul! No synonyms! One-all.
	GUIL:	What in God's name is going on?
30	ROS:	Foul! No rhetoric. Two-one.
	GUIL:	What does it all add up to?
	ROS:	Can't you guess?
	GUIL:	Were you addressing me?
	ROS:	Is there anyone else?
35	GUIL:	Who?
	ROS:	How would I know?
	GUIL:	Why do you ask?
	ROS:	Are you serious?
	GUIL:	Was that rhetoric?
40	ROS:	No.
	GUIL:	Statement! Two-all. Game point.
	ROS:	What's the matter with you today?
	GUIL:	When?
	ROS:	What?
45	GUIL:	Are you deaf?
	ROS:	Am I dead?
	GUIL:	Yes or no?
	ROS:	Is there a choice?
	GUIL:	Is there a God?
50	ROS:	Foul! No non sequiturs, three-two, one game all.
	GUIL:	[*Seriously*] What's your name?
	ROS:	What's yours?
	GUIL:	I asked first.
	ROS:	Statement. One-love.
55	GUIL:	What's your name when you're at home?
	ROS:	What's yours?
	GUIL:	When I'm at home?
	ROS:	Is it different at home?
	GUIL:	What home?
60	ROS:	Haven't you got one?
	GUIL:	Why do you ask?

	ROS:	What are you driving at?
	GUIL:	[*With emphasis*] What's your name?!
	ROS:	Repetition. Two-love. Match point to me.
65	GUIL:	[*Seizing him violently*] WHO DO YOU THINK YOU ARE?
	ROS:	Rhetoric! Game and match! [*Pause.*] Where's it going to end?
	GUIL:	That's the question.
	ROS:	It's all questions.
	GUIL:	Do you think it matters?
70	ROS:	Doesn't it matter to you?
	GUIL:	Why should it matter?
	ROS:	What does it matter why?
	GUIL:	[*Teasing gently*] Doesn't it matter why it matters?
	ROS:	[*Rounding on him*] What's the matter with you?
75		[*Pause.*]
	GUIL:	It doesn't matter.
	ROS:	[*Voice in the wilderness*] . . . What's the game?
	GUIL:	What are the rules?

How characteristic is this extract of Stoppard's dramatic approach, not only in *Rosencrantz and Guildenstern are Dead*, but also in *Arcadia*?

10. Wilde

To what extent, in your view, can Wilde's plays be considered to be critiques of Victorian values?

In your answer you should refer to all **three** of the specified texts.

11. Williams

Discuss Williams's treatment of loneliness in *Sweet Bird of Youth* and in *A Streetcar Named Desire*.

POETRY

12. Burns

EITHER

(a) Make a close comparative study of the poetic means by which, in **three** or **four** poems, Burns criticises aspects of the society of his day.

OR

(b) "*The typical Burns lyric is almost beyond criticism; it is transparent and artless. And yet it speaks of intense emotion, it is powerful, it resonates.*"

Account for the lasting emotional impact of a number of Burns's "transparent and artless" songs.

13. Chaucer

With reference to the *General Prologue* and to **either** or to **both** of the specified *Canterbury Tales*, illustrate what you consider to be the subtlety of Chaucer's characterisation.

14. Donne

"*It is a characteristic of the metaphysical poets that profound emotion stimulates their powers of intellectual analysis and argument.*"

Examine in detail the relationship between profound emotion and intellect in **three** or **four** poems by Donne.

15. Duffy

By making reference to both content and technique in a range of her poems, evaluate the extent to which Duffy could be termed "a poet for our times".

16. Heaney

Read the following poem from the sequence *Clearances* and answer the question that follows it.

> *In Memoriam M.K.H., 1911–1984*
>
> When all the others were away at Mass
> I was all hers as we peeled potatoes.
> They broke the silence, let fall one by one
> Like solder weeping off the soldering iron:
> 5 Cold comforts set between us, things to share
> Gleaming in a bucket of clean water.
> And again let fall. Little pleasant splashes
> From each other's work would bring us to our senses.
> So while the parish priest at her bedside
> 10 Went hammer and tongs at the prayers for the dying
> And some were responding and some crying
> I remembered her head bent towards my head,
> Her breath in mine, our fluent dipping knives --
> Never closer the whole rest of our lives.

It has been said that Heaney "*never allows elegy to sentimentalise actual, intractable human difficulty*".

How far is this statement true of **this** poem and of **two** or **three** other elegies on the death of friends or family members?

17. **Henryson**

    EITHER

    (a) "*I have pietie thou suld fall sic mischance.*"

         By what means does Henryson communicate his compassion for Cresseid and her plight?

    OR

    (b) What do you consider to be the principal poetic features of Henryson's *Morall Fabillis*?

18. **Keats**

    "*In **Ode to a Nightingale** Keats presents the speaker's engagement with the fluid music of the bird's song; in **Ode on a Grecian Urn** with the static immobility of sculpture.*"

    Make a comparative study of the poet's use of key images and symbols to express his principal thematic concerns in **both** of these poems.

19. **MacDiarmid**

    EITHER

    (a) Do you find *A Drunk Man Looks at the Thistle* a satisfying poetic unity?

    OR

    (b) Read the following poem and answer the questions that follow it.

    THE EEMIS STANE

    > I' the how-dumb-deid o' the cauld hairst nicht
    > The warl' like an eemis stane
    > Wags i' the lift;
    > An' my eerie memories fa'
    > 5 Like a yowdendrift.
    >
    > Like a yowdendrift so's a couldna read
    > The words cut oot i' the stane
    > Had the fug o' fame
    > An' history's hazelraw
    > 10 No' yirdit thaim.

    (i) Make a close critical appreciation of this poem.

    (ii) To what extent can this poem be taken as representative of the themes and techniques of MacDiarmid's lyrics?

20. Muir

Discuss in detail the means by which, in **three** or **four** poems, Muir explores the relationship between mankind and nature.

21. Plath

"*The reading of Sylvia Plath's poetry is a disturbing . . . even frightening experience.*"

How far has this been your experience of reading her poetry?

You should make detailed reference to **three** or **four** poems in your answer.

22. Yeats

Discuss the principal poetic means by which, in *Sailing to Byzantium* **and** in *Byzantium*, Yeats explores the relationship between nature and art.

PROSE FICTION

23. Atwood

"*Her female protagonists are forced to remake themselves, to achieve courage and self-reliance in their attitudes and relationships with others and with the world around them.*"

Make a close evaluative study of the characterisation of **either** Elaine **or** Grace in the light of this assertion.

24. Austen

Discuss the scope and function of irony in *Pride and Prejudice* and in *Persuasion*.

25. Dickens

Dickens has often been described as the most dramatic of our novelists.

Illustrate what you consider to be the essentially dramatic qualities of *Great Expectations* and *Hard Times*.

26. Fitzgerald

To what extent is Fitzgerald concerned with exposing the destructive power of wealth and materialism in *The Beautiful and Damned* and in *Tender is the Night*?

27. Galloway

How effectively does Galloway explore alienation in *The Trick is to Keep Breathing* and in *Foreign Parts*?

28. Gray

Gray has been described as "*a master of the playful nightmare*".

With reference to *Lanark* and *Poor Things*, discuss the validity of this description.

29. Hardy

"There are no innocent victims in Hardy's mature novels. What is innocent or fine is tragically linked with what is sentimental, blind, or self-injuring."

How far is this true of the central characters in *The Return of the Native* **and** *Tess of the d'Urbervilles?*

30. Hogg

Discuss the presentation of the duality of human nature in *The Private Memoirs and Confessions of a Justified Sinner* and in **one** of the specified short stories.

31. Joyce

Read the following extract from *A Portrait of the Artist as a Young Man* and then answer the question that follows it.

Publisher's note. In the original exam paper, an extract from the final few pages of chapter 4 of *A Portrait of the Artist as a Young Man* was supplied. However, due to copyright restrictions, we are unable to publish this extract and apologise for any inconvenience caused. We would therefore advise you to use a copy of the book alongside this question.

Comment on some of the literary and linguistic means by which Joyce makes Stephen's vision of the girl seem special.

Go on to discuss in some detail the significance of this episode in the novel as a whole.

32. Stevenson

Compare and contrast Stevenson's treatment of moral conflict in *The Master of Ballantrae* **and** in **two** of the specified short stories.

33. Waugh

". . . *no new mad thing brought to his notice could add a jot to the all-encompassing chaos that shrieked about his ears.*"

A Handful of Dust

". . . *man had deserted his post and the jungle was creeping back into its old strongholds.*"

Brideshead Revisited

To what extent can these two novels be regarded as elegies for the passing of a way of life?

PROSE NON-FICTION

34. "*The heart of any place is the relationships you have there. Geography is people.*"

(William McIlvanney)

Discuss any **two** of the specified texts in the light of this comment.

35. It has been suggested that we "*turn to autobiography to see how others have managed to secure their sense of a self*".

Examine the means by which a sense of the author's "self" has emerged from your reading of **one** or **more than one** of the specified autobiographies.

Section 2—Language Study

You must answer **one question only** in this section.

N.B. *This Specimen Paper contains only **one** question on each of the specified Language Study topics.*

*The actual examination paper will contain **two** questions on each topic.*

One (or even both) of these questions may be text-based—as in Question 4, Question 6 and Question 7 of this Specimen Paper.

TOPIC A —VARIETIES OF ENGLISH OR SCOTS

1. Describe the principal linguistic features of **one** particular variety of English **or** Scots you have studied and go on to discuss
   - who uses it
   - the contexts in which it is used
   - its relationship to other varieties of English or Scots.

TOPIC B—THE HISTORICAL DEVELOPMENT OF ENGLISH OR SCOTS

2. Show how **two** or **three** key historical events or movements or writers or texts have influenced the development of contemporary English **or** Scots.

TOPIC C—MULTILINGUALISM IN CONTEMPORARY SCOTLAND

3. What evidence is there in the conversation of contemporary Scottish multilingual speakers **either** of the structural and functional patterns associated with codeswitching **or** of the ongoing process of language shift?

TOPIC D—THE USE OF SCOTS IN CONTEMPORARY LITERATURE

4. Comment in detail on the linguistic characteristics of **two** of the following extracts.

Extract 1

"Gie's a bottle o vodka an twa o Eddie's peels," he spiered o a loon ower bi the kitchie. "I dinna ken fit's in Eddie's peels," the loon telt him. "They could be Smarties, or E's, or onythin."

"So?" quo Derek. "It's just fur a lauch. I'm gonna spike yon Laurie's punch, the wee scrubber. It'll be funny . . . wyte an see."

He cowped some o the punch frae Laurie's glaiss inno the bowl, syne tappit it up wi vodka an twa peels. Syne he gaed ower tae the CD player, tae pit on a rave album.

Dauncin made Laurie droothy. Efter twa tracks o the album, she teemed her glaissie ina wunner. Efter, she gied a bit grue. "It disna taste richt," quo she. Steven dippit the ladle inno the punch bowl, takkin a sup o the reid bree. "It tastes aaricht tae me," he replied. "Ach, forget it, an come up fur anither daunce."

Hauf ben the dance, she sterted tae feel shuggily. Ferlies bleared an furled. The room gaed tapsalteerie. Music skirled. Lichts grew skyrie. Her heid stooned. Her een played trickes. Faces aroon her ran an dreepit like meltin wax, like a widdendreme.

Her pulse quickened, her braith grew ticht, her moo dried. Fleg, set bricht reid roses in her chikks. "Fit's adee wi me Steven?" she cried. "Fit's adee? Ah'm needin hame. An'm wantin ma. Ah want tae lie doon . . ."

Wi a sough, she slippit doon tae the fleer, like an auld cloot. "Fit's gaun on here?" cried Sarah Broon. "Fit neep-heid spiked the puir quine's drink?"

Naebody spukk fur a meenit, syne a loon clypit.

"It's Derek's wyte . . . speir at him."

(from Leddy-Bird, Leddy-Bird by Sheena Blackhall)

Extract 2

"Hallo, Sandy," she smilit, as if it wis nae mair than ten days instead o ten years sin they'd seen ane anither. "A'm sorry A wisnae right wakin when A seen ee in the toon."

"Sorry?" He wis slow in the uptak.

"It wis yow, wis eet no, that gien iz a light? A wis walkin the dog in the High Street."

"Wis it yow, then?" He wis thunnerstruck. He'd seen his childhood sweethairt an thocht it wis some dreich, ill-faured, nameless woman he micht hae seen somewhaur afore. Whit wis wrang wi him?

"A'm no at my best early in the mornin," she chirmed.

May didnae jine in the joke. Her face wis wan an dowie.

"Sandy," she said. "Mum's gey hard up. She'll hev ti gaun ti the hospital."

"When did it happen?" Sandy wis bumbazed. He'd been up the hill for nae mair nor an oor.

"Oh, she can tak a bad turn gey quick," May said. "She's been hingin on jist ti see ee. Now ee're here, she's happy."

They gae intil the bedroom whaur his mother was white as the bedsheets unner the blue quilt.

"She's hed her pille, an the doctor'll gie her an injection. She's in nae pain. The ambulance'll no be lang."

Luikin doun at her face, he kent she wis deein. A terrible knot o dule fankled his kist, forcin oot his raith. Toronto seemed no jist thoosans, but millions o miles away fae him noo.

(from The Hamecomin by Sheila Douglas)

Extract 3

He goat the idea offy the telly. Heard oan the news this Chinese boy hud ritten 2000 characters oan a singul grainy rice. Well o coarse, he kidny rite Chinese an he dooted if thur wiz any rice in the hoose (unless mebby in the chinky cartons fi last nite). Butty liked the idea. Whit wi the asbestos fi wurk damajin his lungs an him oan the invalidity an that. Well, he hudda loatty time tay himsel an no much munny ti day anyhin wi it. Anny didny reckon he hud long tay go noo. It wid be nice, yi ken, jist tay day sumhin, tay leeve sumhin behind that peepul wid mebby notice. Jist a wee thing.

So wunce the bairnz wur offty skule an the wife wiz offty wurk, he cleared the kitchin table an hud a luke in the cubburds. Rite enuff, nay rice. He foond sum tattys but. Thottyd better scrub thum furst. So he did. Then he took thum back tay the table. He picked the smollist wun soze it wizny like he wiz cheatin too much, anny began tay rite aon it wi a byro. He stied ther aw day. Kept on gawn, rackiniz brains an straynin tay keepiz hand fi shakin.

Efter 7 oors o solid con-sen-tray-shun, he ran ooty space. Heed manijd tay rite 258 swayr wurds oan the wee tatty. He sat back tae huv a luke. Even tho heed scrubd it, it wiz still a bit durty-lukin an it wuz that fully ize yi kidny see the ritin very well. Bit still. He felt heed acheeved sumhin.

(from *A Wee Tatty* by Alison Kermack)

TOPIC E—LANGUAGE AND SOCIAL CONTEXT

5. *"People's perception of linguistic differences across social classes, genders or age-groups has more to do with their prejudices than with any substantial variations in vocabulary, grammar and pronunciation."*

How far do you agree?

TOPIC F—THE LINGUISTIC CHARACTERISTICS OF INFORMAL CONVERSATION

6. The following short text is an extract from a transcript of an informal interview with a father of two children (Stephen and Sally) about his attitudes to parenthood.

It contains the following transcription codes:
   { indicates overlapping speech
   (.) indicates minor pauses.

Written punctuation, such as full stops and commas, has been avoided.

Read the extract carefully and then answer the question that follows it.

INTERVIEWER: what about erm Stephen do you s

FATHER: {he comes to Aikido with me now

INTERVIEWER: oh yeh

FATHER: I try to er encourage him to do it (.)

                      I've tried the painting on 'em all

INTERVIEWER: yeh

FATHER:	tried to find if there's anything there you know
	anything that's been passed on (.)
	Sally's quite good (.) for her age like you know
INTERVIEWER:	mm
FATHER:	erm she seems to be able to put things in the right place (.)
	which is the main thing really (.)
	and er (.) I try and get them to do the things you know
	but (.) they sort of go their own way (.) you know

In what ways do you consider the linguistic characteristics of this extract to be typical of informal conversation?

In answering this question, you should make a detailed analysis of the lexical, grammatical, syntactical and structural features of the extract.

TOPIC G—THE LINGUISTIC CHARACTERISTICS OF POLITICAL COMMUNICATION

7. The following text has been transcribed from a televised party election broadcast made by the Conservative Party in the run-up to the 1997 General Election. At the time of the broadcast, the Conservative Party was the party of government, but Labour, the main opposition party, had a strong lead in the opinion polls.

    The broadcast presented viewers with a representation, set in the future, of what life would be like (in the opinion of the Conservative Party) under a future Labour government. In the representation, actors, using carefully scripted dialogue, took the role of unidentified speakers in everyday settings talking directly to camera.

    The transcript includes pauses, indicated by (.); and each spoken sentence or clause complex has been numbered [1,2,3 etc]. Material which has been difficult to transcribe is enclosed within parentheses: for example, (the). "Er" and "erm" are vocalised pause fillers. Written punctuation, such as commas and capital letters, has been avoided.

    Read the transcript carefully and then answer the question that follows it.

    CONSERVATIVE PARTY ELECTION BROADCAST: 1997

    Voice One:
    [1] she said (.) you don't know what it's like living under a Labour Government
    [2] you haven't experienced it
    [3] you're too young to remember (.)
    [4] and (.) you know I mean obviously that was true
    [5] but (.) I just thought well (.) I mean nobody believes their mother do they
    [6] you know I just wanted to (.) see it for myself (.) basically (.)
    [7] and (.) well I certainly have

Voice Two:
[8]   it's affected me personally much more than I would have expected (.)

[9]   erm I mean for example talk about unemployment figures

[10]   well it's just numbers

[11]   it doesn't mean anything to you

[12]   but when you actually when I actually lost my job a few weeks ago cos I was made redundant (.) erm then it's a whole different story

[13]   it was a difficult decision (.) cos I'd voted Tory before (.)

[14]   but (.) I thought they really had learned their lesson the Labour Party

[15]   erm (.) Tories had that slogan erm (.) Britain's booming don't let Labour mess it up (.)

[16]   and I thought (.) you know they won't do that Blair won't do that (.)

[17]   erm (.) but they have (.) hheh

Voice Three:
[18]   things were nice and calm (.)

[19]   I mean (.) how much damage can you do eh (.)

[20]   interest rates have gone up (.)

[21]   unemployment's rising (.)

[22]   I'm having to pay an extra thirty or forty pounds a week now because of them

Voice Four:
[23]   yeh well they('ve) had their chance

[24]   and they made a complete mess of it

[25]   me mortgage has gone through the roof

[26]   and they've put tax up (.) almost straight after they got in when they promised they wouldn't

[27]   you know don't worry they said (.) we're different

[28]   now I suppose it was our fault for trusting them in the first place

[29]   but basically we're back in recession aren't we

Voice Five:
[30]   my son is looking for a job for over a year now

[31]   he can't get one because of minimum wage

[32]   nobody can afford to take him on

[33]   I don't know how long he'll have to wait

Voice Six:
[34]   well (ob) it's democracy you know (.)

[35]   Tories had had their day

[36]   we thought maybe somebody else (.)

[37]   see what they've done

[38]   I mean it's just been a total downhill total downhill for three years

[39]   but what gets to me you see I went for it

[40]   we all went for it

[41]   we thought you know a change equals something better (.)

[42]   course it wasn't (.)

[43]   something heck of a lot worse

Voice Seven:

[44]   we voted Labour

[45]   and (.) you know like most people thought fresh blood you know (.)

[46]   er (.) and we believed all that stuff about (.) government running out of steam and sleaze

[47]   and (.) well (.) it seems the further we get into the Labour term the more it was just (.) change for change sake (.)

[48]   you know look at us now I mean weren't badly informed

[49]   we (.) most of us we (.) you know read decent newspapers

[50]   and we kept up with the news

[51]   but I mean we knew about we knew about erm the the great state the economy was in

[52]   and we knew about government's record on employment and inflation all that

[53]   but (.) well we knew it but I suppose we didn't value it

Voice Eight:

[54]   every time you open the newspaper there's more bad news things going wrong (.)

[55]   every time I go to the shops prices gone up again

[56]   inflation's just going through the roof (.)

Voice Nine:

[57]   so I had a good job (.) had a low mortgage (.)

[58]   and (the) inflation was low (.)

[59]   an(d) I was stupid enough to vote for Blair (.)

[60]   whew (.) those were the good days

[61]   d'you know I never thought I'd say that

Voice Ten:

[62]   I'm here in the future (.)

[63]   I know what it's like (.)

[64]   don't do this to Britain (.)

[65]   that's my advice

Make a detailed analysis of the above transcript, evaluating its effectiveness as a piece of political communication in terms of as many of the following as you think appropriate:

- its overall style and tone
- its orientation to audience
- the ways in which its discourse is structured and organised
- the effects created by the linguistic characteristics of its various "voices"
- any other aspects of it you consider significant.

Section 3—Textual Analysis

You must answer **one question only** in this section.

1. **Prose fiction (*Pages seventeen to nineteen*)**

   The following extract is the first part of the opening chapter of Elizabeth Gaskell's novel **Wives and Daughters** *(1866).*

   Read the extract carefully and then answer the question that follows it (Page twenty).

      To begin with the old rigmarole of childhood. In a country there was a shire, and in that shire there was a town, and in that town there was a house, and in that house there was a room, and in that room there was a bed, and in that bed there lay a little girl; wide awake and longing to get up, but not daring to do so for fear of the unseen
5   power in the next room; a certain Betty, whose slumbers must not be disturbed until six o'clock struck, when she wakened of herself 'as sure as clockwork', and left the household very little peace afterwards. It was a June morning, and early as it was, the room was full of sunny warmth and light.

      On the drawers opposite to the little white dimity bed in which Molly Gibson lay, was
10   a primitive kind of bonnet-stand on which was hung a bonnet, carefully covered over from any chance of dust with a large cotton handkerchief; of so heavy and serviceable a texture that if the thing underneath it had been a flimsy fabric of gauze and lace and flowers, it would have been altogether 'scomfished' (again to quote from Betty's vocabulary). But the bonnet was made of solid straw, and its only trimming was a
15   plain white ribbon put over the crown, and forming the strings. Still, there was a neat little quilling inside, every plait of which Molly knew, for had she not made it herself the evening before, with infinite pains? and was there not a little blue bow in this quilling, the very first bit of such finery Molly had ever had the prospect of wearing?

      Six o'clock now! the pleasant, brisk ringing of the church bells told that; calling every
20   one to their daily work, as they had done for hundreds of years. Up jumped Molly, and ran with her bare little feet across the room, and lifted off the handkerchief and saw once again the bonnet; the pledge of the gay bright day to come. Then to the window, and after some tugging she opened the casement, and let in the sweet morning air. The dew was already off the flowers in the garden below, but still rising
25   from the long hay-grass in the meadows directly beyond. At one side lay the little town of Hollingford, into a street of which Mr Gibson's front door opened; and delicate columns, and little puffs of smoke were already beginning to rise from many a cottage chimney where some housewife was already up, and preparing breakfast for the bread-winner of the family.

30   Molly Gibson saw all this, but all she thought about it was, 'Oh! it will be a fine day! I was afraid it never never would come; or that, if it ever came, it would be a rainy day!' Five-and-forty years ago, children's pleasures in a country town were very simple, and Molly had lived for twelve long years without the occurrence of any event so great as that which was now impending. Poor child! it is true that she had lost her
35   mother, which was a jar to the whole tenour of her life; but that was hardly an event in the sense referred to; and besides, she had been too young to be conscious of it at the time. The pleasure she was looking forward to to-day was her first share in a kind of annual festival in Hollingford.

The little straggling town faded away into country on one side close to the entrance-
40 lodge of a great park, where lived my Lord and Lady Cumnor: 'the earl' and 'the
countess', as they were always called by the inhabitants of the town; where a very
pretty amount of feudal feeling still lingered, and showed itself in a number of
simple ways, droll enough to look back upon, but serious matters of importance at
the time. It was before the passing of the Reform Bill, but a good deal of liberal talk
45 took place occasionally between two or three of the more enlightened freeholders
living in Hollingford; and there was a great Whig family in the county who, from time
to time, came forward and contested the election with the rival Tory family of
Cumnor.   One would have thought that the above-mentioned liberal-talking
inhabitants of Hollingford would have, at least, admitted the possibility of their
50 voting for the Hely-Harrison who represented their own opinions. But no such thing.
'The earl' was lord of the manor, and owner of much of the land on which
Hollingford was built; he and his household were fed, and doctored, and, to a certain
measure, clothed by the good people of the town; their fathers' grandfathers had
always voted for the eldest son of Cumnor Towers, and following in the ancestral
55 track, every man-jack in the place gave his vote to the liege lord, totally irrespective
of such chimeras as political opinion.

This was no unusual instance of the influence of the great landowners over their
humbler neighbours in those days before railways, and it was well for a place where
the powerful family, who thus overshadowed it, were of so respectable a character as
60 the Cumnors. They expected to be submitted to, and obeyed; the simple worship of
the townspeople was accepted by the earl and countess as a right; and they would
have stood still in amazement, and with a horrid memory of the French *sansculottes*
who were the bugbears of their youth, had any inhabitant of Hollingford ventured to
set his will or opinions in opposition to those of the earl's. But, yielded all that
65 obeisance, they did a good deal for the town, and were generally condescending, and
often thoughtful and kind in their treatment of their vassals. Lord Cumnor was a
forbearing landlord; putting his steward a little on one side sometimes, and taking the
reins into his own hands from time to time, much to the annoyance of the agent, who
was, in fact, too rich and independent to care greatly for preserving a post where his
70 decisions might any day be overturned by my lord's taking a fancy to go 'pottering'
(as the agent irreverently expressed it in the sanctuary of his own home), which,
being interpreted, meant that occasionally the earl asked his own questions of his
own tenants, and used his own eyes and ears in the management of the smaller details
of his property. But his tenants liked my lord all the better for this habit of his. Lord
75 Cumnor had certainly a little turn for gossip, which he contrived to combine with the
failing of personal intervention between the old land-steward and the tenantry. But,
then, the countess made up by her unapproachable dignity for this weakness of the
earl's. Once a year she was condescending. She and the ladies, her daughters, had set
up a school; not a school after the manner of schools now-a-days, where far better
80 intellectual teaching is given to the boys and girls of labourers and work-people than
often falls to the lot of their betters in worldly estate; but a school of the kind we
should call 'industrial', where girls were taught to sew beautifully, to be capital
housemaids, and pretty fair cooks, and, above all, to dress neatly in a kind of charity
uniform devised by the ladies of Cumnor Towers;—white caps, white tippets, check
85 aprons, blue gowns, and ready curtseys, and 'please, ma'ams', being *de rigueur*.

Now, as the countess was absent from the Towers for a considerable part of the year,
she was glad to enlist the sympathy of the Hollingford ladies in this school, with a
view to obtaining their aid as visitors during the many months that she and her

90 daughters were away. And the various unoccupied gentlewomen of the town responded to the call of their liege lady, and gave her their service as required; and along with it, a great deal of whispered and fussy admiration. 'How good of the countess! So like the dear countess—always thinking of others!' and so on; while it was always supposed that no strangers had seen Hollingford properly, unless they had been taken to the countess's school, and been duly impressed by the neat little pupils,

95 and the still neater needlework there to be inspected. In return, there was a day of honour set apart every summer, when with much gracious and stately hospitality, Lady Cumnor and her daughters received all the school visitors at the Towers, the great family mansion standing in aristocratic seclusion in the centre of the large park, of which one of the lodges was close to the little town. The order of this annual

100 festivity was this. About ten o'clock one of the Towers' carriages rolled through the lodge, and drove to different houses, wherein dwelt a woman to be honoured; picking them up by ones or twos, till the loaded carriage drove back again through the ready portals, bowled along the smooth tree-shaded road, and deposited its covey of smartly-dressed ladies on the great flight of steps leading to the ponderous doors of

105 Cumnor Towers. Back again to the town; another picking up of womenkind in their best clothes, and another return, and so on till the whole party were assembled either in the house or in the really beautiful gardens. After the proper amount of exhibition on the one part, and admiration on the other, had been done, there was a collation for the visitors, and some more display and admiration of the treasures inside the house.

110 Towards four o'clock, coffee was brought round; and this was a signal of the approaching carriage that was to take them back to their own homes; whither they returned with the happy consciousness of a well-spent day, but with some fatigue at the long-continued exertion of behaving their best, and talking on stilts for so many hours. Nor were Lady Cumnor and her daughters free from something of the same

115 self-approbation, and something, too, of the same fatigue; the fatigue that always follows on conscious efforts to behave as will best please the society you are in.

For the first time in her life, Molly Gibson was to be included among the guests at the Towers. She was much too young to be a visitor at the school, so it was not on that account that she was to go; but it had so happened that one day when Lord

120 Cumnor was on a 'pottering' expedition, he had met Mr Gibson, the doctor of the neighbourhood, coming out of the farm-house my lord was entering; and having some small question to ask the surgeon (Lord Cumnor seldom passed any one of his acquaintance without asking a question of some sort—not always attending to the answer; it was his mode of conversation), he accompanied Mr Gibson to the out-

125 building, to a ring in the wall of which the surgeon's horse was fastened. Molly was there too, sitting square and quiet on her rough little pony, waiting for her father. Her grave eyes opened large and wide at the close neighbourhood and evident advance of 'the earl'; for to her little imagination the grey-haired, red-faced, somewhat clumsy man, was a cross between an archangel and a king.

130 'Your daughter, eh, Gibson?—nice little girl, how old? Pony wants grooming though,' patting it as he talked. 'What's your name, my dear? He is sadly behindhand with his rent, as I was saying, but if he is really ill, I must see after Sheepshanks, who is a hardish man of business. What's his complaint? You'll come to our school-scrimmage on Thursday, little girl—what's-your-name? Mind you

135 send her, or bring her, Gibson; and just give a word to your groom, for I'm sure that pony was not singed last year, now, was he? Don't forget Thursday, little girl— what's-your-name?—it's a promise between us, is it not?' And off the earl trotted.

Question

How successfully in this first part of the opening chapter of the novel has Elizabeth Gaskell engaged the reader in her narrative?

In answering this question, you should examine the narrative and linguistic means by which she

- introduces the main characters
- creates an impression of the community of Hollingford
- encourages the reader to read further.

2. **Prose non-fiction** *(Pages twenty-one to twenty-two)*

The following extract is from **Moon Country** *(1996), an account by Simon Armitage and Glyn Maxwell of their travels in Iceland. In this extract, on the last day of their visit, Simon Armitage reflects upon the place and upon himself as a writer.*

Read the extract carefully and then answer the question that follows it (Page twenty-two).

I'm sitting way above the farm, high up at the back of the bay. This is Europe's most westerly point; set out from here and you finish up on the tip of Greenland or the coast of America, the way the Vikings did. It's two in the afternoon. A headland at either side curves out into the ocean, like two arms protecting everything within
5   reach—the track uncoiling out of the hills, the boulders and rocks in the middle distance, the strip of grassland that makes up the apron of the beach, then a mile or so of sand, and then the sea. I can count seven buildings down there, all of them huddled together under the hill for shelter, beginning with the farm itself, a rectangular white bungalow, connected to a three-storey dormitory or bunk-house
10 that looks like a lunatic asylum imported from Eastern Europe. Close by, there are two free-standing wooden sheds, a breeze-block garage, and a long-by-narrow greenhouse with polythene instead of glass, most of it shredded by the wind. And then there's the church. Anywhere else, it probably wouldn't be much more than a pigeon loft or a dovecote, but it does well for itself here, its miniature spire taking
15 whatever elements the Atlantic can throw at it, and the metal cross on top making its point. To the left, a chain-gang of telegraph poles lines up across the hillside, tethered by a single cable.

Glyn's gone wandering off along the coast, around the peninsula, out of sight. I've come inland, turning stones over and following paths that dry up after a couple of
20 hundred yards or go to ground like hunted animals. Behind me there's a steep valley leading to higher ground, but I think I've come far enough. I've lost all sense of perspective and scale this last week, and every time I look over my shoulder towards the horizon I can't decide if it's two miles away or twenty, if it's a walk I can make before dark or not. In and amongst the rocks I can make out a couple of rooks or
25 ravens or crows, scavenging on the ground, and another one just launching itself into mid-air, more like a pair of big black gloves in the shape of a bird than a bird itself, throwing a huge feathered shadow against the side of the hill.

This is the last day and these are the last hours. I should be writing but haven't managed a single word as yet, and I'm hovering with a pen about an inch above a
30 notebook, like the teleprinter in the old sports reports, waiting for the results to come in. On the opposite page, I can just about decipher a few scribbled lines from a piece I once wrote about my sister, and for some reason I'm more interested in that than in all this epic geography going on in the foreground. Maybe I'm just homesick at the moment, but even back at home I don't seem to be able to make anything of anything
35 until it's gone down in history, until it's been transmuted into memory. And the fact that I've written nothing doesn't surprise me, because I'm very slowly coming to the conclusion that all writing comes from the past, from childhood or innocence or naivety, and from loss, lost lives and lives gone by, even the loss of only eight, nine, ten, eleven seconds ago.

40 Maybe there's some unwritten rule of inversion, to do with distance, a rule that makes the spaceman think of his house, and a room in his house, and a box in that room, and inside that box his most treasured possession, a rule that makes him open

the box and look inside it, while orbiting the Earth. It's the rule that brings out the *there and then* from the *here and now*, a rule that I'm very much aware of this precise

45   minute, from the *here and now*, a rule that I'm very much aware of this precise minute, because this is the sort of place where you rub noses with yourself, catch up with yourself, meet yourself coming back the other way; this is the place where your own face looks back at you, where the days happen in real time, where every moment is simultaneous to itself, synchronised, and where all actions are true to life,

50   unimaginary, right now. This is actuality, the present, and according to the rule I have to get as far away from it as possible.

Question

How effectively does this piece of writing enable you to understand why Simon Armitage feels he has "to get as far away from it as possible"?

You should support your answer to this question by detailed reference to the language, imagery, structural features and patterning of ideas in the extract.

3. **Poetry (*Page twenty-three*)**

Read the poem **At Marsden Bay** *by Peter Reading and then answer the question that follows it.*

AT MARSDEN BAY

Arid hot desert stretched here in the early
Permian Period—sand dune fossils
are pressed to a brownish bottom stratum.
A tropical saline ocean next silted
5   calcium and magnesium carbonates
over this bed, forming rough Magnesian
Limestone cliffs on the ledges of which
Rissa tridactyla colonizes—
an estimated four thousand pairs
10   that shuttle like close-packed tracer bullets
against dark sky between nests and North Sea.
The call is a shrill "kit-e-wayke, kit-e-wayke",
also a low "uk-uk-uk" and a plaintive
"ee-e-e-eeh, ee-e-e-eeh".

15   Four boys about sixteen years old appear
in Army Stores combat-jackets, one wearing
a Balaclava with a long narrow eye-slit
(such as a rapist might find advantageous),
bleached denims rolled up to mid calf, tall laced boots
20   with bright polished toe-caps, pates cropped to stubble.
Three of the four are crosseyed, all are acned.
Communication consists of bellowing
simian ululations between
each other at only a few inches range:
25   "Gibbo, gerrofforal getcher yaffuga",
also a low "lookadembastabirdsmon".

Gibbo grubs up a Magnesian Limestone
chunk and assails the ledges at random,
biffing an incubating kittiwake
30   full in the sternum—an audible slap.
Wings facing the wrong way, it thumps at the cliff base,
twitching, half closing an eye. Gibbo seizes
a black webbed foot and swings the lump joyously
round and round his head. It emits
35   a strange wheezing noise. Gibbo's pustular pal
is smacked in the face by the flung poultry, yowls,
and lobs it out into the foam. The four
gambol euphoric like drunk chimps through rock pools.
Nests are dislodged, brown-blotched shells crepitate
40   exuding thick rich orange embryo goo
under a hail of hurled fossilized desert
two hundred and eighty million years old.

Question

How do you react to the poem *At Marsden Bay*?

In answering this question, you should consider the effectiveness of the poetic techniques used in the presentation of

- the place and the birds
- the boys and their actions.

4. Drama (*Pages twenty-four to twenty-eight*)

*The following extract is taken from the end of Arthur Miller's play **All My Sons** (1947). The play not only exposes the evils of wartime profiteering, but also confronts the ideological conflict between father and son, and its tragic consequences.*

The characters who appear in the extract are listed below, with some of Miller's own introductory description of them. Larry does not actually appear in the extract, but plays an important part in the play.

Joe Keller: *nearly sixty, "a business man, with the imprint of the machine-shop worker and boss still upon him . . . a man whose judgements must be dredged out of him". His firm manufactured parts for aircraft.*

Kate (**Mother** *in the script*): *early fifties, Keller's wife, "a woman of uncontrolled inspirations and an overwhelming capacity for love".*

Chris: *thirty-two, Keller's son, "capable of immense affection and loyalty".*

Larry: *Keller's other son, presumed dead, except by his mother, who cannot accept that he is dead.*

Ann: *twenty-six, "gentle, but despite herself capable of holding fast to what she knows". She was Larry's girl when he was alive—but is now in love with Chris.*

At this point in the play, Keller is struggling to face up to the fact that those close to him (Chris in particular) have discovered that he knowingly allowed his firm to fit faulty cylinder heads into fighter planes. As a direct consequence, many pilots died—but up to this point Keller has always managed to avoid taking responsibility. Having just had a showdown with Chris, who has recently found out about the cylinder heads, Keller is with Kate bemoaning the family's inability to understand that his business decisions were driven by the importance of providing for the family.

Keller and Kate are just outside the Keller house. Chris has run off in despair. The time is 2 a.m. Ann enters from the house. Her first words refer to Chris.

Read the extract carefully and then answer questions (a), (b) and (c) that follow it (Page twenty-seven).

	ANN:	Why do you stay up? I'll tell you when he comes.
	KELLER	[*rises, goes to her*]: You didn't eat supper, did you? [*To* MOTHER] Why don't you make her something?
	MOTHER:	Sure, I'll—
5	ANN:	Never mind, Kate, I'm all right. [*They are unable to speak to each other.*] There's something I want to tell you. [*She starts, then halts.*] I'm not going to do anything about it.
	MOTHER:	She's a good girl! [*To* KELLER] You see? She's a—
10	ANN:	I'll do nothing about Joe, but you're going to do something for me. [*Directly to* MOTHER] You made Chris feel guilty with me. Whether you wanted to or not, you've crippled him in front of me. I'd like you to tell him that Larry is dead and that you know it. You understand me? I'm not going out of here alone. There's no life for me that way. I want you to set him free. And then I promise you, everything will end, and we'll go away, and that's
15		all.
	KELLER:	You'll do that. You'll tell him.
	ANN:	I know what I'm asking, Kate. You had two sons. But you've only got one now.
	KELLER:	You'll tell him.

20	ANN:	And you've got to say it to him so he knows you mean it.
	MOTHER:	My dear, if the boy was dead, it wouldn't depend on my words to make Chris know it . . . The night he gets into your bed, his heart will dry up. Because he knows and you know. To his dying day he'll wait for his brother! No, my dear, no such thing. You're going in the morning and you're going alone. That's your life, that's your lonely life. [*She goes to porch, and starts in.*]
25		
	ANN:	Larry is dead, Kate.
	MOTHER	[*—she stops*]: Don't speak to me.
30	ANN:	I said he's dead. I know! He crashed off the coast of China November twenty-fifth! His engine didn't fail him. But he died, I know . . .
	MOTHER:	How did he die? You're lying to me. If you know, how did he die?
	ANN:	I loved him. You know I loved him. Would I have looked at anyone else if I wasn't sure? That's enough for you.
35	MOTHER	[*moving on her*]: What's enough for me? What're you talking about? [*She grasps* ANN's *wrists.*]
	ANN:	You're hurting my wrists.
	MOTHER:	What are you talking about! [*Pause. She stares at* ANN *a moment, then turns and goes to* KELLER.]
	ANN:	Joe, go in the house.
40	KELLER:	Why should I—
	ANN:	Please go.
	KELLER:	Lemme know when he comes. [KELLER *goes into house.*]
	MOTHER	[*as she sees* ANN *taking a letter from her pocket*]: What's that?
45	ANN:	Sit down. [MOTHER *moves left to chair, but does not sit.*] First you've got to understand. When I came, I didn't have any idea that Joe—I had nothing against him or you. I came to get married. I hoped . . . So I didn't bring this to hurt you. I thought I'd show it to you only if there was no other way to settle Larry in your mind.
	MOTHER:	Larry? [*Snatches letter from* ANN's *hand.*]
50	ANN:	He wrote it to me just before he—[MOTHER *opens and begins to read letter.*] I'm not trying to hurt you, Kate. You're making me do this, now remember you're—Remember. I've been so lonely, Kate . . . I can't leave here alone again. [*A long, low moan comes from* MOTHER's *throat as she reads.*] You made me show it to you. You wouldn't believe me. I told you a hundred times, why wouldn't you believe me!
55		
	MOTHER:	Oh, my God . . .
	ANN	[*with pity and fear*]: Kate, please, please . . .
	MOTHER:	My God, my God . . .
	ANN:	Kate, dear, I'm so sorry . . . I'm so sorry.
60		[CHRIS *enters from driveway. He seems exhausted.*]
	CHRIS:	What's the matter—?
	ANN:	Where were you? . . . You're all perspired. [MOTHER *doesn't move.*] Where were you?
	CHRIS:	Just drove around a little. I thought you'd be gone.
65	ANN:	Where do I go? I have nowhere to go.

CHRIS [*to* MOTHER]: Where's Dad?

ANN: Inside lying down.

CHRIS: Sit down, both of you. I'll say what there is to say.

MOTHER: I didn't hear the car . . .

70 CHRIS: I left it in the garage. Mother . . . I'm going away. There are a couple of firms in Cleveland, I think I can get a place. I mean, I'm going away for good. [*To* ANN *alone*] I know what you're thinking, Annie. It's true. I'm yellow. I was made yellow in this house because I suspected my father and I did nothing about it, but if I knew that night when I came home what I 75 know now, he'd be in the district attorney's office by this time, and I'd have brought him there. Now if I look at him, all I'm able to do is cry.

MOTHER: What are you talking about? What else can you do?

CHRIS: I could jail him! I could jail him, if I were human any more. But I'm like everybody else now. I'm practical now. You made me practical.

80 MOTHER: But you have to be.

CHRIS: The cats in that alley are practical, the bums who ran away when we were fighting were practical. Only the dead ones weren't practical. But now I'm practical, and I spit on myself. I'm going away. I'm going now.

ANN [*going up to him*]: I'm coming with you.

85 CHRIS: No, Ann.

ANN: Chris, I don't ask you to do anything about Joe.

CHRIS: You do, you do.

ANN: I swear I never will.

CHRIS: In your heart you always will.

90 ANN: Then do what you have to do!

CHRIS: Do what? What is there to do? I've looked all night for a reason to make him suffer.

ANN: There's reason, there's reason!

CHRIS: What? Do I raise the dead when I put him behind bars? Then what'll I do 95 it for? We used to shoot a man who acted like a dog, but honour was real there, you were protecting something. But here? This is the land of the great big dogs, you don't love a man here, you eat him! That's the principle; the only one we live by—it just happened to kill a few people this time, that's all. The world's that way, how can I take it out on him? What 100 sense does that make? This is a zoo, a zoo!

ANN [*to* MOTHER]: You know what he's got to do! Tell him!

MOTHER: Let him go.

ANN: I won't let him go. You'll tell him what he's got to do . . .

MOTHER: Annie!

105 ANN: Then I will!

[KELLER *enters from house.* CHRIS *sees him, goes down near arbour.*]

KELLER: What's the matter with you? I want to talk to you.

CHRIS: I've got nothing to say to you.

KELLER [*taking his arm*]: I want to talk to you!

110 CHRIS [*pulling violently away from him*]: Don't do that, Dad. I'm going to hurt you if you do that. There's nothing to say, so say it quick.

KELLER: Exactly what's the matter? What's the matter? You got too much money? Is that what bothers you?

CHRIS [*with an edge of sarcasm*]: It bothers me.

115 KELLER: If you can't get used to it, then throw it away. You hear me? Take every cent and give it to charity, throw it in the sewer. Does that settle it? In the sewer, that's all. You think I'm kidding? I'm tellin' you what to do, if it's dirty then burn it. It's your money, that's not my money. I'm a dead man, I'm an old dead man, nothing's mine. Well, talk to me! What do you want
120 to do!

CHRIS: It's not what I want to do. It's what you want to do.

KELLER: What should I want to do? [CHRIS *is silent.*] Jail? You want me to go to jail? If you want me to go, say so! Is that where I belong? Then tell me so! [*Slight pause.*] What's the matter, why can't you tell me? [*Furiously*]
125 You say everything else to me, say that! [*Slight pause.*] I'll tell you why you can't say it. Because you know I don't belong there. Because you know! [*With growing emphasis and passion, and a persistent tone of desperation*] Who worked for nothin' in that war? When they work for nothin', I'll work for nothin'. Did they ship a gun or a truck outa Detroit before they got
130 their price? Is that clean? It's dollars and cents, nickels and dimes; war and peace, it's nickles and dimes, what's clean? Half the goddam country is gotta go if I go! That's why you can't tell me.

CHRIS: That's exactly why.

KELLER: Then . . . why am *I* bad?

135 CHRIS: *I* know you're no worse than most men but I thought you were better. I never saw you as a man. I saw you as my father. [*Almost breaking*] I can't look at you this way, I can't look at myself!

[*He turns away, unable to face* KELLER. ANN *goes quickly to* MOTHER, *takes letter from her and starts for* CHRIS. MOTHER *instantly rushes to intercept her.*]

140 MOTHER: Give me that!

ANN: He's going to read it! [*She thrusts letter into* CHRIS's *hand.*] Larry. He wrote it to me the day he died.

KELLER: Larry!

MOTHER: Chris, it's not for you. [*He starts to read.*] Joe . . . go away . . .

145 KELLER [*mystified, frightened*]: Why'd she say, Larry, what—?

MOTHER [*desperately pushes him towards alley, glancing at* CHRIS]: Go to the street, Joe, go to the street! [*She comes down beside* KELLER.] Don't, Chris . . . [*Pleading from her whole soul*] Don't tell him.

CHRIS [*quietly*]: Three and one half years . . . talking, talking. Now you tell me
150 what you must do . . . This is how he died, now tell me where you belong.

KELLER [*pleading*]: Chris, a man can't be a Jesus in this world!

CHRIS: I know all about the world. I know the whole crap story. Now listen to this, and tell me what a man's got to be! [*Reads.*] 'My dear Ann: . . .' You listening? He wrote this the day he died. Listen, don't cry . . . Listen! 'My
155 dear Ann: It is impossible to put down the things I feel. But I've got to tell you something. Yesterday they flew in a load of papers from the States and I read about Dad and your father being convicted. I can't express myself. I can't tell you how I feel—I can't bear to live any more. Last night I circled the base for twenty minutes before I could bring myself in. How

160   could he have done that? Every day three or four men never come back and he sits back there doing business . . . I don't know how to tell you what I feel . . . I can't face anybody . . . I'm going out on a mission in a few minutes. They'll probably report me missing. If they do, I want you to know that you mustn't wait for me. I tell you, Ann, if I had him there now

165   I could kill him—' [KELLER *grabs letter from* CHRIS's *hand and reads it. After a long pause*] Now blame the world. Do you understand that letter?

KELLER   [*speaking almost inaudibly*]: I think I do. Get the car. I'll put on my jacket. [*He turns and starts slowly for the house.* MOTHER *rushes to intercept him.*]

MOTHER: Why are you going? You'll sleep, why are you going?

170 KELLER: I can't sleep here. I'll feel better if I go.

MOTHER: You're so foolish. Larry was your son too, wasn't he? You know he'd never tell you to do this.

KELLER   [*looking at the letter in his hand*]: Then what is this if it isn't telling me? Sure, he was my son. But I think to him they were all my sons. And I guess

175   they were, I guess they were. I'll be right down. [*Exits into house.*]

MOTHER   [*to* CHRIS, *with determination*]: You're not going to take him!

CHRIS: I'm taking him.

MOTHER: It's up to you, if you tell him to stay he'll stay. Go and tell him!

CHRIS: Nobody could stop him now.

180 MOTHER: You'll stop him! How long will he live in prison? Are you trying to kill him?

CHRIS   [*holding out letter*]: I thought you read this!

MOTHER   [*of Larry, the letter*]: The war is over! Didn't you hear? It's over!

CHRIS: Then what was Larry to you? A stone that fell into the water? It's not enough for him to be sorry. Larry didn't kill himself to make you and Dad sorry.

185 MOTHER: What more can we be!

CHRIS: You can be better! Once and for all you can know there's a universe of people outside and you're responsible to it, and unless you know that, you threw away your son because that's why he died.

    [*A shot is heard in the house. They stand frozen for a brief second.* CHRIS

190   *starts for porch, pauses a step, turns to* ANN. *He goes on into the house and* ANN *runs up driveway.* MOTHER *stands alone, transfixed.*]

MOTHER   [*softly, almost moaning*]: Joe . . . Joe . . . Joe . . . Joe . . .

    [CHRIS *comes out of the house, down to* MOTHER's *arms.*]

CHRIS   [*almost crying*]: Mother, I didn't mean to—

195 MOTHER: Don't dear. Don't take it on yourself. Forget now. Live. [CHRIS *stirs as if to answer.*] Shhh . . . [*She puts his arms down gently and moves towards porch.*] Shhh . . . [*As she reaches porch steps she begins sobbing.*]

CURTAIN

Questions

(a) Trace the role of Mother in the above extract from *All My Sons*.

(b) Discuss the dramatic significance of the letter in the extract.

(c) Imagine you are directing a performance of the play. How would you advise the actors to deliver their lines in the final part of the extract (from "MOTHER [*to* CHRIS, *with determination*]: You're not going to take him!" to the end)? You should base your answer on a detailed exploration of the language of lines 176 to 197.

Section 4—Reading the Media

*N.B. This section of the specimen paper contains only **one question** on each of the five specified media categories. The actual examination paper will contain **two questions** on each category.*

You must answer **one question only** in this section.

Category A—Film

1. *"Genre films allow little scope for innovation."*

   With reference to **at least two** films, from **one** or **more than one** genre, indicate to what extent you agree or disagree that genre inhibits innovation.

Category B—Television

2. *"Modern television drama equals cops, docs or frocks."* [crime, medical or costume]

   Discuss the potential of **one** or **more than one** of the above categories to provide the audience with challenging television drama. You should support your discussion with evidence drawn from **at least two** television dramas.

Category C—Radio

3. Discuss, with detailed reference to **a range** of programmes, how radio responds to the challenge of communicating purely through sound.

Category D—Print journalism

4. With reference to **a range** of examples from **one** or **more than one** newspaper, consider how journalists employ the devices of narrative and representation to create news stories out of real life events.

Category E—Advertising

5. In this question you are provided with **two** advertisements (*Pages thirty and thirty-one*).

   How effectively, in your judgement, do these advertisements convey the message(s) of the advertisers?

   You should support your answer to this question by making detailed reference to:
   - the use of technical codes (camera, lighting, black and white film, composition)
   - the cultural codes which establish the representation of each woman
   - how the written text (caption and copy) contributes to our interpretation of each woman
   - the cultural assumptions—and social expectations—that underlie both written text and image in each advertisement
   - any other features of the advertisements you consider significant.

[END OF QUESTION PAPER]

[BLANK PAGE]

ADVANCED HIGHER

2008

[BLANK PAGE]

X115/701

NATIONAL QUALIFICATIONS 2008	THURSDAY, 15 MAY 1.00 PM – 4.00 PM	ENGLISH ADVANCED HIGHER

There are four sections in this paper.

Section 1–Literary Study	pages	2 — 6
Section 2–Language Study	pages	7 —12
Section 3–Textual Analysis	pages	13 —33
Section 4–Reading the Media	pages	34 —35 (plus Insert)

Depending on the options you have chosen, you must answer **one** or **two** questions.

If you have submitted a Creative Writing folio, you must answer only **one** question.

Otherwise, you must answer **two** questions.

If you are required to answer only **one question**

- it must be taken from **Section 1–Literary Study**
- you must leave the examination room **after 1 hour 30 minutes**.

If you are required to answer **two questions**

- your first must be taken from **Section 1–Literary Study**
- your second must be taken from **a different section**
- each answer must be written in **a separate answer booklet**
- the maximum time allowed for any question is **1 hour 30 minutes**.

You must identify each question you attempt by indicating clearly

- **the title of the section** from which the question has been taken
- **the number of the question** within that section.

You must also write inside the front cover of your Literary Study answer booklet

- **the topic** of your Specialist Study (Dissertation)
- **the texts** used in your Specialist Study (Dissertation).

Section 1—Literary Study

This section is **mandatory** for all candidates.

You must answer **one question only** in this section.

DRAMA

1. **Beckett**

   "In a Beckett play, the audience is often tricked into laughter at situations which are bleak, anguished, desperate."

   Keeping this statement in mind, discuss the uses Beckett makes of humour in *Waiting for Godot* **and** in *Endgame*.

2. **Byrne**

   *"While the three plays exist as compelling works in their own right, **The Slab Boys Trilogy** is best appreciated as a dramatic whole."*

   How far do you agree?

3. **Chekhov**

   Discuss the dramatic means by which Chekhov gives significance to the effects of change in *The Cherry Orchard* **and** in *Uncle Vanya*.

4. **Friel**

   How effectively in *Translations* **and** in *Dancing at Lughnasa* does Friel dramatise the impact on the individual of large-scale social change?

5. **Lindsay**

   According to one critic, *"Lindsay's great play has endured the passage of time not for the strength of its themes or the universal appeal of its subject matter but for its grand theatrical effect."*

   Why, in your view, has *Ane Satyre of the Thrie Estaitis* endured the passage of time?

6. **Lochhead**

   Make a detailed study of the nature and function of characterisation in *Mary Queen of Scots Got Her Head Chopped Off*.

7. **Pinter**

   Discuss the means by which an atmosphere of menace is created in *The Homecoming*, *One for the Road* and *Mountain Language*.

8. **Shakespeare**

   EITHER

   (a) ***Othello* and *Antony and Cleopatra***

   "*In these plays, what finally gives the protagonists tragic stature is their power to transcend—even in defeat—the forces ranged against them.*"

   How far, in your view, does this assertion apply to *Othello* **or** to *Antony and Cleopatra* **or** to both plays?

   OR

   (b) ***The Winter's Tale* and *The Tempest***

   Make a detailed study of Shakespeare's treatment of reconciliation and forgiveness in *The Winter's Tale* **or** in *The Tempest* **or** in both plays.

9. **Stoppard**

   EITHER

   (a) Make a detailed study of the uses Stoppard makes of *Hamlet* in *Rosencrantz and Guildenstern are Dead*.

   OR

   (b) Make a detailed study of the dramatic effects created by Stoppard's juxtaposition of different historical periods in *Arcadia*.

10. **Wilde**

    With close reference to *The Importance of Being Earnest* **and** to **one** of the other specified plays, discuss the principal dramatic means by which Wilde explores some of the serious issues and conflicts that existed within Victorian society.

11. **Williams**

    "*For Williams, Time is the enemy: things go; things fade; things end. And yet, in the face of these certainties, there emerges a sense of nobility in his characters.*"

    Discuss *A Streetcar Named Desire* **and** *Sweet Bird of Youth* in the light of this statement.

POETRY

12. **Burns**

    EITHER

    (a) Discuss the techniques of satire employed by Burns in *The Twa Dogs* **and** in *The Holy Fair*.

    OR

    (b) "*Whether a love song or a political song or a melancholy song, what marks it out is Burns's mastery of tone and idiom to express deep feeling.*"

    Discuss a range of Burns's songs in the light of this statement.

13. **Chaucer**

Discuss the principal means by which, in the General Prologue **and** in **either** or **both** of the specified Tales, Chaucer exposes the *"sinne of Pryde"*.

14. **Donne**

"Donne's love poetry reveals an obsession with the darker aspects of love—its dissatisfactions, resentments and pains."

Discuss Donne's treatment of "the darker aspects of love" in **three** or **four** poems.

15. **Duffy**

Make a study of **three** or **four** poems in which Duffy makes use of dramatised voices—in monologue and/or in dialogue. In your study, you should examine the poetic techniques Duffy uses to create these voices and consider the effects achieved.

16. **Heaney**

Referring to the outbreak of sectarian violence in 1969 that led to The Troubles, Heaney wrote: *". . . from that moment the problems of poetry moved . . . to being a search for images and symbols adequate to our predicament."*

(*Feelings into Words*, 1974)

How successful, in your view, was Heaney in finding images and symbols to convey the effects of The Troubles on society and on the individual?

17. **Henryson**

EITHER

(*a*) Analyse the means by which Henryson explores Cresseid's spiritual and psychological development following her abandonment by Diomede.

OR

(*b*) *"Henryson is a master of the beast-fable: his mastery is based on the relationship he creates between the world of beasts and the world of men."*

Discuss the means by which, in **two** or **three** of the *Morall Fabillis*, Henryson creates a relationship between *"the world of beasts"* and *"the world of men"*.

18. **Keats**

*"Far from being merely an amiable parody of a medieval court romance, **The Eve of St Agnes** is a complex exploration of the relationship between poetic vision and real life."*

How far do you agree?

19. MacDiarmid

EITHER

(a) Discuss MacDiarmid's use of the symbol of the thistle in *A Drunk Man Looks at the Thistle*.

OR

(b) *"MacDiarmid's early poems constitute perfectly crafted examples of the capacity of the short lyric to address themes of profound significance."*

Discuss with reference to **three** or **four** of MacDiarmid's early lyrics.

20. Muir

Discuss the uses Muir makes of elements of religion in **three** or **four** poems.

21. Plath

Discuss the uses Plath makes of aspects of the natural world in **three** or **four** poems.

22. Yeats

Make a detailed study of *The Stolen Child*, *The Host of the Air* and *The Song of Wandering Aengus* in which you identify those aspects of theme and technique that characterise Yeats's early poetry.

PROSE FICTION

23. Atwood

Discuss Atwood's use of narrative voice in *Cat's Eye* **and** in *Alias Grace*.

24. Austen

"A key aspect of Austen's narrative technique is her use of contrast—in characters, in situations, in setting."

Discuss with reference to *Pride and Prejudice* **and** to *Persuasion*.

25. Dickens

Discuss Dickens's treatment of issues of social class in *Hard Times* **or** in *Great Expectations* **or** in both novels.

26. Fitzgerald

"In Fitzgerald's depiction of marriage, failure and waste are given a tragic grandeur of their own."

Keeping this statement in mind, make a detailed study of Fitzgerald's depiction of the relationship between Anthony and Gloria in *The Beautiful and Damned* **and** of the relationship between Dick and Nicole in *Tender is the Night*.

27. **Galloway**

Analyse and evaluate Galloway's treatment of gender issues in *The Trick is to Keep Breathing* **and** in *Foreign Parts*.

28. **Gray**

Discuss the function of the dual narrative in *Lanark*.

29. **Hardy**

EITHER

(a) Discuss the significance of Egdon Heath in *The Return of the Native*.

OR

(b) Blackmoor Vale . . . Talbothays . . . Flintcomb-Ash . . . Stonehenge.

Discuss the uses Hardy makes of these settings in *Tess of the D'Urbervilles*.

30. **Hogg**

Discuss Hogg's treatment of moral issues in *The Private Memoirs and Confessions of a Justified Sinner* **and** in **one** or **more than one** of the other specified texts.

31. **Joyce**

Discuss the fictional means by which Joyce explores the individual's response to the condition of Ireland in *A Portrait of the Artist as a Young Man* **and** in any **two** of the stories in *Dubliners*.

32. **Stevenson**

Discuss Stevenson's portrayal of evil in *The Master of Ballantrae* **and** in **one** or **two** of the specified short stories.

33. **Waugh**

Discuss the importance of religion in *A Handful of Dust* **and** in *Brideshead Revisited*.

PROSE NON-FICTION

34. How successful, in your view, are any **two** of the specified texts in their reconstruction of childhood experience?

35. How effectively do any **two** of the specified texts convey a sense of the distinctive identity of Scotland **or** of a part (or parts) of Scotland?

Section 2—Language Study

You must answer **one question only** in this section.

Topic A—Varieties of English or Scots

1. Describe and account for some of the principal features of the English **or** Scots used in a particular geographical area.

2. From your research, discuss how the use of a particular variety of English **or** Scots contributes to the creation of a distinct regional and/or cultural identity.

Topic B—The historical development of English or Scots

3. Which language do you consider to have had the greatest influence on the historical development of English **or** Scots? Give reasons for your decision.

4. Discuss some of the ways in which English **or** Scots words have changed over time. You may wish to consider some or all of the following:

   * changes in meaning
   * changes in word-formation patterns
   * the effects of borrowing from other languages
   * the effects of standardisation.

Topic C—Multilingualism in contemporary Scotland

5. In what ways can minority languages in Scotland be protected and encouraged?

6. What issues about multilingualism in contemporary Scotland are raised in the following extract from the novel *Bhudda Da* by Anne Donovan?

Ah started tae edge oot towards the door. Ah kind of wanted tae say ah was sorry too but didnae want tae interrupt. Then he started speakin even lower, in a language ah didnae understaund but mixed up wi English words and Nisha was answerin him in the same way. Ah stood just outside the room till Nisha came oot and shut the door behind her. She never said a word, just made a face, crossin her eyes and stickin her tongue oot at me. Ah managed tae haud in the laughter till we went through tae Nisha's room, then the two of us collapsed on the bed, gigglin.

"Ah don't believe it—he's never home at this time. Just ma luck."

"Was he really mad? What were yous sayin? Do yous speak Punjabi in the hoose then?"

"No really. When ma da was alive we used tae – he wanted us to speak the mother tongue – but Kamaljit and me just speak English maist of the time. Even my ma doesnae really speak it tae us a lot. But Gurpreet likes tae mix it in, especially when he's DJin. Thinks it makes him a bit different fae the others."

Nisha looked oot the windae. "It's rainin. Chuckin it doon. Don't want tae go oot in that."

"Naw."

"Fancy watchin a video?"

Topic D—The use of Scots in contemporary literature

For both questions on this topic, you are provided with three poems written in Scots: *SOS SOS* by Sheena Blackhall, *A Manifesto for MSPs* by James Robertson and *"The Corrie" Sailin* by John Law.

Read the poems carefully and then answer **either** Question 7 **or** Question 8.

7. Make a detailed study of the ways in which Scots is used in any **two** or in all **three** of the poems.

    In your study, you should consider features such as vocabulary, grammar, orthography, implied pronunciation.

8. Compare the use of Scots in any **one** of the poems provided with the use of Scots in the work of **one** other writer you have studied.

SOS SOS

SOS SOS I am a phone box in distress!
Jeannie Murphy's quine wis greetin,
Said she catched her boyfreen cheatin.
Big Joe Christie's giro's tint,
Phoned the Broo tae say he's skint.
Auld Ma Sangster's neebor telt her
Vandals smashed the new bus shelter.
Jocky Todd is stottin fu,
Baxter's laddie's sniffin glue.

SOS SOS I am a phone box in distress!
If the news I gie is bad,
Ten tae wan the fowk get mad,
And they catch me by the lug,
Gie ma wires and heid a rug.
Tak me Lord, frae cooncil scheme
Tae be a phone box on the meen!

A Manifesto for MSPs

Dinna be glaikit, dinna be ower smert,
dinna craw croose, dinna be unco blate,
dinna breenge in, dinna be ayewis late,
dinna steek yer lugs, dinna steek yer hert.
Dinna be sleekit, dinna be a sook,
dinna creesh nae loof for future favour,
dinna swick nor swither, hash nor haiver,
dinna be soor o face, and dinna jouk.
Open yer airms and minds tae folk in need,
hain frae fylin and skaith the land and sea,
tak tent o justice and the commonweal,
ding doon hypocrisy, wanthrift and greed,
heeze up the banner o humanity,
seek oot the truth and tae the truth be leal.

"The Corrie" Sailin
(Owreset frae Siubhal a' Choire, bi George Campbell Hay)

Up an awa oot wi us on the green sea machairs liftit
an we pit past dour Garvel o the gurlin storms –
lowps on us syne a sair blast wast bi sooth, an hard rain.
Up wi her heid, prow fornent cauld wave-heids
stoondin an stunnin, a slim dark lassie,
up wi her sang an surgin forrit.

She streikit her lee sheet ticht as steel
she streikit her hainch til the thies o the brekkers
she streikit her gait til the gait o the ocean
she gaed dunt wi her gunnel gin yaw
an dunt wi the seam of her shouther gaed she
an ryvit the wave wi her beak at the pitch.

Come Eilean Aoidh she raired oot joyfu
Ardlamont haerd her prood bellin
bi Inchmarnock she crooned a douce air.
Oorsels wappit in her smeik – smoorit-nane –
that stang in oor een frae the ram-stam o her
in a spelder o speindrift an saut spray
an nocht cuid we hear but the pulse o her pechin.

Topic E—Language and social context

9. Why is knowledge of the social context of language use important for our understanding of linguistic variation?

10. Using evidence from your own reading and research, illustrate some of the ways in which studies of language and social context reveal people's attitudes towards language variation.

[Turn over

Topic F—The linguistic characteristics of informal conversation

11. Discuss some of the functions of interruptions in informal conversation.

12. For this question, you are provided with an extract from a transcript of an informal conversation between three adolescent males, Andrew, Adrian and Mashuk, and two anonymous females, Anon F and Anon F2, who are discussing some homework they have to do.

    Read the extract carefully and then answer the question that follows it.

Transcription Key:

The lines have been numbered individually.

[overlapping turns
(.)   pause of less than one second
(   )   speech inaudible
(text)   speech hard to discern: the analyst's guess is provided as text, as in (ished) in line 9

Extract

```
 1  Anon F:    what lesson have we got last
 2  Andrew:    ma ⌈ ths
 3  Adrian:       ⌊ we got maths
 4  Anon F:    oh cor
 5  Andrew:    the assignment
 6  Anon F:    I know but um- I haven't finished my- task one yet
 7  Andrew:    ain't you
 8  Anon F:    no
 9  Andrew:    I ain't fin(ished) my task four
10  Anon F:    I ain't (started on) task one and (     ) two  (I
11             haven't finished) task three and I havent done task
12             four
13  Mashuk:    ain't you done none of the tasks
14  Anon F:    no ⌈ no we've got 'em but I ain't done 'em
15  Adrian:       ⌊ I've done all of 'em I've done all of 'em
16             ⌈ I'm on task six
17  Mashuk:    ⌊ have you got 'em in rough
18  Anon F:    yeh- no (.) I ain't done anything
19  Anon F2:   I've done it in rough
20  Mashuk:    when does it have to be in by this-
21             ⌈ this Monday init
22  Anon F2:   ⌊ Monday
```

(Source: Rampton, Ben (1995) *Crossing: language and ethnicity among adolescents*. London: Longman. Pages 210–211.)

To what extent do you consider the linguistic characteristics of this exchange to be typical of informal conversation?

Topic G—The linguistic characteristics of political communication

13. Below is a transcript of part of President George W. Bush's State of the Union address to the American Congress in 2002. For ease of reference, the paragraphs have been numbered.

   Make a detailed analysis of the linguistic characteristics of political communication evident in this speech. In your analysis, you should examine as many of the following as you consider appropriate:

   - the degree of formality
   - the choice of vocabulary
   - grammatical complexity
   - the use of figurative language.

[1] Our nation will continue to be steadfast, and patient, and persistent, in the pursuit of two great objectives. First, we will shut down terrorist camps, disrupt terrorist plans and bring terrorists to justice. And second, we must prevent the terrorists and regimes who seek chemical, biological or nuclear weapons from threatening the United States and the world.

[2] Our military has put the terror training camps of Afghanistan out of business, yet camps still exist in at least a dozen countries. A terrorist underworld – including groups like Hamas, Hezbollah, Islamic Jihad and Jaish-i-Mohammed – operates in remote jungles and deserts, and hides in the centres of large cities.

[3] While the most visible military action is in Afghanistan, America is acting elsewhere. We now have troops in the Philippines helping to train that country's armed forces to go after terrorist cells that have executed an American and still hold hostages. Our soldiers, working with the Bosnian government, seized terrorists who were plotting to bomb our embassy. Our Navy is patrolling the coast of Africa to block the shipment of weapons and the establishment of terrorist camps in Somalia. My hope is that all nations will heed our call and eliminate the terrorist parasites who threaten their countries and our own.

[4] Many nations are acting forcefully. Pakistan is now cracking down on terror, and I admire the strong leadership of President Musharraf. But some governments will be timid in the face of terror. And make no mistake about it: if they do not act, America will.

[5] Our second goal is to prevent regimes that sponsor terror from threatening America or our friends and allies with weapons of mass destruction. Some of these regimes have been pretty quiet since September 11, but we know their true nature. North Korea is a regime arming with missiles and weapons of mass destruction, while starving its citizens. Iran aggressively pursues these weapons and exports terror, while an unelected few repress the Iranian people's hope for freedom. Iraq continues to flaunt its hostility toward America and to support terror. The Iraqi regime has plotted to develop anthrax and nerve gas and nuclear weapons for over a decade. This is a regime that has already used poison gas to murder thousands of its own citizens, leaving the bodies of mothers huddled over their dead children. This is a regime that agreed to international inspections then kicked out the inspectors. This is a regime that has something to hide from the civilized world.

[6] States like these, and their terrorist allies, constitute an axis of evil, arming to threaten the peace of the world. By seeking weapons of mass destruction, these regimes pose a grave and growing danger. They could provide these arms to terrorists, giving them the means to match their hatred. They could attack our allies or attempt to blackmail the United States. In any of these cases, the price of indifference would be catastrophic.

14. David Crystal has suggested that political debate is conducted in "a style of language which is at times opaque, inspecific, or empty". Does your own reading and research suggest that this is true of political communication generally?

Justify your answer.

Section 3—Textual Analysis

You must answer **one question only** in this section.

1. **Prose fiction [*Pages thirteen to nineteen*]**

Read carefully the short story **Soldier's Home** *(1939) by Ernest Hemingway and then answer the question that follows it (Page nineteen).*

KREBS went to the war from a Methodist college in Kansas. There is a picture which shows him among his fraternity brothers, all of them wearing exactly the same height and style collar. He enlisted in the Marines in 1917 and did not return to the United States until the second division returned from the Rhine in the summer of
5   1919.

There is a picture which shows him on the Rhine with two German girls and another corporal. Krebs and the corporal look too big for their uniforms. The German girls are not beautiful. The Rhine does not show in the picture.

By the time Krebs returned to his home town in Oklahoma the greeting of heroes
10   was over. He came back much too late. The men from the town who had been drafted had all been welcomed elaborately on their return. There had been a great deal of hysteria. Now the reaction had set in. People seemed to think it was rather ridiculous for Krebs to be getting back so late, years after the war was over.

At first Krebs, who had been at Belleau Wood, Soissons, the Champagne, St
15   Mihiel, and in the Argonne, did not want to talk about the war at all. Later he felt the need to talk but no one wanted to hear about it. His town had heard too many atrocity stories to be thrilled by actualities. Krebs found that to be listened to at all he had to lie, and after he had done this twice he, too, had a reaction against the war and against talking about it. A distaste for everything that had happened to him in the war set in
20   because of the lies he had told. All of the times that had been able to make him feel cool and clear inside himself when he thought of them; the times so long back when he had done the one thing, the only thing for a man to do, easily and naturally, when he might have done something else, now lost their cool, valuable quality and then were lost themselves.

25   His lies were quite unimportant lies and consisted in attributing to himself things other men had seen, done, or heard of, and stating as facts certain apocryphal incidents familiar to all soldiers. Even his lies were not sensational at the pool-room. His acquaintances who had heard detailed accounts of German women found chained to machine guns in the Argonne forest and who could not comprehend, or were barred by
30   their patriotism from interest in, any German machine-gunners who were not chained, were not thrilled by his stories.

Krebs acquired the nausea in regard to experience that is the result of untruth or exaggeration, and when he occasionally met another man who had really been a soldier and they talked a few minutes in the dressing-room at a dance he fell into the easy pose
35   of the old soldier among other soldiers: that he had been badly, sickeningly frightened all the time. In this way he lost everything.

[Turn over

During this time, it was late summer, he was sleeping late in bed, getting up to walk down town to the library to get a book, eating lunch at home, reading on the front porch until he became bored, and then walking down through the town to spend the
40 hottest hours of the day in the cool dark of the pool-room. He loved to play pool.

In the evening he practised on his clarinet, strolled down town, read, and went to bed. He was still a hero to his two young sisters. His mother would have given him breakfast in bed if he had wanted it. She often came in when he was in bed and asked him to tell her about the war, but her attention always wandered. His father was non-
45 committal.

Before Krebs went away to the war he had never been allowed to drive the family motor-car. His father was in the real-estate business and always wanted the car to be at his command when he required it to take clients out into the country to show them a piece of farm property. The car always stood outside the First National Bank building
50 where his father had an office on the second floor. Now, after the war, it was still the same car.

Nothing was changed in the town except that the young girls had grown up. But they lived in such a complicated world of already defined alliances and shifting feuds that Krebs did not feel the energy or the courage to break into it. He liked to look at
55 them, though. There were so many good-looking young girls. Most of them had their hair cut short. When he went away only little girls wore their hair like that or girls that were fast. They all wore sweaters and shirt waists with round Dutch collars. It was a pattern. He liked to look at them from the front porch as they walked on the other side of the street. He liked to watch them walking under the shade of the trees. He liked
60 the round Dutch collars above their sweaters. He liked their silk stockings and flat shoes. He liked their bobbed hair and the way they walked.

When he was in town their appeal to him was not very strong. He did not like them when he saw them in the Greek's ice-cream parlour. He did not want them themselves really. They were too complicated. There was something else. Vaguely he wanted a
65 girl but he did not want to have to work to get her. He would have liked to have a girl but he did not want to have to spend a long time getting her. He did not want to get into the intrigue and the politics. He did not want to have to do any courting. He did not want to tell any more lies. It wasn't worth it.

He did not want any consequences. He did not want any consequences ever again.
70 He wanted to live along without consequences. Besides he did not really need a girl. The army had taught him that. It was all right to pose as though you had to have a girl. Nearly everybody did that. But it wasn't true. You did not need a girl. That was the funny thing. First a fellow boasted how girls meant nothing to him, then a fellow boasted that he could not get along without girls, that he had to have them all the time,
75 that he could not go to sleep without them.

That was all a lie. It was all a lie both ways. You did not need a girl unless you thought about them. He learned that in the army. Then sooner or later you always got one. When you were really ripe for a girl you always got one. You did not have to think about it. Sooner or later it would come. He had learned that in the army.

80   Now he would have liked a girl if she had come to him and not wanted to talk. But here at home it was all too complicated. He knew he could never get through it all again. It was not worth the trouble. That was the thing about French girls and German girls. There was not all this talking. You couldn't talk much and you did not need to talk. It was simple and you were friends. He thought about France and then
85 he began to think about Germany. On the whole he had liked Germany better. He did not want to leave Germany. He did not want to come home. Still, he had come home. He sat on the front porch.

He liked the girls that were walking along the other side of the street. He liked the look of them much better than the French girls or the German girls. But the world
90 they were in was not the world he was in. He would like to have one of them. But it was not worth it. They were such a nice pattern. He liked the pattern. It was exciting. But he would not go through all the talking. He did not want one badly enough. He liked to look at them all, though. It was not worth it. Not now when things were getting good again.

95   He sat there on the porch reading a book on the war. It was a history and he was reading about all the engagements he had been in. It was the most interesting reading he had ever done. He wished there were more maps. He looked forward with a good feeling to reading all the really good histories when they would come out with good detail maps. Now he was really learning about the war. He had been a good soldier.
100 That made a difference.

One morning after he had been home about a month his mother came into his bedroom and sat on the bed. She smoothed her apron.

"I had a talk with your father last night, Harold," she said, "and he is willing for you to take the car out in the evenings."

105 "Yeah?" said Krebs, who was not fully awake. "Take the car out? Yeah?"

"Yes. Your father has felt for some time that you should be able to take the car out in the evenings whenever you wished, but we only talked it over last night."

"I'll bet you made him," Krebs said.

"No. It was your father's suggestion that we talk the matter over."

110 "Yeah. I'll bet you made him," Krebs sat up in bed.

"Will you come down to breakfast, Harold?" his mother said.

"As soon as I get my clothes on," Krebs said.

His mother went out of the room and he could hear her frying something downstairs while he washed, shaved, and dressed to go down into the dining-room for
115 breakfast. While he was eating breakfast his sister brought in the mail.

"Well, Hare," she said. "You old sleepy-head. What do you ever get up for?"

Krebs looked at her. He liked her. She was his best sister.

"Have you got the paper?" he asked.

120 She handed him the *Kansas City Star* and he shucked off its brown wrapper and opened it to the sporting page. He folded the *Star* open and propped it against the water pitcher with his cereal dish to steady it, so he could read while he ate.

"Harold," his mother stood in the kitchen doorway, "Harold, please don't muss up the paper. Your father can't read his *Star* if it's been mussed."

"I won't muss it," Krebs said.

125 His sister sat down at the table and watched him while he read.

"We're playing indoor over at school this afternoon," she said. "I'm going to pitch."

"Good," said Krebs. "How's the old wing?"

"I can pitch better than lots of the boys. I tell them all you taught me. The other 130 girls aren't much good."

"Yeah?" said Krebs.

"I tell them all you're my beau. Aren't you my beau, Hare?"

"You bet."

"Couldn't your brother really be your beau just because he's your brother?"

135 "I don't know."

"Sure you know. Couldn't you be my beau, Hare, if I was old enough and if you wanted to?"

"Sure. You're my girl now."

"Am I really your girl?"

140 "Sure."

"Do you love me?"

"Uh, huh."

"Will you love me always?"

"Sure."

145 "Will you come and watch me play indoor?"

"Maybe."

"Aw, Hare, you don't love me. If you loved me, you'd want to come over and watch me play indoor."

Krebs's mother came into the dining-room from the kitchen. She carried a plate of
150 two fried eggs and some crisp bacon on it and a plate of buckwheat cakes.

"You run along, Helen," she said. "I want to talk to Harold."

She put the eggs and bacon down in front of him and brought in a jug of maple
syrup for the buckwheat cakes. Then she sat down across the table from Krebs.

"I wish you'd put down the paper a minute, Harold," she said.

155 Krebs took down the paper and folded it.

"Have you decided what you are going to do yet, Harold?" his mother said, taking
off her glasses.

"No," said Krebs.

"Don't you think it's about time?" His mother did not say this in a mean way. She
160 seemed worried.

"I hadn't thought about it," Krebs said.

"God has some work for everyone to do," his mother said. "There can be no idle
hands in His Kingdom."

"I'm not in His Kingdom," Krebs said.

165 "We are all of us in His Kingdom."

Krebs felt embarrassed and resentful as always.

"I've worried about you so much, Harold," his mother went on. "I know the
temptations you must have been exposed to. I know how weak men are. I know what
your own dear grandfather, my own father, told us about the Civil War, and I have
170 prayed for you. I pray for you all day long, Harold."

Krebs looked at the bacon fat hardening on his plate.

"Your father is worried, too," his mother went on. "He thinks you have lost your
ambition, that you haven't got a definite aim in life. Charley Simmons, who is just
your age, has a good job and is going to be married. The boys are all settling down;
175 they're all determined to get somewhere; you can see that boys like Charley Simmons
are on their way to being really a credit to the community."

Krebs said nothing.

"Don't look that way, Harold," his mother said. "You know we love you and I want
to tell you for your own good how matters stand. Your father does not want to hamper
180 your freedom. He thinks you should be allowed to drive the car. If you want to take
some of the nice girls out riding with you, we are only too pleased. We want you to
enjoy yourself. But you are going to have to settle down to work, Harold. Your father
doesn't care what you start in at. All work is honourable as he says. But you've got to
make a start at something. He asked me to speak to you this morning and then you can
185 stop in and see him at his office."

"Is that all?" Krebs said.

"Yes. Don't you love your mother, dear boy?"

"No," Krebs said.

His mother looked at him across the table. Her eyes were shiny. She started crying.

190   "I don't love anybody," Krebs said.

It wasn't any good. He couldn't tell her, he couldn't make her see it. It was silly to have said it. He had only hurt her. He went over and took hold of her arm. She was crying with her head in her hands.

"I didn't mean it," he said. "I was just angry at something. I didn't mean I didn't
195 love you."

His mother went on crying. Krebs put his arm on her shoulder.

"Can't you believe me, mother?"

His mother shook her head.

"Please, please, mother. Please believe me."

200   "All right," his mother said chokily. She looked up at him. "I believe you, Harold."

Krebs kissed her hair. She put her face up to him.

"I'm your mother," she said. "I held you next to my heart when you were a tiny
baby."

Krebs felt sick and vaguely nauseated.

205   "I know, Mummy," he said. "I'll try to be a good boy for you."

"Would you kneel and pray with me, Harold?" his mother asked.

They knelt down beside the dining-room table and Krebs's mother prayed.

"Now, you pray, Harold," she said.

"I can't," Krebs said.

210   "Try, Harold."

"I can't."

"Do you want me to pray for you?"

"Yes."

So his mother prayed for him and then they stood up and Krebs kissed his mother
215 and went out of the house. He had tried so to keep his life from being complicated.
Still, none of it had touched him. He had felt sorry for his mother and she had made
him lie. He would go to Kansas City and get a job and she would feel all right about it.
There would be one more scene maybe before he went away. He would not go down to
his father's office. He would miss that one. He wanted his life to go smoothly. It had
220 just gotten going that way. Well, that was all over now, anyway. He would go over to
the schoolyard and watch Helen play indoor baseball.

Question

In what ways in this short story does Hemingway explore the state of mind of the soldier
returned from war?

2. **Prose non-fiction [*Pages nineteen to twenty-three*]**

*Read carefully **The Old Silk Route** (1989) by Colin Thubron and then answer the
question that follows it (Page twenty-three).*

The trees were neither living nor dead: a Grimm forest of willows convulsed by
vanished winds. Their roots sank so deep that they found moisture which never
reached the surface, but the thinning sap had desiccated their leaves, and their bark had
loosened and split. Behind them a grey piedmont gravel, pushed down from the
5 Tianshan snows, was smeared across hundreds of square miles of sand. In front, the
true desert began.

Our spirits rose, as if the weight of eastern China, which lay far behind us, was
suddenly lifted. For a moment, I think, my companions too wanted to be alone. As for
me, solitude seemed the natural condition of travel. Alone, I was at once more
10 vulnerable and more sensitized, and even China appeared no longer precisely a strange
land. I was just a stranger in it, my identity thinned. And this solitude carried an
inner excitement, which has been perfectly distinct to me since childhood.

But now the company of my own people—a television camera team—filled me with
misgiving. In a film, the lone traveller's windfalls—the chance intimacies and
15 impulses—are gone. Solitude can only be recreated. Yet our film aimed to record the
Chinese Silk Road through my eyes, and I nursed a fantasy that our journey would
somehow bifurcate. I would experience it, and they would shoot it. The two processes
could be decently separated, just as the writing of a travel book is separate from the
journey it records.

20 Such a daydream must have belonged to a time of innocence twenty-five years
before, when I made freelance documentaries alone, wandering about Morocco and
Japan with a cine-camera and a tape-recorder slung over my back. The films' ideas,
script, shooting had all been mine, and their technical naivety had been balanced, I
suppose, by some raw freshness.

25 But now I was only the visual tip of a corporate iceberg. Behind me trudged a
two-man camera crew, a sound-recordist, the director, his assistant, a Mandarin
interpreter, a Turkic interpreter, two camel-drivers and seven camels loaded with
cameras, tripods and stock-boxes.

Yet for the screen we were fabricating solitude.

30   We journeyed in the unnatural silence of huge beasts treading in softness. The wind had dropped to nothing. The camels' hooves left dim circles in the powdery earth. Once or twice we crossed the tracks of intermittent rivers, now dry. Their starved reeds splintered at our touch; our feet crunched through their beds. Then the forest gave way to stunted red willows until even these had reverted to dust—ancient-
35 looking mounds of roots and crumbled wood littered over the sand.

       If I had charted the most landlocked spot on earth, the arms of my compass would have intersected here, in China's far north-west. Its heart is a howling wilderness, 600 miles wide, where the winds have buried and mummified whole caravans. The native Uighurs call it Taklimakan, "You enter and you never return." Aurel Stein thought
40 Arabia tame by comparison. Sven Hedin called it the world's most dangerous desert. Its dunes rise to 300 feet, and in sudden temperature changes the moving sands make hallucinatory noises, as if caravans or troupes of musicians were passing nearby. So at night, wrote Marco Polo, "the stray traveller will hear as it were the tramp and hum of a great cavalcade of people away from the real line of march, and taking this to be their
45 own company they will follow the sound; and when day breaks they find that a cheat has been put on them and that they are in an ill plight. Even in daytime one hears those spirits talking . . ."

       But I could hear nobody talking, except my own countrymen—shared gossip, jokes, assumptions. We sheltered in our own culture. We plodded across the sand in
50 disparate groups, complaining about Chinese bureaucracy and the cameleers. Nobody else seemed to be missing a lonely fraternization with the land. Perhaps, I thought, the habit of living alone had paradoxically exacerbated my awareness of people: until their presence obliterated everything else. But it seemed now that this companionship enfolded us all in a balloon of Britishness: amiable, safe, uncreative.

55   We intruded on the desert like a regiment. Only in the lens were some of us—three select camels, my guide and I—effortlessly, romantically isolated. We five moved in the borrowed glory of Lawrence and Doughty. Even my guide, in his flat cap and loose trousers, was touched by a shambling glamour. As we went, the horizon was closed by shallow hills stubbled with tamarisk, and in front of us range upon range of stark
60 dunes came beating in out of emptiness. The land was simplifying itself, shedding its stones first, then its trees, then its shrubs. Horses were useless in this terrain—their hooves burned in the sand—and donkeys slowly weakened. Only the twin-humped Bactrian camel, which can go waterless for two weeks, travelled the wastes at all. Its long, slender legs lift its body as if on stilts above the surface heat, and its spatular feet
65 dissipate the impact of its tread. It only starts to sweat—mildly—in a temperature at which a man would be dead.

       I watch these three sauntering in train behind us. They carried plastic water-containers, bedding, tent-poles, food-boxes. (They carried film equipment too, but it was concealed under a native rug.) They were like emissaries of the desert's
70 strangeness. Their rhythmic swaying echoed the surge of its dunes. Shaggy fringes dribbled down the underside of their necks like inverted manes, and each head rose to a punkish tuft far back on the forehead, above long-lashed eyes and vain lips. They shared an air of randy contempt.

Before us the desert wrinkled to the horizon in a tumult of ghostly curves. The
75 deepening silence, the intensifying heat, the ever-purer slopes, suggested that we were
approaching some presence—or primal absence—in the wastes. Was this, the viewer
might have wondered, a paradigm of the ultimate journey, the paring away of
everything essential, little by little, as we advanced into the heart of Nothing?

But no. We were conscious mainly of mild boredom and an unheroic thirst (we had
80 plenty of water). Our glamour rested only in the eyes of others. It is uncertain if we
were really journeying at all. We were creating the likeness of a journey.

In fact, we were undergoing not one voyage, but two. The first of these was real
but stayed unfilmed—the director's battle for transport and locations, the crew's
struggling with light and angles; whereas the second—the imaginary journey which it
85 produced—was a celluloid narrative of premeditated images, the voyage whose
destination was always known (since everything had to be prepared in advance),
fostered in an illusion of naturalness by camera-shots repeated over and over. This was
the ghost-journey, in which I was an actor. It was produced only for the screen.

So I became nostalgic for writing. A travel-book is an account: it records the real.
90 A travel-film is an illusion: it reconstructs it. And the confusion of this harassed both
the director and me. He was an austerely sensitive man, who instinctively wanted to
mould the film to a travel-writer's energies. But travelling like this, I could only
imagine those energies. I could not feel them. So while he tried to envisage our
journey through the eyes of a writer. I perversely began to see it through the lens of a
95 film director.

But this was obscured by more brutal confusions. We were at the mercy of four
Uighurs, local Turkomen more volatile than the native Chinese, who dwindle to a
minority in this far north-west. The Uighur had once made the Silk Road work:
opportunists trading between the static hierarchies of China and the empires to the
100 west. But as far as our film was concerned, only one Uighur (my guide) existed. The
other three—two camel herdsmen and an interpreter—accompanied us invisibly: part
of the true journey which lurked beneath the film. They belonged to the chaos of real
travel. They split into factions. The guide and interpreter came from one village, the
cameleers from another. They wrangled, and fell into bitter silences.

105 The camels, too, were not what they seemed. They had been assembled in advance
from different regions of the province, but were less beasts of burden than herd
animals. They bellowed resentment at their loads, and suddenly broke loose and
rampaged over the desert, scattering boxes and blankets in their wake. It was a star
performance. But we could not film it: because our cameras were on their backs. The
110 cameleers followed them, mutinously. And all afternoon we marched on south, looking
for sand unblemished by any speck of scrub, ranges which would say to the camera:
this is the harshest desert on earth.

The camera, after its fashion, was demanding truth.

[Turn over

At last, by evening, we arrived. Long, virgin dunes curved photogenically in front
115 of us, and the camels were back in harness. We had reconvened the mythic elements of
our journey. The three most filmic beasts, their loads reassembled for continuity,
paraded along the dune-lips behind the guide and me. But we were, of course, going
nowhere in particular. We were completing patterns of backlit beauty for the lens,
creating compositions, lending proportion and drama. The director and camera crew,
120 squatting like guerrillas on strategic hillocks, directed our passage through walkie-
talkies. We gazed hypocritically through them into solitude. The four camels which
did not officially exist coughed unseen in a dip of the sands. How did we look?

The cameraman worried about the slant of evening light. The dunes, he said, were
pointing the wrong way. The director pondered and shuffled unsurely. Wherever the
125 lens swung, there was cliché: skyline, camel-train, sunset, us. We were trapped in other
people's daydreams.

I tried to imagine how we appeared. Compared to our surroundings, I felt, we must
look weirdly insubstantial. Again I was reminded of ghosts, trying pathetically to
integrate with the real. Perhaps the paranoia of Hollywood directors, I thought, was
130 due to the terrifying precariousness of their control. A film seemed to belong to
nobody. It was in the hands not only of financiers and the elements, but of cameramen
and actors (myself now) and of the sheer recalcitrance of images, which never
reproduced themselves predictably. And in the end, for all the arts of editing and
commentary, the lens would give back to the viewer his own vision: he would see
135 simply what he would have seen if he were standing where the camera stood.

By comparison, my trade as a writer seemed megalomaniac. I was the lens, even the
viewer. Everything I wrote was subjective.

Then reality broke in. As the guide and I ascended too steep a slope, the camels
floundered to their knees. They collapsed in sequence, like cards. Their leading-ropes
140 broke. They struggled and roared. I tried to beat the hindmost to its feet, but the
baggage was slipping over its humps. Its buried legs gained no purchase in the sand.
Its slobbering face sank level with mine. I struck its flank several times before I
noticed it was defecating—a piece of cruelty faithfully recorded by the cameras on the
far dune. For minutes the sand writhed and slithered away under us, as if we were
145 treading water. And even after we had painfully reassembled on the dune's crest, the
reputation of camels was confirmed. The lead beast flailed out and lacerated my
guide's shin.

I felt suddenly guilty. It was as if a fictional character had lunged out of our film,
and kicked. All at once I imagined the film eating up everyone around it. Except me.
150 I was its supposed hero, already incarnate in it. Yet I was accompanied by people who
had traversed precisely the same land as I had, and who would appear on screen only as
names at the end.

At dusk we put up a makeshift wind-break. Our camp-fire blazed and subsided,
while an invisible haze, reaching far up the horizon, obliterated the stars. Since we had
155 to rise for the dawn light, the camels were fed in darkness, and for hours I was kept
awake by the crash of their teeth into piles of brittle foliage, and watched their profiles
as they shambled back and forth between the fodder and a futile search for plants.
Sometimes they would squeak in a peculiar, unofficial way, as if in distress; and one
great beast, passing the shelter where we lay, sank its fangs into the newly cut
160 tent-poles and brought them crashing on to our heads before it trotted contemptuously
into the night.

The unfilmed moment touched us only with dazed ill temper. It belonged merely to life. There was no light by which to film it and besides, the journey was not meant to be happening to the others, only to me.

165   But next morning, the dawn shone perfect. The most docile beasts fell into line behind me with their baggage and continuity intact. The backlit dunes were pronounced correct, and rippled accommodatingly. And I stepped again into the legend of a real journey—a voyage through random light and circumstance, to an unknown horizon, alone.

Question

"Yet our film aimed to record the Chinese Silk Road through my eyes" (lines 15 and 16)

How effectively does Colin Thubron describe and reflect on his experience of the making of this film?

[Turn over

3.   Poetry (*Page twenty-four*)

*Read carefully the poem **Wind** (1957) by Ted Hughes and then answer the question that follows it.*

Wind

This house has been far out at sea all night,
The woods crashing through darkness, the booming hills,
Winds stampeding the fields under the window
Floundering black astride and blinding wet

5   Till day rose; then under an orange sky
The hills had new places, and wind wielded
Blade-like, luminous black and emerald,
Flexing like the lens of a mad eye.

At noon I scaled along the house-side as far as
10   The coal-house door. I dared once to look up—
Through the brunt wind that dented the balls of my eyes
The tent of the hills drummed and strained its guyrope,

The fields quivering, the skyline a grimace,
At any second to bang and vanish with a flap:
15   The wind flung a magpie away and a black-
Back gull bent like an iron bar slowly. The house

Rang like some fine green goblet in the note
That any second would shatter it. Now deep
In chairs, in front of the great fire, we grip
20   Our hearts and cannot entertain book, thought,

Or each other. We watch the fire blazing,
And feel the roots of the house move, but sit on,
Seeing the window tremble to come in,
Hearing the stones cry out under the horizons.

Question

Make a critical evaluation of this poem.

Your evaluation should be based on careful analysis of key aspects of its language and form.

4. **Drama (*Pages twenty-five to thirty-three*)**

The following extract is the opening to the play **The Voysey Inheritance** *(1905) by Harley Granville Barker.*

Central to the play is Voysey and Son, a firm of family solicitors at the heart of the London legal establishment. As head of the firm, Mr Voysey *is entrusted with the financial affairs of many families, including the safe investment of their money.*

The characters in the extract are Mr Voysey, Peacey, *the firm's head clerk, and* Edward, Mr Voysey's *son and a partner in the firm.*

Read the extract carefully and then answer the question that follows it (Page thirty-three).

THE VOYSEY INHERITANCE

ACT I

The Office of Voysey and Son is in the best part of Lincoln's Inn. Its panelled rooms give out a sense of grandmotherly comfort and security, very grateful at first to the hesitating investor, the dubious litigant. Mr Voysey's own room, into which he walks about twenty past ten of a morning, radiates enterprise besides. There is polish on everything; on the
5 *windows, on the mahogany of the tidily packed writing-table that stands between them, on the brasswork of the fireplace in the other wall, on the glass of the firescreen which preserves only the pleasantness of a sparkling fire, even on* Mr Voysey's *hat as he takes it off to place it on the little red-curtained shelf behind the door.* Mr Voysey *is sixty or more and masterful; would obviously be master anywhere from his own home outwards, or wreck the*
10 *situation in his attempt. Indeed there is sometimes a buccaneering air in the twist of his glance, not altogether suitable to a family solicitor. On this bright October morning,* Peacey, *the head clerk, follows just too late to help him off with his coat, but in time to take it and hang it up with a quite unnecessary subservience. Relieved of his coat,* Mr Voysey *carries to his table the bunch of beautiful roses he is accustomed to bring to the*
15 *office three times a week and places them for a moment only near the bowl of water there ready to receive them while he takes up his letters. These lie ready too, opened mostly, one or two private ones left closed and discreetly separate. By this time the usual salutations have passed,* Peacey's *"Good morning, sir";* Mr Voysey's *"Morning, Peacey." Then as he gets to his letters* Mr Voysey *starts his day's work.*

20 *Mr Voysey.*	Any news for me?
Peacey.	I hear bad accounts of Alguazils Preferred, sir.
Mr Voysey.	Oh . . . who from?
Peacey.	Merrit and James's head clerk in the train this morning.
Mr Voysey.	They looked all right on . . . Give me *The Times*.
25	Peacey *goes to the fireplace for* The Times; *it is warming there.* Mr Voysey *waves a letter, then places it on the table.*
	Here, that's for you . . . Gerrard's Cross business. Anything else?
Peacey.	[*as he turns* The Times *to its Finance page*] I've made the usual notes.

	Mr Voysey.	Thank'ee.
30	*Peacey.*	Young Benham isn't back yet.
	Mr Voysey.	Mr Edward must do as he thinks fit about that. Alguazils, Alg—oh, yes.

He is running his eye down the columns. Peacey *leans over the letters.*

	Peacey.	This is from Mr Leader about the codicil . . . You'll answer that?
35	*Mr Voysey.*	Mr Leader. Yes. Alguazils. Mr Edward's here, I suppose.
	Peacey.	No, sir.
	Mr Voysey.	[*his eye twisting with some sharpness*] What!
	Peacey.	[*almost alarmed*] I beg pardon, sir.
	Mr Voysey.	Mr Edward.
40	*Peacey.*	Oh, yes, sir, been in his room some time. I thought you said Headley; he's not due back till Thursday.

Mr Voysey *discards* The Times *and sits to his desk and his letters.*

	Mr Voysey.	Tell Mr Edward I've come.
	Peacey.	Yes, sir. Anything else?
45	*Mr Voysey.*	Not for the moment. Cold morning, isn't it?
	Peacey.	Quite surprising, sir.
	Mr Voysey.	We had a touch of frost down at Chislehurst.
	Peacey.	So early!
50	*Mr Voysey.*	I want it for the celery. All right, I'll call through about the rest of the letters.

Peacey *goes, having secured a letter or two, and* Mr Voysey *having sorted the rest (a proportion into the waste-paper basket) takes up the forgotten roses and starts setting them into a bowl with an artistic hand. Then his son* Edward *comes in.* Mr Voysey *gives him one glance and goes on arranging the roses, but says cheerily . . .*

	Mr Voysey.	Good morning, my dear boy.

Edward *has little of his father in him and that little is undermost. It is a refined face, but self-consciousness takes the place in it of imagination, and in suppressing traits of brutality in his character it looks as if the young man had suppressed his sense of humour too. But whether or no, that would not be much in evidence now, for* Edward *is obviously going through some experience which is scaring him (there is no better word). He looks not to have slept for a night or two, and his standing there, clutching and unclutching the bundle of papers he carries, his eyes on his father, half appealingly but half accusingly too, his whole being altogether so unstrung and desperate, makes* Mr Voysey's *uninterrupted arranging of the flowers seem very calculated indeed. At last the little tension of silence is broken.*

	Edward.	Father . . .
70	*Mr Voysey.*	Well?
	Edward.	I'm glad to see you.

This is a statement of fact. He doesn't know that the commonplace phrase sounds ridiculous at such a moment.

	Mr Voysey.	I see you've the papers there.
75	*Edward.*	Yes.
	Mr Voysey.	You've been through them?
	Edward.	As you wished me . . .
	Mr Voysey.	Well?

Edward doesn't answer. Reference to the papers seems to overwhelm him
80 *with shame.* Mr Voysey *goes on with cheerful impatience.*

Now, now, my dear boy, don't take it like this. You're puzzled and worried, of course. But why didn't you come down to me on Saturday night? I expected you . . . I told you to come. Your mother was wondering why you weren't with us for dinner yesterday.

85	*Edward.*	I went through everything twice. I wanted to make quite sure.
	Mr Voysey.	I told you to come to me.
	Edward.	[*he is very near crying*] Oh, Father!
	Mr Voysey.	Now look here, Edward, I'm going to ring and dispose of these letters. Please pull yourself together.

90 *He pushes the little button on his table.*

	Edward.	I didn't leave my rooms all day yesterday.
	Mr Voysey.	A pleasant Sunday! You must learn, whatever the business may be, to leave it behind you at the office. Life's not worth living else.

Peacey *comes in to find* Mr Voysey *before the fire ostentatiously warming*
95 *and rubbing his hands.*

Oh, there isn't much else, Peacey. Tell Simmons that if he satisfies you about the details of this lease it'll be all right. Make a note for me of Mr Granger's address at Mentone.

	Peacey.	Mr Burnett . . . Burnett and Marks . . . has just come in, Mr Edward.
100	*Edward.*	[*without turning*] It's only fresh instructions. Will you take them?
	Peacey.	All right.

Peacey *goes, lifting his eyebrows at the queerness of* Edward's *manner. This* Mr Voysey *sees, returning to his table with a little scowl.*

	Mr Voysey.	Now sit down. I've given you a bad forty-eight hours, have I? Well,
105		I've been anxious about you. Never mind, we'll thresh the thing out now. Go through the two accounts. Mrs Murberry's first . . . how did you find it stands?
	Edward.	[*his feelings choking him*] I hoped you were playing some joke on me.

	Mr Voysey.	Come now.
110		Edward *separates the papers precisely and starts to detail them; his voice quite toneless. Now and then his father's sharp comments ring out in contrast.*
	Edward.	We've got the lease of her present house, several agreements . . . and here's her will. Here's an expired power of attorney . . . over her securities and her property generally . . . it was made out for six months.
115		
	Mr Voysey.	She was in South Africa.
	Edward.	Here's the Sheffield mortgage and the Henry Smith mortgage with Banker's receipts . . . her Banker's to us for the interest up to date . . . four and a half and five per cent. Then . . . Fretworthy Bonds. There's a note scribbled in your writing that they are at the Bank; but you don't say what bank.
120		
	Mr Voysey.	My own.
125	*Edward.*	[*just dwelling on the words*] Your own. I queried that. There's eight thousand five hundred in three and a half India stock. And there are her Banker's receipts for cheques on account of those dividends. I presume for those dividends.
	Mr Voysey.	Why not?
130	*Edward.*	[*gravely*] Because then, Father, there are her Banker's half-yearly receipts for other sums amounting to an average of four hundred and twenty pounds a year. But I find no record of any capital to produce this.
	Mr Voysey.	Go on. What do you find?
135	*Edward.*	Till about three years back there seems to have been eleven thousand in Queenslands which would produce . . . did produce exactly the same sum. But after January of that year I find no record of them.
	Mr Voysey.	In fact the Queenslands are missing, vanished?
	Edward.	[*hardly uttering the word*] Yes.
	Mr Voysey.	From which you conclude?
140	*Edward.*	I supposed at first that you had not handed me all the papers . . .
	Mr Voysey.	Since Mrs Murberry evidently still gets that four twenty a year somehow; lucky woman.
	Edward.	[*in agony*] Oh!
	Mr Voysey.	Well, we'll return to the good lady later. Now let's take the other.
145	*Edward.*	The Hatherley Trust.
	Mr Voysey.	Quite so.
	Edward.	[*with one accusing glance*] Trust.
	Mr Voysey.	Go on.

Edward.	Father . . .
150	*His grief comes uppermost again and* Mr Voysey *meets it kindly.*
Mr Voysey.	I know, my dear boy. I shall have lots to say to you. But let's get quietly through with these details first.
Edward.	[*bitterly now*] Oh, this is simple enough. We're young Hatherley's trustees till he comes of age. The property was thirty-eight thousand invested in Consols. Certain sums were to be allowed for his education; we seem to be paying them.
155	
Mr Voysey.	Regularly?
Edward.	Quite. But where's the capital?
Mr Voysey.	No record?
160 *Edward.*	Yes . . . a note by you on a half sheet: Refer Bletchley Land Scheme.
Mr Voysey.	Oh . . . we've been out of that six years or more! He's credited with the interest on his capital?
Edward.	With the Consol interest.
Mr Voysey.	Quite so.
165 *Edward.*	The Bletchley scheme paid seven and a half.
Mr Voysey.	At one time. Have you taken the trouble to calculate what will be due from us to the lad?
Edward.	Yes . . . capital and interest . . . about forty-six thousand pounds.
Mr Voysey.	A respectable sum. In five years' time?
170 *Edward.*	When he comes of age.
Mr Voysey.	That gives us, say, four years and six months in which to think about it.
	Edward *waits, hopelessly, for his father to speak again; then says . . .*
Edward. 175	Thank you for showing me these, sir. Shall I put them back in your safe now?
Mr Voysey.	Yes, you'd better. There's the key.
	Edward *reaches for the bunch, his face hidden.*
180	Put them down. Your hand shakes . . . why, you might have been drinking. I'll put them away later. It's no use having hysterics, Edward. Look your trouble in the face.
	Edward's *only answer is to go to the fire, as far from his father as the room allows. And there he leans on the mantelpiece, his shoulders heaving.*
	I'm sorry, my dear boy. I wouldn't tell you if I could help it.
185 *Edward.*	I can't believe it. And that you should be telling me . . . such a thing.
Mr Voysey.	Let yourself go . . . have your cry out, as the women say. It isn't pleasant, I know. It isn't pleasant to inflict it on you.

	Edward.	[*able to turn to his father again; won round by the kind voice*] How long has it been going on? Why didn't you tell me before? Oh, I know you thought you'd pull through. But I'm your partner . . . I'm responsible too. Oh, I don't want to shirk that . . . don't think I mean to shirk that, Father. Perhaps I ought to have discovered . . . but those affairs were always in your hands. I trusted . . . I beg your pardon. Oh it's us . . . not you. Everyone has trusted us.
190		
195	*Mr Voysey.*	[*calmly and kindly still*] You don't seem to notice that I'm not breaking my heart like this.
	Edward.	What's the extent of . . . ? Are there other accounts . . . ? When did it begin? Father, what made you begin it?
	Mr Voysey.	I didn't begin it.
200	*Edward.*	You didn't? Who then?
	Mr Voysey.	My father before me.
		Edward *stares.*
		That calms you a little.
	Edward.	But how terrible! Oh, my dear father . . . I'm glad. But . . .
205	*Mr Voysey.*	[*shaking his head*] My inheritance, Edward.
	Edward.	My dear father!
	Mr Voysey.	I had hoped it wasn't to be yours.
	Edward.	But you mean to tell me that this sort of thing has been going on here for years? For more than thirty years!
210	*Mr Voysey.*	Yes.
	Edward.	That's a little hard to understand . . . just at first, sir.
	Mr Voysey.	[*sententiously*] We do what we must in this world, Edward. I have done what I had to do.
215	*Edward.*	[*his emotion well cooled by now*] Perhaps I'd better just listen while you explain.
	Mr Voysey.	[*concentrating*] You know that I'm heavily into Northern Electrics.
	Edward.	Yes.
220	*Mr Voysey.*	But you don't know how heavily. When I got the tip the Municipalities were organising the purchase, I saw of course the stock must be up to a hundred and forty-five—a hundred and fifty in no time. Now Leeds has quarrelled with the rural group . . . there'll be no general settlement for ten years. I bought at ninety-five. What are they today?
	Edward.	Seventy-two.
225	*Mr Voysey.*	Seventy-one and a half. And in ten years I may be . . . ! I'm not a young man, Edward. That's mainly why you've had to be told.
	Edward.	With whose money are you so heavily into Northern Electrics?
	Mr Voysey.	The firm's money.
	Edward.	Clients' money?
230	*Mr Voysey.*	Yes.

Edward.	[*coldly*] Well . . . I'm waiting for your explanation, sir.
Mr Voysey.	[*with a shrug*] Children always think the worst of their parents, I suppose. I did of mine. It's a pity.
Edward.	Go on, sir, go on. Let me know the worst.
235 *Mr Voysey.*	There's no immediate danger. I should think anyone could see that from the figures there. There's no real risk at all.
Edward.	Is that the worst?
Mr Voysey.	[*his anger rising*] Have you studied these two accounts or have you not?
240 *Edward.*	Yes, sir.
Mr Voysey.	Well, where's the deficiency in Mrs Murberry's income . . . has she ever gone without a shilling? What has young Hatherley lost?
Edward.	He stands to lose . . .
Mr Voysey. 245	He stands to lose nothing if I'm spared for a little, and you will only bring a little common sense to bear and try to understand the difficulties of my position.
Edward.	Father, I'm not thinking ill of you . . . that is, I'm trying not to. But won't you explain how you're justified . . . ?
Mr Voysey.	In putting our affairs in order?
250 *Edward.*	Are you doing that?
Mr Voysey.	What else?
Edward.	[*starting patiently to examine the matter*] How bad were things when you came into control?
Mr Voysey.	Oh, I forget.
255 *Edward.*	You can't forget.
Mr Voysey.	Well . . . pretty bad.
Edward.	How was it my grandfather . . . ?
Mr Voysey. 260	Muddlement . . . timidity! Had a perfect mania for petty speculation. He'd no capital . . . no real credit . . . and he went in terror of his life. My dear Edward, if I hadn't found out in time, he'd have confessed to the first man who came and asked for a balance sheet.
Edward.	How much was he to the bad then?
Mr Voysey.	Oh . . . a tidy sum.
Edward.	But it can't have taken all these years to pay off . . .
265 *Mr Voysey.*	Oh, hasn't it!
Edward.	[*making his point*] Then how does it happen, sir, that such a recent trust as young Hatherley's has been broken into?
Mr Voysey.	Well, what could be safer? There is no one to interfere, and we haven't to settle up for five years.
270 *Edward.*	[*utterly beaten*] Father, are you mad?

	Mr Voysey.	Mad? I wish everybody were as sane. As a trustee the law permits me to earn for a fund three and a half per cent . . . and that I do . . . punctually and safely. Now as to Mrs Murberry . . . those Fretworthy Bonds at my bank . . . I've borrowed five thousand on them. But I can release them tomorrow if need be.
275		
	Edward.	Where's the five thousand?
	Mr Voysey.	I needed it . . . temporarily . . . to complete a purchase . . . there was that and four thousand more out of the Skipworth fund.
	Edward.	But, my dear father—
280	*Mr Voysey.*	Well?
	Edward.	[*summing it all up very simply*] It's not right.

Mr Voysey *considers his son for a moment with a pitying shake of the head.*

	Mr Voysey.	That is a word, Edward, which one should learn to use very carefully. You mean that from time to time I have had to go beyond the letter of the law. But consider the position I found myself in. Was I to see my father ruined and disgraced without lifting a finger to help him? I paid back to the man who was most involved in my father's mistakes every penny of his capital . . . and he never even knew the danger he'd been in . . . never had one uneasy moment. It was I that lay awake. I have now somewhere a letter from that man written as he lay dying . . . I'll tell you who it was, old Thomson the physiologist . . . saying that only his perfect confidence in our conduct of his affairs had enabled him to do his life's work in peace. Well, Edward, I went beyond the letter of the law to do that service . . . to my father . . . to old Thomson . . . to Science . . . to Humanity. Was I right or wrong?
285		
290		
295		
	Edward.	In the result, sir, right.
	Mr Voysey.	Judge me by the result, I took the risk of failure . . . I should have suffered. I could have kept clear of the danger if I'd liked.
300	*Edward.*	But that's all past. The thing that concerns me is what you are doing now.
	Mr Voysey.	[*gently reproachful*] My boy, can't you trust me a little? It's all very well for you to come in at the end of the day and criticise. But I who have done the day's work know how that work had to be done. And here's our firm, prosperous, respected and without a stain on its honour. That's the main point, isn't it?
305		
	Edward.	[*quite irresponsive to this pathetic appeal*] Very well, sir. Let's dismiss from our minds any prejudice about behaving as honest firms of solicitors do behave . . .
310	*Mr Voysey.*	We need do nothing of the sort. If a man gives me definite instructions about his property, I follow them. And more often than not he suffers.
	Edward.	But if Mrs Murberry knew . . .

Mr Voysey.		Well, if you can make her understand her affairs . . . financial or other
315		. . . it's more than I ever could. Go and knock it into her head, then, if you can, that four hundred and twenty pounds of her income hasn't, for the last eight years, come from the place she thinks it's come from, and see how happy you'll make her.
Edward.		But is that four hundred and twenty a year as safe as it was before you
320		. . . ?
Mr Voysey.		Why not?
Edward.		What's the security?
Mr Voysey.		[*putting his coping stone on the argument*] My financial ability.

Question

Make a detailed study of the dramatic means by which in this opening to the play the playwright establishes key aspects of plot, character and theme.

[Turn over

Section 4—Reading the Media

You must answer **one question only** in this section.

Category A—Film

1. *"Editing is a crucial element in the making of films."*

   Drawing evidence from particular sequences, discuss the contribution of editing to the effectiveness of any **one** film you have studied.

2. Choose any **two** films by one director. Analyse the particular aspects of style and content that mark these films as the work of that director.

Category B—Television

3. Discuss the distinctive technical and cultural codes employed in any **one** television drama—soap, serial, series or single play—you have studied.

4. *"Essential to the success of documentary is the construction of effective narrative."*

   How far do you agree?

   You should support your answer with evidence drawn from **two** or **more than two** television documentary programmes you have studied.

Category C—Radio

5. *"Radio is a non-visual medium; so much depends on voice."*

   Discuss the importance of voice in **one** or **two** of the following radio genres: news and current affairs, sport, drama, comedy, documentary, magazine, music.

6. By what means has any **one** radio channel created its distinctive identity?

   In your answer, you should consider aspects such as programme content, scheduling, mode of address.

Category D—Print journalism

7. *"The best print journalism entertains at the same time as it informs, enlightens and educates."*

   Discuss.

   You should support your answer with evidence drawn from at least **two** newspapers.

   NB In your answer to Question 7, you **may** refer to the material provided for Question 8, but your answer must also include evidence from at least **one other** newspaper.

8. In January 2006, a bottle-nosed whale dominated the news for several days before its eventual demise.

   For this question, you are provided with an extract (*see Insert*) from the coverage of this event in *The Independent on Sunday* of 22 January, 2006.

   In a careful study of the extract, show how, through devices such as narrative and representation, the newspaper turns an event into a "legend".

Category E—Advertising

9. *"Advertising is an art—the art of persuasion."*

   How effectively, in your view, is the "*art of persuasion*" employed in a range of advertisements **or** in an advertising campaign you have studied?

   NB In your answer to Question 9, you may refer to the advertisements provided for Question 10, but your answer must also refer to **other** advertisements.

10. For this question, you are provided with two advertisements (*see Insert*) published in the *Radio Times* magazine for Vodafone.

    Make a detailed analysis of these two advertisements in which you consider:

    •   technical, cultural and written codes
    •   the stereotyping of gender and the extent to which it is confirmed or subverted
    •   the narrative of each advertisement.

[END OF QUESTION PAPER]

Insert for Section 4 – Reading the Media Question 8

The legend of the London
Whale

Lost and in distress, its plight touched the city and the world

The Thames was lined with crowds and camera crews as rescuers tried to help the animal to the open sea.
By **Cole Moreton**

For a while there was a chance of a happy ending. As darkness fell at the end of an emotional day. The Whale Who Came to London was heading for the open sea again, albeit in a harness and blanket on the back of a Port of London Authority (PLA) barge.

The gentle, incongruous giant spotted swimming past the House of Commons on Friday had been rescued from the shallow, polluted waters of the Thames and given the best possible odds for survival. But as television pictures of the barge heading for Tilbury were broadcast around the world, the RSPCA announced that the condition of the whale had deteriorated in transit.

Despite the supporting inflatables and a constant spray of water, it was not now fit enough to be released into the English Channel, as had been the plan. As darkness descended on the windswept Thames Estuary, vets were trying to decide whether to let the whale take its chances in the waters there. The 18ft northern bottlenosed whale should have been out in the Atlantic diving for squid. Instead, it had somehow wandered up river into the city late on Thursday, far from its mother who had been heard calling 40 miles away, off the coast of Essex.

Londoners lined the river to see it but the plight of the whale captured imaginations all round the world, not least because its story had all the elements of a modern fairytale: the child lost and lonely in an alien and dangerous place; the desperate parent calling out, and the rescuers who waded into the water and comforted the whale with their bare hands yesterday before helping with its bid for freedom.

They were members of the charity British Divers Marine Life Rescue (BDMLR), who put an inflatable pontoon under the whale and lifted it by crane on to the PLA barge *Crossness*. As a deep sea creature, it needed to go to the Channel, where it could find food, or best of all the Atlantic. But as time wore on, those on board the barge faced what they called "an awful choice". "The longer the whale stays on the barge – the further we go to get to deeper water – the more the animal's condition could deteriorate," said Tony Woodley of the BDMLR. The whale was being given antibiotics and its breathing rate monitored, but its muscles were stiffening.

"The animal has been in distress for the past couple of days," said Mr Woodley. "When it is out of the water for this length of time, the pressure on its internal organs is a problem." If the whale was released into the estuary there was still a chance it would swim back up river, or die quickly, he said. "We are pessimistic."

JOURNEY HOME			
Race against time to save the whale	**08.10** **The sighting** After the first sighting, in the Albert Bridge area, rescuers try to take control of the 15ft adolescent whale. An attempt is made to assess its health for possible transport to outside the Thames Estuary. They also weigh up the option of a mercy killing if it is too ill to travel.	**12.30** **The wrapping** At low tide, rescuers wrap the whale in a blanket and cocoon it between floating pontoons for transport. As the whale thrashes around in distress, attempts are made to assess its breathing rate. Blood and blubber samples are taken. Rescuers lubricate its eyes and blow-holes.	**13.09** **The calming** Medics soothe the animal before giving the go-ahead for it to be dragged gently towards a barge that will take it out of the crowded Thames. No decision has yet been made on whether it is well enough to be released, or needs to be put out of its misery.
From dawn, experts fought to return the stranded mammal to open water			

THE SIGHTINGS

1 11am Thursday: first sighting of a northern bottlenosed whale near Dagenham rouses national interest

2 3pm Thursday: as it passes the Thames Barrier, spectators start to line riverbanks, hoping to catch a glimpse of the creature

3 2pm Friday: whale spotted by the Palace of Westminster. The last time that a live whale was seen in the Thames was in 1913

4 2.30pm Friday: the whale continues to swim upstream against a strong current, reaches Albert Bridge then appears to turn back, raising hopes that it might head downstream to the sea of its own volition. It soon becomes clear that it is disorientated

5 12.30pm yesterday: rescuers attach the beached whale to floating pontoons before towing it towards a barge, on to which it is lifted by crane

6 3.45pm yesterday: the barge carrying the whale, the "Crossness", sets off for the Thames estuary. But the whale's health deteriorates. Unable to support its own weight out of the water, it starts to suffocate

7 5pm: with regret medics cancel their appeal for an ocean-going vessel to take the whale out to sea, having decided it is now too ill to be transported to the Atlantic

8 8pm: the whale is due to be released into the Thames estuary

---

The first sighting of the whale had been on Thursday, when fishermen saw it out by the mouth of the Thames. Later that day it was spotted by staff at the Thames Barrier – which seems to have been no barrier at all. Then on Friday morning, a sharp-eyed rail commuter crossing a central London bridge looked out of the window and had the presence of mind to ring the authorities. "Unless I'm hallucinating," he said, "I've just seen a whale in the Thames."

'Unless I'm hallucinating I've seen a whale in the Thames'

This was no hallucination. Neither was it a dolphin: these visit London quite often. A dead harbour porpoise was found at Putney yesterday, by what appeared to be coincidence, although there was speculation that it might have been frightened into swimming up the Thames in the same way as the whale, possibly by naval sonar activity.

There were hopes that the whale would swim back out to sea on its own, then fears that it had died. But it was sighted again early yesterday morning by the blue and white PLA launch that then shadowed its progress up and down the river, between Battersea and Chelsea.

Noon was the deadline: that was when the vets and marine biologists expected to be able to get close to the whale, as it beached in shallow water. Trying to catch it while it swam would be too dangerous, they said. Playing whale song from closer to the mouth of the river would not work because of the level of river noise.

It was a clear, bright day, but to listen for the calls and bellows of the whale was to become aware again of the traffic, the sirens, shouts, rumbling trains and thundering jets that form the soundtrack to city life, not to mention the police and news helicopters hovering at a respectful distance overhead.

The children were mildly amused to see a huge animal surfacing to blow air in such an unlikely place. But it was the thousands of adults alongside them, lining the bridges and riverside walks, who watched for hours with childlike intensity.

Children were amused; adults watched with childlike intensity

Why are we drawn to such creatures? The size is one thing, and the grace of movement as they slip through the water, but yesterday there was something profoundly moving and attractive about the combination of power and apparent gentleness. A flick of the tail could have capsized the dinghy, but whales are curious creatures that get themselves in trouble because they like to be friendly to boats. And above all there was the curiosity value.

A whale in the Thames is not something you see every century, let alone every day. The last sighting was in 1913.

"Get back!" screamed a woman in a black rubber suit from the water as a member of the public waded in, intent on helping to rescue the whale which had become beached at low tide. "Get back you fool!" shouted her colleague and the man slowly waded away embarrassed. As the water level dropped, 18 people in rubber suits surrounded the whale, which bellowed and thrashed its tail but then became quiet and still. The hands were to calm it. Yellow bands were passed under its body, then inflated.

Mark Stevens of the BDMLR waded ashore to tell the crowds, "The whale is comfortable; it likes the pressure of the pontoons. The blood you saw in the water is because the river bed is full of dirty great boulders, and one of them cut the skin, but a whale has a lot of blood, so it is nothing to worry about."

They were waiting for the results of blood tests taken in the river, he said. But as the tide rose again it became a race against time. After a certain time the barge would not have enough room to pass under the bridges. So the *Crossness* set out without the test results, in the hope that the whale would be declared fit enough to be set free. "Go on, fella," whispered a policeman, as he helped clear spectators off the rapidly shrinking beach. "Best of luck."

14.35
The lifting
Bystanders cheer as rescuers brave cold and fast-moving currents to manouver slings under the animal's belly and lift it on to the barge. It is uncertain the exhausted whale will survive this traumatic event, but everything goes like clockwork and there is hope it may see it through.

15.50
The journey begins
Vets assess the whale's health as better than they had feared during its arduous journey on the barge towards the estuary. But they are still unsure whether they will be in a position to release it into the Channel, or have to transport it further out to open water.

Around 20.00
An uncertain end
After all the effort, spirits sink as the medics report their grim news: the whale is too ill to be transferred to another vessel for a second leg out to the Atlantic. Instead, the plan was to release it into the Channel –a worrying finale to a story that touched the nation.

Insert for Section 4 – Reading the Media Question 10

Today, Matthew, I'm going to be a parent, a child, a grandchild, an animal handler, a man manager, an employee, a friend, a lover, an ex-friend, an ex-lover, a music lover, a bad singer, a good Samaritan, a social commentator, a philosopher, a psychologist, an interior designer, a personal shopper, a cook, a washer-upper, a player, a spectator, a film critic, a TV critic, a writer, a reader, a kids' entertainer and the beautiful princess in the bedtime story who lives happily ever after ●

Make the most of now.

It's the most

precious thing in the world. It only exists for an instant. It's here. Then it's gone. So cherish it. Love it. Use it to make someone smile. Use it to tell someone you love them. Discover great things. Laugh at daft things. Take it in your hands and stretch it. Eloooongate it. Put it through its paces. Make it earn its keep. Fill it to the brim with your favourlte things. Squeeze every drop of enjoyment out of it. Whatever you do make the most of it ●

Make the most of now.

vodafone

[BLANK PAGE]

ADVANCED HIGHER

2009

[BLANK PAGE]

X115/701

NATIONAL
QUALIFICATIONS
2009

FRIDAY, 15 MAY
1.00 PM – 4.00 PM

ENGLISH
ADVANCED HIGHER

There are four sections in this paper.

Section 1–Literary Study	pages	2 — 9	
Section 2–Language Study	pages	10 —17	
Section 3–Textual Analysis	pages	18 —36	
Section 4–Reading the Media	pages	37 — 40	**(plus 2 colour inserts)**

Depending on the options you have chosen, you must answer **one** or **two** questions.

If you have submitted a Creative Writing folio, you must answer only **one** question.

Otherwise, you must answer **two** questions.

If you are required to answer only **one question**

- it must be taken from **Section 1–Literary Study**
- you must leave the examination room **after 1 hour 30 minutes**.

If you are required to answer **two questions**

- your first must be taken from **Section 1–Literary Study**
- your second must be taken from **a different section**
- each answer must be written in **a separate answer booklet**
- the maximum time allowed for any question is **1 hour 30 minutes**.

You must identify each question you attempt by indicating clearly

- **the title of the section** from which the question has been taken
- **the number of the question** within that section.

You must also write inside the front cover of your Literary Study answer booklet

- **the topic** of your Specialist Study (Dissertation)
- **the texts** used in your Specialist Study (Dissertation).

Section 1—Literary Study

This section is **mandatory** for all candidates.

You must answer **one question only** in this section.

Unless otherwise indicated, your answer must take the form of a **critical essay** appropriately structured to meet the demands of your selected question.

DRAMA

1. **Beckett**

   "Although often at odds with each other, what is striking about Beckett's central characters is their need for each other, their dependence on each other."

   Discuss with reference to Vladimir and Estragon in *Waiting for Godot* **and** Hamm and Clov in *Endgame*.

2. **Byrne**

   *"Central to **The Slab Boys Trilogy** is Byrne's use of the unexpected—in terms of character, action and tone."*

   Discuss.

3. **Chekhov**

   Write an essay on the importance of time in *The Cherry Orchard*.

4. **Friel**

   Make a detailed study of the dramatic function of Owen O'Donnell in *Translations* **and** of Jack Mundy in *Dancing at Lughnasa*.

5. **Lindsay**

   Analyse and evaluate some of the principal dramatic techniques employed by Lindsay in *Ane Satyre of the Thrie Estaitis* to press for reform of Church and State and to remind those in power of their duties to the common people.

6. **Lochhead**

   Make a detailed study of the role of La Corbie in *Mary Queen of Scots Got Her Head Chopped Off* **and** of Renfield in *Dracula*.

7. **Pinter**

   Discuss Pinter's dramatic presentation of aspects of power, political or otherwise, in any **two** of the specified plays.

8. **Shakespeare**

EITHER

(a) ***Othello* and *Antony and Cleopatra***

"*Excellent wretch! Perdition catch my soul
But I do love thee; and when I love thee not,
Chaos is come again.*"

(Othello in Act III, Scene iii of *Othello*)

"*Look where they come.
Take but good note, and you shall see in him
The triple pillar of the world transformed
Into a strumpet's fool.*"

(Philo in Act I, Scene i of *Antony and Cleopatra*)

Keeping these quotations in mind, discuss Shakespeare's treatment of love in *Othello* **or** in *Antony and Cleopatra* **or** in **both** plays.

OR

(b) ***The Winter's Tale* and *The Tempest***

"*The relationships between Florizel and Perdita **and** between Ferdinand and Miranda are central to the dramatic development and resolution of these plays.*"

Discuss.

9. **Stoppard**

"*We can't even predict the next drip from a dripping tap when it gets irregular. Each drip sets up the conditions for the next, the smallest variation blows prediction apart, and the weather is unpredictable the same way, will always be unpredictable. When you push the numbers through the computer you can see it on the screen. The future is disorder.*"

(Valentine speaking to Hannah in Act One Scene Four of *Arcadia*)

Discuss some of the principal dramatic means by which unpredictability and disorder are explored in *Arcadia* **and** in *Rosencrantz and Guildenstern are Dead*.

10. **Wilde**

"*Not social analysis but social subversion by laughter through wit, style and fantasy—that was Wilde's forte.*"

Discuss with reference to any **two** or to all **three** of the specified plays.

11. **Williams**

"*In a Williams play, the climax of the drama comes when the central characters suffer the confrontation of past and present, when the thing they have fled from corners them . . .*"

In the light of this assertion, make a detailed study of the climax of *A Streetcar Named Desire* **and** the climax of *Sweet Bird of Youth*.

POETRY

12. **Burns**

Read carefully the following extract from **The Cotter's Saturday Night** *and then answer questions (a)* **and** *(b) that follow it (Page five).*

November chill blaws loud wi' angry sough;
    The short'ning winter-day is near a close;
The miry beasts retreating frae the pleugh;
    The black'ning trains o' craws to their repose:
    The toil-worn Cotter frae his labour goes,
This night his weekly moil is at an end,
    Collects his spades, his mattocks, and his hoes,
Hoping the morn in ease and rest to spend,
And weary, o'er the moor, his course does hameward bend.

At length his lonely cot appears in view,
    Beneath the shelter of an agèd tree;
Th' expectant wee-things, toddling, stacher through
    To meet their Dad, wi' flichterin' noise an' glee,
    His wee bit ingle, blinkin bonnilie,
His clean hearth-stane, his thrifty wifie's smile,
    The lisping infant, prattling on his knee,
Does a' his weary kiaugh and care beguile,
An' makes him quite forget his labour an' his toil.

Belyve, the elder bairns come drapping in,
    At service out, amang the farmers roun';
Some ca' the pleugh, some herd, some tentie rin
    A cannie errand to a neibor town:
    Their eldest hope, their Jenny, woman-grown,
In youthfu' bloom, love sparkling in her e'e,
    Comes hame, perhaps to shew a braw new gown,
Or deposite her sair-won penny-fee,
To help her parents dear, if they in hardship be.

With joy unfeign'd, brothers and sisters meet,
    An' each for other's welfare kindly spiers:
The social hours, swift-wing'd, unnoticed fleet;
    Each tells the uncos that he sees or hears;
    The parents, partial, eye their hopeful years;
Anticipation forward points the view.
    The mother, wi' her needle an' her sheers,
Gars auld claes look amaist as weel's the new;
The father mixes a' wi' admonition due.

Their master's an' their mistress's command,
   The younkers a' are warnèd to obey;
An' mind their labours wi' an eydent hand,
   An' ne'er, tho' out o' sight, to jauk or play:
   "And O! be sure to fear the Lord alway,
An' mind your duty, duly, morn an' night!
   Lest in temptation's path ye gang astray,
Implore His counsel and assisting might:
They never sought in vain that sought the Lord aright!"

But hark! a rap comes gently to the door;
   Jenny, wha kens the meaning o' the same,
Tells how a neebor lad cam o'er the moor,
   To do some errands, and convoy her hame.
   The wily mother sees the conscious flame
Sparkle in Jenny's e'e, and flush her cheek;
   With heart-struck anxious care, enquires his name,
While Jenny hafflins is afraid to speak;
Weel-pleas'd the mother hears it's nae wild, worthless rake.

Wi' kindly welcome, Jenny brings him ben;
   A strappin' youth; he takes the mother's eye;
Blythe Jenny sees the visit's no ill ta'en;
   The father cracks of horses, pleughs and kye.
   The youngster's artless heart o'erflows wi' joy,
But blate and laithfu', scarce can weel behave;
   The mother, wi' a woman's wiles, can spy
What makes the youth sae bashfu' an' sae grave;
Weel-pleased to think her bairn's respected like the lave.

(a)   Make a detailed analysis of Burns's treatment of Scottish rural life in this extract.

and

(b)   Go on to discuss Burns's treatment of Scottish rural life elsewhere in *The Cotter's Saturday Night* **and** in **one** or **two** other poems.

13. Chaucer

Examine the poetic means by which Chaucer creates characters that extend beyond social or moral stereotypes.

In your answer you should refer to **three** or **four** characters. These characters should be drawn **both** from the General Prologue **and** from **either** or **both** of the specified Tales.

14. Donne

Discuss the uses Donne makes of aspects of Renaissance learning and discovery in *The Good Morrow, The Sun Rising, Aire and Angels* and *A Valediction: forbidding mourning.*

15. Duffy

Analyse Duffy's poetic treatment of the past in *Originally, The Captain of the 1964 "Top of the Form" Team* and *Litany*.

16. Heaney

"Heaney explores the past to try to understand the present and to offer solutions for the future."

Keeping this statement in mind, discuss the principal means by which Heaney explores the past in *The Tollund Man, Funeral Rites* and *Punishment*.

17. Henryson

EITHER

    (a)   *Read carefully the following extract from* **The Testament of Cresseid** *and then answer questions (i)* **and** *(ii) that follow it (Page seven).*

> And first of all Saturne gave his sentence,
> Quhilk gave to Cupide litill reverence,
> Bot as ane busteous churle on his maneir
> Came crabitlie with auster luik and cheir.
>
> His face fronsit, his lyre was lyke the leid,
> His teeth chatterit and cheverit with the chin,
> His ene drowpit, how sonkin in his heid,
> Out of his nois the meldrop fast can rin,
> With lippis bla and cheikis leine and thin;
> The ice schoklis that fra his hair doun hang
> Was wonder greit, and as ane spear als lang:
>
> Atouir his belt his lyart lokkis lay
> Felterit unfair, ouirfret with froistis hoir
> His garmound and his gyte full gay of gray,
> His widderit weid fra him the wind out woir
> Ane busteous bow within his hand he boir,
> Under his girdill ane flasche of felloun flanis
> Fedderit with ice and heidit with hailstanis.
>
> Than Juppiter, richt fair and amiabill,
> God of the starnis in the firmament
> And nureis to all things generabill;
> Fra his father Saturne far different,
> With burelie face and browis bricht and brent,
> Upon his heid ane garland wonder gay
> Of flouris fair, as it had been in May.

His voice was cleir, as crystal were his ene,
As goldin wyre sa glitterand was his hair,
His garmound and his gyte full gay of grene
With goldin listis gilt on everie gair;
Ane burelie brand about his middill bair,
In his richt hand he had ane groundin speir,
Of his father the wraith fra us to weir.

(i) Identify and analyse in detail some of the principal poetic techniques employed in this extract to convey the character of Saturne and the character of Juppiter.

and

(ii) Go on to examine some of the principal poetic techniques employed elsewhere in the poem to convey the character of Cresseid.

OR

(b) "In the **Morall Fabillis** the relationship between tale and moral is rarely straightforward."

Examine **two** or **three** of the *Morall Fabillis* in the light of this statement.

18. Keats

Discuss some of the principal means by which, in **two** or **three** poems, Keats explores the nature and importance of beauty.

19. MacDiarmid

EITHER

(a) Discuss some of the principal poetic means by which the search for identity, both personal and national, is explored in *A Drunk Man Looks at the Thistle*.

OR

(b) "The impact of MacDiarmid's early lyrics derives from their blend of earthly and cosmic elements."

Discuss.

20. Muir

Discuss some of the principal means by which, in *The Good Town*, *The River* and *The Refugees*, Muir explores some of the tensions he found in contemporary Europe.

21. Plath

Analyse and evaluate Plath's use of images and symbols in *The Arrival of the Bee Box*, *Daddy* and *Lady Lazarus*.

22. Yeats

Discuss in detail Yeats's poetic treatment of loss and change in *In Memory of Major Robert Gregory*, *An Irish Airman Foresees his Death* and *Easter 1916*.

PROSE FICTION

23. Atwood

Discuss some of the principal means by which Atwood presents the motivations of her characters in *Cat's Eye* **and** in *Alias Grace*.

24. Austen

*"We can all **begin** freely—a slight preference is natural enough; but there are very few of us who have heart enough to be really in love without encouragement. In nine cases out of ten, a woman had better shew **more** affection than she feels."*

(Charlotte Lucas to Elizabeth Bennet)

"I am no matchmaker, as you know well . . . being much too well aware of the uncertainty of all human events and calculations. I only mean that if Mr. Elliot should some time hence pay his addresses to you, and if you should be disposed to accept him, I think there would be every possibility of your being happy together. A most suitable connection everybody must consider it, but I think it might be a very happy one."

(Lady Russell to Anne Elliot)

Consider the advice offered by a range of characters to Elizabeth Bennet **and** to Anne Elliot, and discuss the effects of that advice.

25. Dickens

Discuss the contribution of humour to Dickens's characterisation in *Hard Times* **and** in *Great Expectations*.

26. Fitzgerald

"The world of a Fitzgerald novel is glamorous but essentially shallow; its characters live in an emotional and spiritual vacuum."

In the light of this statement, discuss some of the principal means by which Fitzgerald presents the worlds of *The Beautiful and Damned* **and** *Tender is the Night*.

27. Galloway

"In her novels Galloway presents to us characters that grow and develop and become stronger."

How effective, in your view, is Galloway's presentation of such characters in *The Trick is to Keep Breathing* **and** in *Foreign Parts*?

28. Gray

Discuss some of the means by which Gray explores concepts of identity in *Lanark* **and** in *Poor Things*.

29. Hardy

Writing of the specified texts, one critic has claimed that *"Hardy's central concerns are the social issues of his day: tradition and change in rural society, class distinctions, attitudes to marriage, the position of women . . . ."*

Discuss *The Return of the Native* **and** *Tess of the d'Urbervilles* in the light of this assertion.

30. Hogg

"In **The Private Memoirs and Confessions of a Justified Sinner**, *the role of the supernatural is to offer an alternative interpretation of reality."*

Discuss.

31. Joyce

Discuss the uses Joyce makes of "epiphanies", moments of intense revelation, in *A Portrait of the Artist as a Young Man* **and** in **one** or **two** of the stories from *Dubliners*.

32. Stevenson

Discuss the role of narrative voice in *The Master of Ballantrae* and in **one** or **two** of the specified short stories.

33. Waugh

Make a comparative study of the importance of houses both as setting and as symbol in *A Handful of Dust* **and** in *Brideshead Revisited*.

PROSE NON-FICTION

34. *"No life is really private or isolated; personal preoccupations are inevitably bound up with the larger movements of mankind."*

Discuss the treatment of "personal preoccupations" and "the larger movements of mankind" in any **one** of the specified texts.

35. It has been suggested that the writer of non-fiction *"preserves in words things that matter to him or her: people, places, events, scenes, incidents, moments"*.

Discuss some of the principal techniques employed by **one** or **two** of the specified writers in order to *"preserve in words things that matter"*.

[Turn over

Section 2—Language Study

You must answer **one question only** in this section.

Unless otherwise indicated, your answer must take the form of an **essay/analytical report** appropriately structured to meet the demands of your selected question.

Topic A—Varieties of English or Scots

1. Show how any **one** variety of English **or** Scots you have studied has been influenced by **one** or **more than one** of the following:

   - mass media
   - population movement
   - globalisation
   - employment patterns
   - political agendas
   - information and communication technology.

2. Describe in detail what you consider to be the distinctive features of any **one** variety of English **or** Scots you have studied.

Topic B—The historical development of English or Scots

If you choose to answer a question on this topic, you must refer to **one** of the two texts provided.

Text A is from Jonathan Swift's *A Proposal for Correcting, Improving and Ascertaining The English Tongue*, published in 1712.

Text B is from Alexander Hume's *Of the Orthographie and Congruitie of the Britan Tongue*, for which the date of publication is uncertain, but possibly 1617 or 1618.

Choose one of these texts and then answer **either** question 3 **or** question 4.

3. What linguistic features of **Text A** differ from those of present-day English **or** what linguistic features of **Text B** differ from those of present-day Scots?

   What explanations can you offer to account for the differences you have identified?

   In your answer, you may wish to consider some or all of the following:

   - spelling
   - punctuation
   - vocabulary
   - grammar.

4. Discuss some of the attitudes towards language in the text you have chosen **and** in other texts from your own reading and research.

Text A

THERE is a another Sett of Men who have contributed very much to the ſpoiling of the *Engliſh* Tongue; I mean the Poets, from the Time of the Reſtoration. Theſe Gentlemen, although they could not be inſenſible how much our Language was already overſtocked with Monoſyllables; yet, to ſave Time and Pains, introduced that barbarous Cuſtom of abbreviating Words, to fit them to the Meaſure of their Verſes; and this they have frequently done, ſo very injudiciouſly, as to form ſuch harſh unharmonious Sounds, that none but a *Northern* Ear could endure: They have joined the moſt obdurate Conſonants without one intervening Vowel, only to ſhorten a Syllable: And their Taſte in time became ſo depraved, that what was at firſt a Poetical Licence not to be juſtified, they made their Choice, alledging, that the Words pronounced at length, ſounded faint and languid. This was a Pretence to take up the ſame Cuſtom in Proſe; ſo that moſt of the Books we ſee now a-days, are full of thoſe Manglings and Abbreviations. Inſtances of this Abuſe are innumerable: What does Your LORDSHIP think of the Words, *Drudg'd, Diſturb'd, Rebuk't, Fledg'd,* and a thouſand others, every where to be met in Proſe as well as Verſe? Where, by leaving out a Vowel to ſave a Syllable, we form ſo jarring a Sound, and ſo difficult to utter, that I have often wondred how it could ever obtain.

ANOTHER Cauſe (and perhaps borrowed from the former) which hath contributed not a little to the maiming of our Language, is a fooliſh Opinion, advanced of late Years, that we ought to ſpell exactly as we ſpeak; which beſide the obvious Inconvenience of utterly deſtroying our Etymology, would be a thing we ſhould never ſee an End of. Not only the ſeveral Towns and Countries of *England*, have a different way of Pronouncing, but even here in *London*, they clip their Words after one Manner about the Court, another in the City, and a third in the Suburbs; and in a few Years, it is probable, will all differ from themſelves, as Fancy or Faſhion ſhall direct: All which reduced to Writing would entirely confound Orthography. Yet many People are ſo fond of this Conceit, that it is ſometimes a difficult matter to read modern Books and Pamphlets; where the Words are ſo curtailed and varied from their original Spelling, that whoever hath been uſed to plain *Engliſh*, will hardly know them by ſight.

Text B

To clere this point, and alsoe to reform an errour bred in the south, and now usurped be our ignorant printeres, I wil tel quhat befel my self quhen I was in the south with a special gud frende of myne. Ther rease, upon sum accident, quhither quho, quhen, quhat, etc., sould be symbolized with q or w, a hoat disputation betuene him and me. After manie conflictes (for we ofte encountered), we met be chance, in the citie of Baeth, with a Doctour of divinitie of both our acquentance. He invited us to denner. At table my antagonist, to bring the question on foot amangs his awn condisciples, began that I was becum an heretik, and the doctour spering how, ansuered that I denyed quho to be spelled with a w, but with qu. Be quhat reason? quod the Doctour. Here, I beginning to lay my grundes of labial, dental, and guttural soundes and symboles, he snapped me on this hand and he on that, that the doctour had mikle a doe to win me room for a syllogisme. Then (said I) a labial letter can not symboliz a guttural syllab. But w is a labial letter, quho a guttural sound. And therfoer w can not symboliz quho, nor noe syllab of that nature. Here the doctour staying them again (for al barked at ones), the proposition, said he, I understand; the assumption is Scottish, and the conclusion false. Quherat al laughed, as if I had bene dryven from al replye, and I fretted to see a frivolouse jest goe for a solid ansuer. My proposition is grounded on the 7 sectio of this same cap., quhilk noe man, I trow, can denye that ever suked the paepes of reason. And soe the question must rest on the assumption quhither w be a labial letter and quho a guttural syllab. As for w, let the exemples of wil, wel, wyne, juge quhilk are sounded befoer the voual with a mint of the lippes, as is said the same cap., sect. 5. As for quho, besydes that it differres from quo onelie be aspiration, and that w, being noe perfect consonant, can not be aspirated, I appele to al judiciouse eares, to quhilk Cicero attributed to mikle, quhither the aspiration in quho be not ex imo gutture, and therfoer not labial.

Topic C—Multilingualism in contemporary Scotland

5. In your own reading and research, what evidence have you found of codeswitching between languages by speakers in contemporary Scotland?

In your answer you should consider some of the forms, contexts and purposes of such codeswitching.

6. To what extent does the Scottish Parliament encourage and support **more than** the three indigenous languages of Scotland?

Topic D—The use of Scots in contemporary literature

For both questions on this topic, you are provided with two texts written in Scots.

Text A is an extract from *The Steamie*, a play by Tony Roper.

Text B is a poem entitled *Tae makk a Martyr* by Sheena Blackhall.

Read the two texts carefully and then answer **either** question 7 **or** question 8.

7. Discuss some of the principal aesthetic effects created by each writer's use of Scots.

8. Select **one** of the texts and contrast the use of Scots in that text—vocabulary, idiom, grammar, orthography—with the use of Scots by a writer other than Tony Roper or Sheena Blackhall.

Text A

Extract from *The Steamie*

DOLLY:	Wait tae ye hear this. Tell them what ye telt me Mrs Culfeathers.
MRS CULFEATHERS:	Well I wis tellin' Dolly that I aye got ma mince oot o' Galloways because it is lovely mince . . . there's hardly any fat in their mince Doreen ye know.
DOREEN (slightly mystified):	Aye, oh, it's good mince.
MRS CULFEATHERS:	D'ye no like their mince Magrit?
MAGRIT:	Aye . . . it's awright. (Looks at DOLLY.)
DOLLY:	Tell them aboot whit Mr Culfeathers says aboot it.
MRS CULFEATHERS:	Well . . . I wis tellin' Dolly aboot how I aye get ma mince oot o' Galloways, but sometimes I get it oot another butchers . . . ye know just for a wee change, and I was saying that when I get it oot another butchers, Mr Culfeathers can always tell, even though I havenae said whit butcher's I got it oot o'. If I pit mince doon tae him, and I havenae got it oot o' Galloways, he aye says tae me, 'where did ye get that mince fae?'

MAGRIT (slight sarcasm):   Does he? . . . (To DOREEN) D'ye hear that?

DOREEN: Aye . . . that's . . . that's . . . that's eh . . . very interesting.

MRS CULFEATHERS: That shows ye what good mince it is.

DOLLY: Oh it is . . . aye it is good mince, isn't it Magrit?

MAGRIT: Oh . . . second tae none.

DOLLY: But that's no the end o' it. There's mair.

DOREEN: Surely not.

MAGRIT: Ye mean even mair interesting than that?

DOLLY: Aye . . . wait tae ye hear this.

MAGRIT: Well I don't see how you can top that but do go on.

Text B

Tae makk a Martyr

Takk ae patriot
Separate him frae kintra, kin an airmy
Croon him wi leaves like ony tattie-bogle
Makk a radge o him an his beliefs

Add nae drap o human kindness, raither
A scoosh o soor grapes, wersh as graveyaird bree
Sprinkle a jeelip o heich wirds ower the proceedins

Wheep yer warrior, bleedin ben the streets
Larded wi gobs an skaith
Beat till nearhaun fooshionless
Afore a fyauchie boorich o yer commons
Hing on the gallows till hauf-smored an thrappled

Neist, remove yer patriot,
Skewer an disembowel
While yet alive . . . hate is a dish best hett

Fry his intimmers aneth his verra een
Syne chop the lave an sen tae aa the airts
Sae his puir pairts micht flegg aff similar craas
Nailin oppression's colours tae life's brig

Sit back an wyte
There's mair nur deid-flesh stewin

[Turn over

Topic E—Language and social context

9. Joan Swann has written *"the language variety you use conveys certain information about you, such as where you come from and what kind of person you are."*

   To what extent does your study of language and social context support this claim?

10. What has your study of language and social context suggested about the effects of audience **and/or** topic on the linguistic choices which speakers make?

Topic F—The linguistic characteristics of informal conversation

For both questions on this topic you are provided with a transcript of a conversation between two women.

Read the transcript carefully and then answer **either** question 11 **or** question 12.

11. What linguistic features characterise this exchange as informal conversation?

12. Using the transcript provided and evidence from your own reading and research, write an essay on turn-taking in informal conversation.

The transcribers have provided the following information regarding transcription methods:

- F631 and F689 are identification numbers given to speakers
- Non-lexical sounds appear in the transcript within square brackets, eg [laugh]
- Stretches of overlapping speech are marked by the use of double slashes: // //
- Stammering, false starts and truncated words are marked by the use of hyphens: -

F631: So, you got married recently, Louise. //Tell us about your,//
F689: //[laugh]//
F631: the whole experience. [inhale]
F689: The whole experience? Oh I don't know. //I don't remember much o it now. [laugh] Sort o wiped from ma memory.//
F631: //[laugh]//
F689: Ehm, it all started, I think, it must have been September or something like that, and David just decided one day "I think we should get married soon". //An I says "Ehm,//
F631: //Mmhm// //[laugh]//
F689: //really?" [laugh]// //[laugh]//
F631: //How romantic! [laugh]//
F689: Och, it was just, I never really thought about it, cause erm, I was quite happy ploddin along, but we'd said like years ago before Rosalyn was even born that we should perhaps get married at some point, [laugh], //so it just sort o//
F631: //Mmhm//
F689: got put on hold and put on hold. And then what with the movin house and stuff. Ehm, so it originally turned out that we'd just go for a really really small do.
F631: Mmhm
F689: And [throat] of course I told Mum and she was like "Oh, we'll need to have a reception" [laugh] and things like that. //So,//
F631: //Right.//

F689: it just started out ehm tryin to keep it as simple an as sort o cheap as possible. [laugh]

F631: Mmhm

F689: Ehm, but it was quite horrendous tryin to find like a place that would accept children, //and stuff like that.//

F631: //Really?//

F689: Mmhm, it was like erm, totally, erm, "You're only allowed kids until half past eight and that's it. No exceptions." //[laugh] Uh-huh//

F631: //Up until half eight, right.//

F689: And, so we tried about four different pubs and phoned other places and it was "no no no no no" //[laugh].//

F631: //Mmhm//

F689: So, and a lot of them were just really small as well, //so I was,//

F631: //Yeah.//

F689: by the time we sort o counted heads it was gonna be like fifty plus, [laugh] //[laugh]]//

F631: //Mmhm//

F689: that's what it started out like, so erm, [throat]. Pa- [tut] What else is there? Eh

F631: But it was a nice place that you had, in the end. //Mmhm//

F689: //Our hotel, uh-huh that was Mum that// sort o said, "Right, we'll go for this", even though it wisnae the cheapest //place.//

F631: //Mmhm//

F689: Ehm, so, //[laugh]//

F631: //And what about ehm// booking the registrar's? Di- when did you do that, for,

F689: Eh, it was as soon as David phoned out and found sort o the, he was like "What date shall we go for?" I was like that "Oh, any date", sort o, "preferably at the end of the month." Ehm, [tut], and, he just phoned up and they told him what dates there [laugh] were an //that was it. [laugh]//

F631: //Yeah.//

F689: oh I just sort of randomly picked that one, the Friday, and I had specifically said to him "Don't pick a Friday", [laugh] or a //a Saturday, [laugh] because you'll never find anywhere like//

F631: //Oh right. [laugh]// //Oh for a reception?//

F689: //that would uh-huh// like for a function in a pub, which was what I was wantin.

F631: Mmhm

F689: Erm so, //that//

F631: //Oops.// //[laugh]//

F689: //wis that [laugh]// that caused a wee argument, so

F631: Mmhm

F689: ehm

[Turn over

Topic G—The linguistic characteristics of political communication

13. Compare and contrast the linguistic characteristics of any **two** types of political communication.

    You may wish to consider:

    • parliamentary debates
    • parliamentary statements (including, if you wish, the statement provided in question 14)
    • political advertising
    • election leaflets
    • interviews with politicians
    • speeches by MPs, MSPs, MEPs, or any other political figures
    • any other types of political communication you have studied.

14. Identify and discuss those features of the following text that are typical of political communication.

    You should support your answer with reference to **some** or **all** of the following:

    • lexical choices
    • grammatical structures
    • rhetorical patterns
    • imagery
    • orientation to audience.

The text is an edited version of part of a statement to the Scottish Parliament made by Jack McConnell, then First Minister of Scotland, on 25 February 2004.

For ease of reference, the text has been subdivided into numbered paragraphs.

[1] Today, I wish to make a statement on our new policy to attract fresh talent to Scotland. The policy is designed to tackle the most serious long-term issue facing our country. Scotland's population is falling; it is declining at a faster rate than that of anywhere else in Europe. That decline, coupled with a significant shift in Scotland's age profile, is making a serious problem even worse. By 2009, Scotland's population will fall below the symbolic 5 million level. By 2027, there could be, on current projections, a quarter of a million fewer people of working age in Scotland. Those projections are a result of there being more deaths in Scotland than births. We know that for centuries Scots emigrated throughout the world, but net emigration is almost insignificant now. Basically, fewer people leave Scotland, but only a few come to live here.

[2] The challenge is now to counter demographic change, but before I lay out the details of our Government's plans to tackle Scotland's declining population, there is one message that I want to make very clear. The first priority of the Government in Scotland must always be to nurture and retain home-grown talent. Helping to meet the hopes and aspirations of the Scottish people should be the motivation of every one of us in this chamber. However, those hopes and aspirations will not be met if our devolved Government does not act to counter what I believe to be the greatest threat to Scotland's future prosperity.

[3] Population decline is serious. Tax revenues will fall. Falling school rolls mean that local schools will close, other local services will become less sustainable and communities will become weaker. The labour market will contract, there will be fewer consumers to underpin a domestic market and our economy will be less dynamic and more likely to contract overall. We can and must do something about that. Although future projections demonstrate demographic shifts of considerable magnitude, taken step by step the challenge looks easier to deal with.

[4] Our first target must be to avoid our population falling below 5 million. To do that, we need an additional 8,000 people living in Scotland each year between now and 2009. We want to meet that target in three ways: by retaining home-grown talent within Scotland; by encouraging Scots who have moved away to come back home; and by attracting some who are completely new to Scotland—from the rest of the United Kingdom, from the European Union and from further afield.

[5] Devolution was created for this precise purpose: to tackle a tough, long-term problem in our national interest. It is absolutely in the interest of every Scottish family that we create a country that is dynamic and growing, with opportunities for our children and our grandchildren. To do that, we need to attract and welcome new people. We need fresh talent. A more diverse, more cosmopolitan country is good for Scots. It will open minds and broaden horizons. It will stimulate ambitions and ideas—to travel, to see some of the world, to learn from others, but to come home, too. Some think that people will move only if there are job opportunities and others think that people locate only according to the quality of life. I believe that the truth is somewhere in between.

[6] Of course, Scotland needs a growing economy and Scotland's economy is growing—not as fast as it could be, but there are signs that it will grow more quickly in the medium term. More ideas are coming out of our universities, there is increased commercialisation, there are greater levels of entrepreneurial activity and more Scots are learning, training and using their skills. There are more jobs and more vacancies and, in a few sectors, there are even shortages.

[7] Scotland has a unique selling point. We are lucky that we are known to be one of the friendliest and most educated peoples in the world. We have a vibrant culture, stunning countryside, excellent schools, decent transport links and good public services. In short, it is good to live in Scotland. I believe that, in the modern world, businesses increasingly choose to locate in the places where people whom they want to employ want to live.

[8] Exactly a year ago today, I made the case that Scotland needs to attract fresh talent to our shores to secure future prosperity for Scotland. In 12 months, we have developed a national consensus that that must be a priority. I believe that the issue is too important to be party political. We cannot allow new people to be welcomed by some and not by others. We will not be able to attract fresh talent to Scotland if our country speaks with different voices. Although we in the chamber might debate the best way of attracting new people to Scotland, I hope that we can agree on one thing—Scotland's projected population decline is something that we must tackle and one important way of doing that is to welcome others to Scotland to contribute to our economy and to our country.

[Turn over

Section 3—Textual Analysis

You must answer **one question only** in this section.

Unless otherwise indicated, your answer must take the form of a **critical analysis** appropriately structured to meet the demands of your selected question.

1. **Prose fiction [*Pages eighteen to twenty-one*]**

*The following extract is a chapter from the novel **No Great Mischief** (2000) by Alistair MacLeod.*

The setting in this chapter is Cape Breton, Nova Scotia, Canada. The year is 1948. The narrator and his family are the descendants of emigrants who left the Scottish Highlands in 1779. They live in a community where Gaelic is still spoken.

Read the extract carefully and then answer the question that follows it (Page twenty-one).

My twin sister and I were the youngest children in our family, and we were three on March 28 when it was decided that we would spend the night with our grandparents.

After he returned from naval service in the war, my father had applied for the position of lightkeeper on the island which seemed almost to float in the channel about
5 a mile and a half from the town which faced the sea. He had long been familiar with boats and the sea and, after passing the examination, was informed in a very formal letter that the job was his. He and my mother were overjoyed because it meant they would not have to go away, and the job reeked of security, which was what they wanted after the disruption of the years of war. The older generation was highly enthusiastic
10 as well. "That island will stay there for a damn long time," said Grandpa appreciatively, although he later apparently sniffed, "Any fool can look after a lighthouse. It is not like being responsible for a *whole* hospital."

On the morning of March 28, which was the beginning of a weekend, my parents and their six children and their dog walked ashore across the ice. Their older sons, who
15 were sixteen, fifteen, and fourteen, apparently took turns carrying my sister and me upon their shoulders, stopping every so often to take off their mitts and rub our faces so that our cheeks would not become so cold as to be frozen without our realising it. Our father, accompanied by our brother Colin, who was eleven, walked ahead of us, testing the ice from time to time with a long pole, although there did not seem much
20 need to do so for he had "bushed" the ice some two months earlier, meaning he had placed spruce trees upright in the snow and ice to serve as a sort of road guide for winter travellers.

During the coldest days of winter, the so-called "dog days", the ice became amazingly solid. It was a combination of drift ice from the region of the eastern Arctic
25 and "made" ice which resulted from the freezing of the local channel. In extremely cold winters if the ice was smooth, it was possible to move freely from the island to the mainland and back again. One could walk, or skate, or fashion an iceboat which would skim and veer with cutting dangerous speed across the stinging surface. People would venture out on the ice with cars and trucks, and on one or two weekends there would be
30 horse races to the delight of all. The sharpshod horses would pull light sleighs or even summer sulkies as they sped around yet another track staked out by temporary spruce. At the conclusion of their races, their owners would hurry to cover them with blankets as the perspiration on their coats began to turn to frost. They seemed almost, for a few brief moments, to be horses who had prematurely aged before the eyes of those
35 who watched them, their coats of black and brown turning to a fragile white. White horses frozen on a field of ice and snow.

My parents welcomed the winter ice because it allowed them to do many practical things that were more difficult to accomplish in the summer. They could truck their supplies over the ice without the difficulty of first hauling everything to the wharf and
40 then trying to load it on the boat which swayed below and then, after transporting it across to the island, having to hoist it up out of the boat to the wharf's cap and then again having to transport it up the cliff to the promontory where the lighthouse stood. They took coal and wood across in the winter, and walked and traded animals, leading them by their halters across the treacherous and temporary bridge.

45 Also in the winter their social life improved, as unexpected visitors crossed to see them, bringing rum and beer and fiddles and accordions. All of them staying up all night, singing songs and dancing and playing cards and telling stories, while out on the ice the seals moaned and cried and the ice itself thundered and snapped and sometimes groaned, forced by the pressures of the tides and currents, running unabated and
50 unseen beneath the cold white surface. Sometimes the men would go outside to urinate and when they would return the others would ask, "*De chuala?*" "What did you hear?" "Nothing," they would say. "*Cha chuala sion.*" "Nothing, only the sound of the ice."

On March 28 there was a lot for my family to do. My older brothers were going to visit their cousins in the country—those who still lived in the old *Calum Ruadh* houses
55 neighbouring the spot which my grandparents had left when they became people of the town. If they could get a ride they were going to spend the weekend there. Even if they could not get a ride, they were planning to walk, saying that ten miles on the inland sheltered roads would not be as cold as a mile and a half straight across the ice. My parents were planning to cash my father's cheque, which they hoped my
60 grandparents had picked up at the post office, and my brother Colin was looking forward to his new parka, which my mother had shrewdly ordered from the Eaton's sale catalogue when such heavy winter garments were reduced by the coming promise of spring. He had been hoping for it since before Christmas. My sister and I were looking forward to the visit with our grandparents, who always made a great to-do
65 about us and always told us how smart we were to make such a great journey from such a far and distant place. And the dog knew where she was going too, picking her way across the ice carefully and sometimes stopping to gnaw off the balls of snow and ice which formed between the delicate pads of her hardened paws.

Everything went well and the sun shone brightly as we journeyed forth together,
70 walking first upon the ice so we could later walk upon the land.

In the late afternoon, the sun still shone, and there was no wind but it began to get very cold, the kind of deceptive cold that can fool those who confuse the shining of the winter sun with warmth. Relatives visiting my grandparents' house said that my brothers had arrived at their destination and would not be coming back until, perhaps,
75 the next day.

My parents distributed their purchases into haversacks, which were always at my grandparents' house, and which they used for carrying supplies upon their backs. Because my parents' backs would be burdened and because my brothers were not there, it was decided that my sister and I would spend the night and that our brothers would
80 take us back to the island when they returned. It was suggested that Colin also might stay, but he was insistent that he go, so that he might test the long-anticipated warmth of the new parka. When they left, the sun was still shining, although it had begun to decline, and they took two storm lanterns which might serve as lights or signs and signals for the last part of the trip. My mother carried one and Colin the other, while
85 my father grasped the ice pole in his hand. When they set out, they first had to walk

about a mile along the shore until they reached the appropriate place to get on the ice and then they started across, following the route of the spruce trees which my father had set out.

Everyone could see their three dark forms and the smaller one of the dog outlined
90   upon the whiteness over which they travelled. By the time they were halfway across, it was dusk and out there on the ice they lit their lanterns, and that too was seen from the shore. And then they continued on their way. Then the lanterns seemed to waver and almost to dance wildly, and one described an arc in what was now the darkness and then was still. Grandpa watched for almost a minute to be sure of what he was seeing
95   and then he shouted to my grandmother, "There is something wrong out on the ice. There is only one light and it is not moving."

My grandmother came quickly to the window. "Perhaps they stopped," she said. "Perhaps they're resting. Perhaps they had to adjust their packs. Perhaps they had to relieve themselves."

100   "But there is only one light," said Grandpa, "and it is not moving at all."

"Perhaps that's it," said Grandma hopefully. "The other light blew out and they're trying to get it started."

My sister and I were playing on the kitchen floor with Grandma's cutlery. We were playing "store", taking turns buying the spoons and knives and forks from each other
105   with a supply of pennies from a jar Grandma kept in her lower cupboard for emergencies.

"The light is still not moving," said Grandpa and he began hurriedly to pull on his winter clothes and boots, even as the phone began ringing. "The light is not moving. The light is not moving," the voices said. "They're in trouble out on the ice."

110   And then the voices spoke in the hurriedness of exchange: "Take a rope." "Take some ice poles." "Take a blanket that we can use as a stretcher." "Take brandy." "We will meet you at the corner. Don't start across without us."

"I have just bought all his spoons and knives," said my sister proudly from the kitchen floor, "and I still have all these pennies left."

115   "Good for you," said Grandma. "A penny saved is a penny earned."

When they were partway to the shore, their lights picked up the dog's eyes, and she ran to Grandpa when he called to her in Gaelic, and she leaped up to his chest and his outstretched arms and licked his face even as he threw his mitts from his hands so he could bury them deep within the fur upon her back.

120   "She was coming to get us," he said. "They've gone under."

"Not under," someone said. "Perhaps down but not under."

"I think under," said Grandpa. "She was under, anyway. She's soaked to the spine. She's smart and she's a good swimmer and she's got a heavy, layered coat. If she just went down, she'd be down and up in a second but she's too wet for that. She must
125   have gone down, and then the current carried her under the ice and she had to swim back to the hole to get herself back out."

They went out on the ice in single file, the string of their moving lights seeming almost like a kind of Christmas decoration; each light moving to the rhythm of the man who walked and carried it in his hand. They followed the tracks and walked
130   towards the light which remained permanent in the ice. As they neared it, they realised

it was sitting on the ice, sitting upright by itself and not held by any hand. The tracks continued until they came to the open water, and then there were no more.

Years later, my sister and I were in Grade XI and the teacher was talking to the class about Wordsworth and, as an example, was reading to us from the poem entitled "Lucy
135   Gray". When she came to the latter lines, both my sister and I started simultaneously and looked towards each other, as if in the old, but new to us, we had stumbled upon the familiar experience:

"They followed from the snowy bank
Those footmarks, one by one,
140   Into the middle of the plank;
And further there were none!"

"And further there were none!" But on March 28 we were tiring of our game of store and putting the cutlery away as our grandmother prepared to ready us for bed while glancing anxiously through the window.

145   Out on the ice the dog began to whine when they came near the open water, and the first men in the line lay on their stomachs, each holding the feet of the man before him, so that they might form a type of human chain with their weight distributed more evenly than if they remained standing. But it was of no use, for other than the light there was nothing, and the ice seemed solid right up to the edge of the dark and
150   sloshing void.

There was nothing for the men to do but wonder. Beyond the crater, the rows of spruce trees marched on in ordered single file in much the same way that they led up to the spot of their interruption. It was thought that perhaps only one tree had gone down and under. The section of the ice that had gone was not large, but as my
155   grandfather said, "It was more than big enough for us."

The tide was going out when they vanished, leaving nothing but a lantern—perhaps tossed on to the ice by a sinking hand and miraculously landing upright and continuing to glow, or perhaps set down after its arc, wildly but carefully by a hand which sought to reach another. The men performed a sort of vigil out on the ice, keeping the hole
160   broken open with their ice poles and waiting for the tide to run its course. And in the early hours of the morning when the tide was in its change, my brother Colin surfaced in one of those half-expected uncertainties known only to those who watch the sea. The white fur hood of his parka broke the surface and the half-frozen men who were crouched like patient Inuit around the hole shouted to one another, and reached for
165   him with their poles. They thought that he had not been a great distance under, or that his clothes had snagged beneath the ice; and they thought that, perhaps, since he was not bearing a backpack, he had not been so heavily burdened and, perhaps, the new material in his parka possessed flotation qualities that had buoyed him to the top. His eyes were open and the drawstrings of his hood were still neatly tied and tucked beside
170   his throat in the familiar manner that my mother always used.

My parents were not found that day, or the next, or in the days or months that followed.

Question

In what ways and how effectively does Alistair MacLeod present what happens on March 28?

2.   **Prose non-fiction [*Pages twenty-two to twenty-five*]**

Read carefully the essay **Where Does Writing Come From?** *(1998) by Richard Ford and then answer the question that follows it (Page twenty-five).*

Where Does Writing Come From?

Where does writing come from? I've often been guilty of trying to answer this question. I've done so, I suppose, in the spirit André Breton must've had in mind when he wrote: *Our brains are dulled by the incurable mania of wanting to make the unknown known.* I've done it on public stages after readings, in panel discussions with
5 dozing colleagues, standing before rows of smirking students, at the suggestion of cruel and cynical journalists in hotel rooms at home and abroad. And I believe I can honestly say that I would never spontaneously have asked myself this question had not someone else seemed interested, or had my financial fortunes not seemed (correctly or incorrectly) tied to such speculation. I must've thought I knew the answer, or thought
10 I didn't need to know it. Yet, once the question was asked, I've over the years taken an interest in the answers I've come up with—which is to say, dreamed up—much in the way I take interest in the progress of any piece of fiction I'm writing. This, after all, is what one does, or what I do anyway when I write fiction: pick out something far-fetched or at least previously unthought of by me, something I feel a kind of
15 language-less yen for, and then see what I can dream up about it or around it that's interesting or amusing to myself in the hope that by making it make sense in words I'll make it interesting and important to someone else.

Plenty of writers for plenty of centuries have furrowed their brows over this question—where does it come from, all this stuff you write? An important part of
20 Wordsworth's answer for instance was that ". . . good poetry is the spontaneous overflow of powerful feelings". And I've seen no reason I shouldn't just as well get my two cents' worth down on the chance I might actually get to or near the bottom of the whole subject and possibly help extinguish literature once and for all—since that seems to be where the enquiry tends: let's get writing explained and turned into a neat
25 theorem, like a teasing problem in plasma physics, so we can forget about it and get back to watching *Seinfeld*. And failing that, I might at least say something witty or charming that could make a listener or a reader seek out the book I really do care about—the one I've just written and hope you'll love.

It may be that this investigation stays alive in America partly because of that
30 principally American institution, the creative writing course—of which I am a bona fide graduate, and about which Europeans like to roll their eyes. The institution has many virtues—time to write being the most precious. But it also has several faults, one of which is the unproven good of constantly having like-minded colleagues around to talk to about what one is doing, as if companionship naturally improved one's
35 important work just when one is doing it. How we do what we do and why we do it may just be a subject a certain kind of anxious person can't help tumbling to at a time in life when getting things written at all is a worry, and when one's body of work is small and not very distinguishable from one's private self, and when one comes to find that the actual thing one is writing is not a very riveting topic of conversation over
40 drinks. Among dedicated novices, the large subject of provenance may be all we have in common and all that will pass for artily abstract speculation of a disinterested kind.

Clearly another socio-literary force which keeps the topic alive is that among many
people who are not writers there's occasionally a flighty belief that writers are special
people, vergers of some kind, in charge of an important interior any person would be
45 wise to come close to as a way of sidling up to a potent life's essence. Questions about
how, why, etc. become just genuflects before the medium. And writers, being generally
undercharged in self-esteem and forever wanting more attention for their work, are
often quite willing to become their work's exponent if not its actual avatar.   I
remember an anecdote about a male writer I know who, upon conducting an interested
50 visitor to his desk overlooking the Pacific, is reported to have whispered as they tiptoed
into the sacred, sun-shot room, "Well, here it is. This is where I make the magic."

Again, nothing's new here: just another instance of supposing an approach upon
the writer will reveal the written thing more fully, more truly; or if not that then it's the
old mistake of confusing the maker with the made thing—an object which may really
55 have some magical pizazz about it, who knows?

Considering an actual set of mechanical connections that might have brought a
piece of writing from nowhere, the "place" it resided before I'd written it, to its final
condition as the book I hope you'll love, actually impresses upon me the romantic view
that artistic invention is a kind of casual magic, one which can't be adequately
60 explained the way, say, a train's arrival in Des Moines can nicely be accounted for by
tracing the tracks and switches and sidings and tunnels all the way to its origin in
Paducah.

You can—and scholars do—try to trace some apparent connections back from the
finished work to the original blank mind and page and even to before that ("He used
65 his father's name for the axe-murderer" . . . hmmm; "she suffered glaucoma just like
the jilted sister who became a Carmelite nun, so how can you argue the whole damn
story isn't about moral blindness?"). But of course such a procedure is famously
unreliable and even sometimes downright impertinent, since in the first place (and
there need not be a second) such investigations start at and take for granted the
70 existence of Des Moines, whereas for the writer (and I mean soon to abandon this train
business) Des Moines is not just a city but a word that has to be not merely found, but
conjured from nothing. In fact the word may not even have been Des Moines to begin
with—it may have been Abilene or Chagrin Falls—but became Des Moines because
the writer inadvertently let Abilene slip his mind, or because Des Moines had that nice
75 diphthong in it and looked neat and Frenchy on the page, whereas Abilene had those
three clunky syllables, and there was already a dopey country song about it. Anyway,
there are at least two Abilenes, one in Texas and another one in Kansas, which is
confusing, and neither has rail service.

You can see what I mean: the true connections might never really be traceable
80 because they exist only in that murky, silent but fecund interstellar night where
impulse, free association, instinct and error reign. And even if I were faithfully to try
explaining the etiological connections in a piece of writing I'd done, I still might lie
about them, or I might just be wrong because I forgot. But in any case I'd finally have
to make something up pretty much the way a scholar does—though not exactly like a
85 writer does who, as I said before, always starts with nothing.

I remember once a complimentary reviewer of a book I'd written singling out for
approval my choice of adjectives, which seemed to him surprising and expansive and of
benefit to the story. One sentence he liked contained a phrase in which I'd referred to a

character's eyes as "old": "He looked on her in an old-eyed way." Naturally, I was
90 pleased to have written something that somebody liked. Only, when I was not long
afterward packing away manuscripts for the attic, my eyes happened to fall upon the
page and the very commended phrase, "old-eyed", and to notice that somehow in the
rounds of fatigued retyping that used to precede a writer's final sign-off on a book in
the days before word processors, the original and rather dully hybridised "cold-eyed"
95 had somehow lost its "c" and become "old-eyed", only nobody'd noticed since they
both made a kind of sense.

This is my larger point writ, admittedly, small, and it calls to mind the joke about
the man from Alabama who couldn't understand how a thermos could keep cold things
cold and hot things always hot, and expressed his wonder in a phrase akin to the title of
100 this very essay: "How do it know?"

Anyone who's ever written a novel or a story or a poem and had the occasion later to
converse about it with an agitated or merely interested reader knows the pinchy feel
that comes when the reader tries to nail down the connections linking the story to some
supposed "source", either as a way of illuminating the procedures that transform life to
105 shapely art, or else of just plain diminishing an act of creation to some problem of
industrial design.

In my case, this enquiry often centres on the potent subject of children, and
specifically writing about children, and more prosecutorily on how it is I can write
about children to such and such effect without actually having or having had any
110 myself. (My wife and I don't have any.)

It's frequently surprising to whomever I'm speaking to that I can write persuasively
about children: although the surprise is often expressed not as pure delight but in a
kind of blinkingly suspicious tone whose spirit is either that I do have children (in
another county, maybe) and don't want to admit it, or else that somebody in a position
115 of authority needs to come down and take a closer look at my little minor inventions to
certify that they're really as finely and truly drawn as they seem.

Myself, I try to stay in happy spirits about such questioning. Some stranger, after
all, has or seems to have read at least a part of some book I've written and been moved
by it, and I'm always grateful for that. He or she could also as easily have been
120 watching *Seinfeld*. And so mostly I just try to smile and chuckle and mumble-mutter
something about having been a child once myself, and if that doesn't work I say
something about there being children pretty much everywhere for the watchful to
study, and that my Jamesian job, after all, is to be a good observer. And finally if that
isn't enough I say that if it were so hard to write about children I of all people
125 wouldn't be able to do it, since I'm no smarter than the next guy.

But the actual truth—the one I know to be true and that sustains my stories—is that
even though I was once a child, and even though there are a God's own slew of bratty
kids around to be studied like lab rats, and even though I'm clearly not the smartest
man in the world, I still mostly write about children by making them up. I make them
130 up out of language bits, out of my memories, out of stories in newspapers, out of
overheard remarks made by my friends and their kids, out of this and out of that, and
sometimes out of nothing at all but the pleasurable will to ascribe something that might
be interesting to a child instead of to an adult or to a spaceman or a horse, after which a
child, a fictive child, begins to take shape on the page as a willed, moral gesture toward

135 a reader. '"All I want for Christmas is to know the difference between that and which," said little Johnny, who was just ten years old but already beginning to need some firmer discipline.' Behold: a child is born.

Occasionally if pushed or annoyed I'll come right out and say it: I make these little beggars up, that's what. So sue me. But an odd restraint almost always makes me
140 revert to my prior explanations. Some delicacy in me simply doesn't want to say, "They're invented things, these characters, you can't track them down like rabbits to their holes. They won't be hiding there." It's as though arguing for invention and its fragile wondrous efficacy was indelicate, wasn't quite nice. And even though arguing for it wouldn't harm or taint invention's marvels (we all know novels are made-up
145 things; it's part of our pleasure to keep such knowledge in our minds), still I always feel queasy doing it—not like a magician who reluctantly shows a rube how to pull a nickel out of his own ear, but more like a local parish priest who upon hearing a small but humiliating confession from a friend, lets the friend off easy just to move matters on to a higher ground.

150 Wallace Stevens wrote once that "in an age of disbelief . . . it is for the poet to supply the satisfactions of belief in his measure and his style". And that takes in how I feel about invention—invented characters, invented landscapes, invented breaks of the heart and their subsequent repairs. I believe that there are important made-up things that resist precise tracing back, and that it's a blessing there are, since our acceptance of
155 them in literature (acting as a substitute for less acceptable beliefs) suggests that for every human problem, every insoluble, every cul-de-sac, every despair, there's a chance we can conjure up an improvement—a Des Moines, where previously there was only a glum Abilene.

Frank Kermode wrote thirty years ago in his wonderful book *The Sense of an*
160 *Ending* that, "It is not that we are connoisseurs of chaos, but that we are surrounded by it, and equipped for coexistence with it only by our fictive powers". To my mind, not to believe in invention, in our fictive powers, to believe that all is traceable, that the rabbit must finally be in the hole waiting is (because it's dead wrong) a certain recipe for the squalls of disappointment, and a small but needless reproach to mankind's
165 saving capacity to imagine what could be better and, with good hope then, to seek it.

Question

"Where does writing come from?"

How effectively, in your view, does the writer explore the ideas raised by this question?

In your answer you should take account of his use of:

- personal experience and anecdote
- language and imagery
- sentence and paragraph structure
- the structure of the essay as a whole
- any other literary or rhetorical devices you consider to be important.

[Turn over

3. **Poetry (*Page twenty-six*)**

Read carefully the poem **The world is too much with us** . . . *(1807) by William Wordsworth and then answer the question that follows it.*

> The world is too much with us; late and soon,
> Getting and spending, we lay waste our powers;
> Little we see in Nature that is ours;
> We have given our hearts away, a sordid boon!
> 5   This Sea that bares her bosom to the moon;
> The winds that will be howling at all hours,
> And are up-gathered now like sleeping flowers;
> For this, for everything, we are out of tune;
> It moves us not.—Great God! I'd rather be
> 10   A Pagan suckled in a creed outworn;
> So might I, standing on this pleasant lea,
> Have glimpses that would make me less forlorn;
> Have sight of Proteus[1] rising from the sea;
> Or hear old Triton[2] blow his wreathèd horn.

[1] An ancient Greek sea god capable of taking many shapes.

[2] An ancient Greek sea god often depicted as trumpeting on a shell.

Question

Write a detailed critical analysis of this poem in which you make clear what you consider to be the significant features of its language and form.

4. **Drama (*Pages twenty-seven to thirty-six*)**

The following extract is taken from the one-act play **Walking Through Seaweed** *(1970) by Ian Hamilton Finlay.*

The play presents a meeting between two girls of sixteen who have previously met casually at a dance.

The scene of the meeting is described as follows: "A city street of the 1960s, at dusk. Two teenage girls have sauntered up to look in a shop window. Three doors away is a café with a juke-box, its raucous or wistful pop songs carrying faintly into the street. Music: any wistful pop song."

The characters are identified only as FIRST GIRL and SECOND GIRL.

Read the extract carefully and then answer the question that follows it (Page thirty-six).

	FIRST GIRL:	I like rock-'n'-roll and jiving.
	SECOND GIRL:	I like that too – it's lovely.
	FIRST GIRL:	Everyone goes jiving.
	SECOND GIRL:	Yep. [*Pause.*] You got a boy friend?
5	FIRST GIRL:	Yep. I got lots of them.
	SECOND GIRL:	You got lots of boy friends?
	FIRST GIRL:	Yep.
	SECOND GIRL:	What d'you do with them?
	FIRST GIRL:	Not much . . . Go jiving.
10	SECOND GIRL:	That all?
	FIRST GIRL:	Go to the pictures.
	SECOND GIRL:	That all?
	FIRST GIRL:	What else?—Go jiving, go to the pictures. Play the juke-box in a café. What else?
15	SECOND GIRL:	I got a boy friend.
	FIRST GIRL:	Have you?
	SECOND GIRL:	Yep. I got a boy friend. And he's sort of special. I mean – I mean I've just the one special boy friend – and do you know what he and I do?
20	FIRST GIRL:	No.
	SECOND GIRL:	Well, guess – go on. Remember about – about the seaweed, and—. Remember he's my special boy friend . . . Now you try and guess what he and I do . . .

	FIRST GIRL:	Go to the pictures?
25	SECOND GIRL:	No.
	FIRST GIRL:	Go jiving?
	SECOND GIRL:	No.
	FIRST GIRL:	If you had enough money, you could go jiving – or something – every night.
30	SECOND GIRL:	Oh, he and I got plenty money. He and I are *loaded*.—But we don't go jiving.
	FIRST GIRL:	No? Can't he jive then?
	SECOND GIRL:	Yep. But he doesn't want to.—He ain't like an ordinary boy. He's special.
35	FIRST GIRL:	All the boys nowadays go jiving.
	SECOND GIRL:	You're supposed to be guessing what he and I do . . .
	FIRST GIRL:	No pictures . . . No jiving . . . I suppose you go in a café and play the juke-box . . .
	SECOND GIRL:	No. We never play a juke-box.
40	FIRST GIRL:	Sounds like your boy must be a square.
	SECOND GIRL:	No, he ain't a square.
	FIRST GIRL:	Well, what d'you do? You'll have to tell me.
	SECOND GIRL:	Me and my boy friend – I told you he's special – *we go walking through seaweed.*
45	FIRST GIRL:	You don't!
	SECOND GIRL:	But we do.—We go – in his car – down to where the sea is, and then – then we take off our shoes . . . and we walk through the seaweed . . . it's ever so lovely!
	FIRST GIRL:	You must be crackers – you and your boy friend.
50	SECOND GIRL:	We are not crackers. He's a very nice boy. [*Pause.*] And while we're walking along through the seaweed – he's ever such a nice boy – he takes hold of my hand . . .
	FIRST GIRL:	What does he do?
	SECOND GIRL:	When we're walking?
55	FIRST GIRL:	No, what does he *do*? What does he work at?
	SECOND GIRL:	He's – he's in advertising.
	FIRST GIRL:	What's his name?
	SECOND GIRL:	His first name's Paul.
	FIRST GIRL:	You ain't just making all of this up, are you?

60 SECOND GIRL: How'd I be making it up? I told you his name, didn't I – Paul. His name is Paul and he's ever so handsome . . . He has nice dark hair and he's . . . kind of smooth . . .

    FIRST GIRL: It doesn't sound to me like a nice, smooth, handsome boy that's in advertising – a kind of a boy like this Paul – would want to go
65   walking through a lot of seaweed . . .

    SECOND GIRL: I beg your pardon, but he *does*. Let me tell you – he wouldn't *mind* getting bit by a crab. [*Pause*] The fact is, he's *fond* of crabs.

    FIRST GIRL: Is he?

70 SECOND GIRL: And we never do get bit.

    FIRST GIRL: What kind of seaweed is that seaweed?

    SECOND GIRL: Well, I'll tell you . . . We walk through every kind of seaweed – the liquorice stuff – and also the other poppy kind . . . And as we walk, we hold hands.

75 FIRST GIRL: It sounds square to me.

    SECOND GIRL: Well, it isn't.—We could take you along with us one day . . . You could come along with me and Paul, and we could all three of us go walking in the seaweed . . .

    FIRST GIRL: I think your Paul must be bats.

80 SECOND GIRL: He is *not* bats. He's a very sensible boy. He only sometimes gets fed-up of being in – the office . . . He gets tired of – the office – and on Saturdays – he wants a change . . . He gets sick-fed up to-the-teeth with that old office . . . So we go and walk through seaweed . . .

85 FIRST GIRL: Where d'you work yourself?

    SECOND GIRL: In a factory.

    FIRST GIRL: How come you happened to meet this Paul fellow who's so handsome and works in advertising?

    SECOND GIRL: You sound like you don't believe me.

90 FIRST GIRL: I'm only asking – how come you met him?

    SECOND GIRL: We met . . . at a dance. [*Pause*] You know – like me and you did. [*Pause*] I suppose you weren't seeing your boy friends that night?

    FIRST GIRL: No.

95 SECOND GIRL: Sometimes . . . you feel like being more on your own . . . Yep . . .

    FIRST GIRL: I never met any handsome smooth fellows – out of advertising – at a dance . . .

    SECOND GIRL: Well, maybe you will . . .

    FIRST GIRL: I never even *saw* any fellows who looked like that . . .

100	SECOND GIRL:	Well, it's just your luck.—And then Paul and I have the same tastes . . .
	FIRST GIRL:	Yep. You both like walking through that seaweed . . .
105	SECOND GIRL:	Yep. That's our favourite thing. [*Pause.*] Don't you ever get fed-up with going to the pictures? Don't you ever get sick-fed-up-to-the-teeth with just ordinary boys? And work? And all that . . . ?
	FIRST GIRL:	I dunno. I don't think about it.
	SECOND GIRL:	Where d'you work?
	FIRST GIRL:	In a factory.
110	SECOND GIRL:	Same as me.
	FIRST GIRL:	Yep. Same as you. But I never met – at a dance – any handsome fellow out of advertising. I *read* of them in magazines. I read of *lots* of them in that magazine my Mum gets . . . Tall, dark and smooth . . . And come to think of it, *their* name was Paul.
115	SECOND GIRL:	Paul is a very common name in advertising.
	FIRST GIRL:	Yep. But I never met one *real* such fellow . . .
	SECOND GIRL:	Maybe you will, though . . . someday.
	FIRST GIRL:	Maybe. Yep. [*Pause.*] I only hope if I do he don't have a taste for walking through seaweed . . .
120	SECOND GIRL:	You have to walk through seaweed sometimes – if you want to get down to where the sea is . . .
	FIRST GIRL:	Who wants to get to the sea?
125	SECOND GIRL:	I do sometimes. I like it. [*Pause.*] It ain't like a factory – the sea. It's big – and it's deep, and—. Well, I dunno. But I like the sea.
	FIRST GIRL:	You're a queer one, you are.
	SECOND GIRL:	What's the name of *your* boy friend?
	FIRST GIRL:	I already told you – I ain't got just *one* boy friend. I got lots of boy friends. I got hundreds.
130	SECOND GIRL:	Who?
	FIRST GIRL:	I can't remember their names off-hand . . .
	SECOND GIRL:	Are they Beats?
	FIRST GIRL:	No they ain't.
	SECOND GIRL:	Do you think I'm a Beat – a Beat girl?
135	FIRST GIRL:	Yep. The things you say – you must be a Beat. Though – well, you ain't *dressed* like a Beat. But walking in seaweed – *that's* sort of a Beat thing . . .

SECOND GIRL:	My Paul walks through seaweed. And he ain't a Beat – he's an advertising man.
140　FIRST GIRL:	What do they do in them places?
SECOND GIRL:	Advertising places?
FIRST GIRL:	Yep. Advertising places. What do they do there?
SECOND GIRL:	Well, I dunno . . . I suppose . . . Well, they sort of – advertise things . . .
145　FIRST GIRL:	What does *he* do?
SECOND GIRL:	Paul?
FIRST GIRL:	Yep. What does Paul do in that advertising place?
SECOND GIRL:	He.—Well, he never talks much about it. You don't think of – of work when you're walking in the seaweed, see? You feel *romantic*.
150	
FIRST GIRL:	All the same you must know what he *does*.
SECOND GIRL:	Well, as a matter of fact I do know. What he does is – is – is go to conferences.
FIRST GIRL:	Conferences?
155　SECOND GIRL:	Yep.
FIRST GIRL:	I read about them conferences in my Mum's magazine . . .
SECOND GIRL:	Uh-huh.
FIRST GIRL:	It seems like advertising's *all* conferences. There's this boy – the one called Paul, you know – the one who's sort of smooth, and dark, and handsome – and what he does is, go to conferences.
160	
SECOND GIRL:	Uh-huh. Well, that's like Paul. Paul goes to conferences.
FIRST GIRL:	Then, after the conferences – when they've knocked off advertising – then this boy Paul – this handsome smoothy – he goes and meets his girl and they go to a rest-ur-ant. They sit and eat lobsters and maybe he's *too* smooth.
165	
SECOND GIRL:	My Paul isn't too smooth.
FIRST GIRL:	Maybe. But what about the other one?
SECOND GIRL:	I ain't *got* another one.
170　FIRST GIRL:	Oh ain't you? Come off it . . .
SECOND GIRL:	But I *told* you – we're special.
FIRST GIRL:	What about the one with ginger hair and a snub nose. The engineer.

[Turn over

	SECOND GIRL:	I don't *know* any engineers.
175	FIRST GIRL:	I bet *he* wouldn't walk through seaweed though. I bet the ginger one with the snub nose spends *his* Saturdays at a football match.
	SECOND GIRL:	I don't love *him*. I love Paul.
	FIRST GIRL:	You don't care about the engineer, eh?
180	SECOND GIRL:	No. If you want to know, I can't stand him.—All he *ever* wants to do is – go and jive.
	FIRST GIRL:	That's what I said. He does the same things like everyone else does.
	SECOND GIRL:	But Paul – he's different.
185	FIRST GIRL:	Yep. He's different. You're telling me he is! Any boy who spends his Saturdays just walking through seaweed is different. He's a head-case. [*Pause.*] Ain't you even *scared* of what might be in it? Ain't you scared of all them crabs and things?
	SECOND GIRL:	No. I'm more scared of every day.
190	FIRST GIRL:	What?
	SECOND GIRL:	Every day. The factory, and all that.—Just working and—. [*Pause.*] You know, when we've walked all through the seaweed– that kind like liquorice and the other poppy kind – when we've walked all the way through the seaweed, hand in hand—.
195	FIRST GIRL:	I thought *you* said you walked with your arms held up.
	SECOND GIRL:	That's right. Like a tight-rope-lady.
	FIRST GIRL:	Then how come you can hold hands?
	SECOND GIRL:	Oh, when Paul and I are walking through the seaweed – we only hold up our *outside* hands.
200	FIRST GIRL:	Then how d'you carry your shoes and socks?
	SECOND GIRL:	What?
	FIRST GIRL:	If the two of you's holding hands and you're holding up your hands like the telly-tight-rope-lady – you only got *two* hands – how d'you carry your shoes and socks? Eh?
205	SECOND GIRL:	Well — well, what d'you think? We left them up where the car is. See?
	FIRST GIRL:	Oh? [*Pause.*] One of these days you and Paul – you're going to be *sorry* for walking through seaweed.
	SECOND GIRL:	Why?
210	FIRST GIRL:	You're going to get bit. That's why.

SECOND GIRL:	We never get bit. But we just *might* though. That's what's nice about walking through seaweed – that you might get bit . . . just a *little* . . . [*Pause.*] Them crabs don't scare *me*. I ain't scared of crabs. They're kind of on *our* side.
215 FIRST GIRL:	What? Whose side?
SECOND GIRL:	Me and Paul's side.
FIRST GIRL:	No one's on your side. Except you.
SECOND GIRL:	Yes they are. The crabs are. All wee things like crabs and – and wee things like that – they *like* me and Paul. [*Pause.*] Do you tell all of them boy friends things?
220	
FIRST GIRL:	No. They're just boy friends.
SECOND GIRL:	I always tell my Paul *lots* of things.
FIRST GIRL:	Do you?
SECOND GIRL:	Yep. He's special. I tell him everything.
225 FIRST GIRL:	I can picture it.
SECOND GIRL:	What?
FIRST GIRL:	You and him – walking in seaweed.—The pair of you standing, walking – right up over the ankles too – in all that seaweed.—All of them crabs ready to bite you – and you and him just standing there telling things . . .
230	
SECOND GIRL:	Well, I always feel like telling things there in the seaweed. [*Pause.*] And then – like I was saying to you – when we've walked right through it all through the seaweed – and us holding hands too – holding our hands and telling our secret things—.
235	
FIRST GIRL:	What sort of secret things?
SECOND GIRL:	Like you tell yourself in bed at night . . .
FIRST GIRL:	When I'm in bed at night I go to sleep. If we had the telly I'd sit up later though. Everyone round us has the telly. Only *we* ain't. You feel right out of it.
240	
SECOND GIRL:	You can come round some night and see our telly.
FIRST GIRL:	That ain't the same as if it was your *own* telly.
SECOND GIRL:	No . . . Well, I was saying – when we've walked all through the seaweed . . .
245 FIRST GIRL:	Yep?
SECOND GIRL:	Then me and Paul – he's a real smooth fellow – we come to where the sea is . . .
FIRST GIRL:	Yep?
SECOND GIRL:	Ain't you listening? We come to the sea.

[Turn over

250 FIRST GIRL: I'm listening. [*Pause.*] I like those records too . . . All we got at home's an old wireless . . . My other sister – she's got a radiogram.

SECOND GIRL: We come to the sea and – it's ever so beautiful.

FIRST GIRL: Some of them's beautiful. I like the cheery ones.

255 SECOND GIRL: I ain't talking about those records on the old juke-box – I'm telling you about Paul and me: we come to *the sea*.

FIRST GIRL: Well, the sea ain't *much* – in my opinion. I don't care *that* much about the sea that I'd risk my life – and spoil my shoes maybe –
260 just walking through a lot of seaweed, all full of crabs and things, to get to it. [*Pause.*] You could get bit like that. It just ain't nice.

SECOND GIRL: What ain't nice?

FIRST GIRL: Ain't I telling you? – Seaweed ain't nice. And the sea ain't nice. And having no telly ain't. I wouldn't put a *toe* in that seaweed . . .

265 SECOND GIRL: But it's – beautiful – the sea.

FIRST GIRL: Yep. I seen it.

SECOND GIRL: Did you ever dream of it?

FIRST GIRL: I don't have dreams.—Only once I dreamed we'd a telly . . .

SECOND GIRL: Yep.

270 FIRST GIRL: A great big telly with a screen as big as the screen in a picture-house. Not one of them wee old-fashioned picture-houses screens . . . . A big screen, about a hundred yards across . . .

SECOND GIRL: Yep?

FIRST GIRL: With a plastic-plated cabinet.

275 SECOND GIRL: I ain't never dreamed of a telly set . . .

FIRST GIRL: Another time I had a dream of a radiogram – and once I dreamed I was married to a disc-jockey.

SECOND GIRL: Well, there you are. You *do* have dreams.

FIRST GIRL: Yep. Well . . . Maybe . . .

280 SECOND GIRL: I dreamed – I dreamed of the sea once. . . . It was all – kind of dark – and – it was all big and dark – and—. Well, it was – beautiful!

FIRST GIRL: It was a beautiful radiogram in my dream. It was kind of Hi-Fi Stereoscopic. Posh! You didn't even have to press the button.
285 You just had to *think* and it went and switched itself on.

SECOND GIRL: Yep? You know what the sea was like in my dream?

FIRST GIRL: It was Hi-Fi Stereoscopic – with *five* extra loudspeakers.

	SECOND GIRL:	It was just kind of like *home* – it was just kind of like what a *real home* is . . .
290	FIRST GIRL:	What?
	SECOND GIRL:	I said – the sea in my dream – it was all big and dark and – just like home!
	FIRST GIRL:	You talk like a funny picture I saw.
	SECOND GIRL:	I could have stayed there by it – forever!
295	FIRST GIRL:	It made me want to giggle. *Everyone* giggled.
	SECOND GIRL:	But my Mum came and waked me up.
	FIRST GIRL:	What?
	SECOND GIRL:	I had to wake up – out of my dream.
	FIRST GIRL:	I wonder why I dreamed of a great big radiogram?
300	SECOND GIRL:	I suppose you'd like to *have* a great big radiogram.
	FIRST GIRL:	Yep.
305	SECOND GIRL:	Maybe you could come with us down to the sea. Or – well, if Paul had to work some Saturday – if he got asked to do overtime – at advertising – we could go there . . . just the two of us.
	FIRST GIRL:	And walk through that seaweed—!?
	SECOND GIRL:	I could hold your hand – like Paul holds my hand –.
	FIRST GIRL:	You ain't like a magazine fellow that would make me feel all right about that seaweed . . .
310 315 320	SECOND GIRL:	I'd hold it tight.—Ever so tight. [*Pause.*] You and I – we could hold hands – we could go walking – like dancers – like on a tight-rope – all down through all that seaweed – and we'd tell each other things – all our secret things.—Yep, you and me – we could walk through the seaweed – all the way – right to the sea! [*Pause.*] You got to walk through seaweed or – or you don't get anywhere. And seaweed – it's full of crabs and things . . . But you got to walk through it – hand in hand – with some other person – because it's lovely too – you got to walk – like a dancer – like two dancers – all through the seaweed – right to the sea . . . !
325	FIRST GIRL:	All my life I kept out of seaweed. I stayed away from seaweed. It ain't well – nice stuff. You can go and walk in all that seaweed – you can go if you want to – but not with *me*! [*Pause.*] Let's go in the café now. [*Pause.*] I like that one that's on the juke-box. Though it's kind of sad . . . Come on, let's go . . .

[Turn over

SECOND GIRL: Yep. Let's go in the café and play the juke-box.—Maybe some of all of them boy friends of yours will be in the café – perhaps.

[*The music grows louder. It is a record – something like – Bobby Darin's* "Beyond The Sea"]

330 Somewhere . . .
Beyond the sea . . .

[*The two girls saunter off as the music grows still louder – then slowly fades*]

Question

Make a detailed study of the ways in which Ian Hamilton Finlay explores the relationship that develops between the two girls.

In your answer you should pay close attention to:

*   setting in time and place
*   language and dialogue
*   the significance of "walking through seaweed"
*   the tone of the closing lines.

Section 4—Reading the Media

You must answer **one question only** in this section.

Unless otherwise indicated, your answer must take the form of a **critical essay** appropriately structured to meet the demands of your selected question.

Category A—Film

1. "*Stars are symbols: they embody the accepted values of the society of their time.*"

   How far do you agree?

   In your answer you should refer to the contribution of the "star" or "stars" to **one** or **more than one** film you have studied.

2. Show how, in **one** or **more than one** film you have studied, the conventions of a particular genre have been reworked or re-presented for a contemporary audience.

Category B—Television

3. Discuss how effectively any **one** television drama you have studied—soap, serial, series or single play—exploits the potential of its particular genre.

4. "*Television is becoming a domestic comforter, no longer watched with concentration or attended to closely.*"

   How far, in your view, does the changing relationship between television and its audience affect the ways in which serious events or issues are presented in news or current affairs programmes?

   You should support your answer with evidence drawn from **a range** of programmes you have studied.

Category C—Radio

5. "*Radio is a solitary medium to which we listen alone—but it is one of the best cures for solitude, providing a convincing illusion of company.*"

   Discuss some of the means by which radio creates a relationship of familiarity with its listeners. You may wish to consider such aspects as programme content, mode of address, channel identity.

6. How effectively does any **one** radio drama you have studied—soap, serial, series or single play—exploit the potential of sound **and** of silence?

Category D—Print journalism

7. What is it about the form, content and ideology of any **one** newspaper you have studied that makes it essential to its target audience?

8. For this question you are provided with two news stories—from *The Independent* of 16 March 2007 and *The Observer* of 18 March 2007.

   Analyse the images and written text employed by each newspaper and evaluate their effectiveness in conveying their views on global warming and climate change.

8. (continued)

FRIDAY 16 MARCH 2007   THE INDEPENDENT

Collapse of Arctic sea ice 'has reached tipping-point'

By Steve Connor
Science Editor

A catastrophic collapse of the Arctic sea ice could lead to radical climate changes in the northern hemisphere according to scientists who warn that the rapid melting is soon be almost totally ice-free at a "tipping point" beyond which it may not recover.

The scientists attribute the loss of some 38,000 square miles of sea ice – an area the size of Alaska – to rising levels of carbon dioxide in the atmosphere as well as to natural variability in Arctic ice.

Ever since satellite measurements of the Arctic sea ice began in 1979, the surface area covered by summer sea ice has retreated from the long-term average. This has increased the rate of coastal erosion from Alaska to Siberia and caused problems for polar bears, which rely on sea ice for hunting seals.

However, in recent years the rate of melting has accelerated and the sea ice is showing signs of not recovering even during the cold, dark months of the Arctic winter. This has led to even less sea ice at the start of the summer melting season.

Mark Serreze, a senior glaciologist at the University of Colorado at Boulder, said the world was heading towards a situation where the Arctic will its reflective cap of ice.

"When the ice thins to a vulnerable state, the bottom will drop out and we may quickly move into a new, seasonally ice-free state of the Arctic," Dr Serreze said.

"I think there is some evidence that we may have reached that tipping point, and the impacts will not be confined to the Arctic region," he said.

Some studies have linked the loss of sea ice in the Arctic to changes in atmospheric weather patterns that influence such things as rainfall in southern and western Europe and the amount of snow and heat. The summer sea ice in the Rocky Mountains of the American Midwest.

The Arctic is one of the fastest warming regions on Earth and scientists fear that temperatures could rise even faster once sea ice melts to expose dark ocean, which absorbs heat more easily without its reflective cap of ice.

"While the Arctic is losing a great deal of ice in the summer months, it now seems that it also is regenerating less ice in the winter. With this increasing vulnerability, a kick to the system just from natural climate fluctuations could send it into a tailspin," Dr Serreze said.

During the late 1980s and early 1990s, changing wind patterns flushed much of the thick sea ice out of the Arctic Ocean and into the Northern Atlantic, where it drifted south and melted away.

A thinner layer of young ice formed in its place, which more readily melts during the warmer, summer months – leading to the appearance of a greater area of open water that absorbs sunlight and heat. The sea ice reached an all-time minimum in September 2005, with September 2006 the second lowest.

"This ice-flushing even could be a small-scale analogue of the sort of kick that could invoke winter sea ice failed again this year sort of kick that could have to recover fully.

"The freeze-up this year was again delayed, and ice extents

The collapse of summer sea ice has already affected the polar bear, which relies on it for hunting seals.

JONATHAN HAYWARD/AP/CP

Dr Serreze said.

Julienne Stroeve from the US National Snow and Ice Data Centre in Colorado said that the Computer models suggest that summer sea ice could disappear altogether by 2080. Some forecasts even predict an ice-free summer by 2040.

from October through to December set new record lows during the satellite era," she said.

Ocean heat blamed for the mysterious disappearance of glaciers

By Steve Connor

A mysterious phenomenon is causing four major glaciers in the Antarctic to shrink in unison, causing a significant increase in sea levels, scientists have found.

The rise in atmospheric temperatures caused by global warming cannot account for the relatively rapid movement of the glaciers into the sea, but scientists suspect that warmer oceans may be playing a role.

"There is a possibility that heat from the ocean is somehow flowing in underneath these glaciers, but it is not related to global warming," said glaciologist Duncan Wingham of University College London. "Something has changed that is causing these glaciers to shrink.

"At this rate the glaciers will all be afloat in 150 years or so."

Satellite measurements have shown that the Antarctic glaciers are retreating in a uniform manner, suggesting a common cause. Air temperatures over Antarctica are much too cold for any significant surface melting, which suggests that the flow of the glaciers into the sea is being aided by melting at their base, lubricating their movement into the ocean.

In a study in the journal Science, Dr Wingham and colleague Andrew Shepherd of Edinburgh University found that major glaciers in the Antarctic identified by Wingham and Shepherd.

"These glaciers are vulnerable over the past decade – about 12 per cent of the current global trend.

While the retreat of the Greenland ice sheet can be linked to melting of the glaciers' surface, the same is not true of the four major glaciers in the Antarctic ocean to reach the underside of the glaciers, which makes it difficult to believe that the present shrinkage is due to global warming, Dr Wingham said.

to small changes in ocean temperature," he said. "A rise of less than 0.5C could have triggered the present imbalance."

However, it would take about 200 years for extra heat from the ocean to reach the underside of a sea level rise of 0.35mm a year sheets have together contributed

8. (continued)

The Observer

18.03.07

Don't exaggerate climate dangers, scientists warn

Hollywood and the media are 'appealing to fear' and confusing the public say experts on global warming

By Juliette Jowit

LEADING CLIMATE change experts have warned of the 'Hollywoodisation' of global warning and criticised American scientists for exaggerating the message of global warming.

Professors Paul Hardaker and Chris Collier of the Royal Meteorological Society said scientists, campaign groups, politicians and the media were all guilty of making out that catastrophic events were more likely to happen when this could not be proved by scientists.

They also criticised the tendency to say individual extreme events – such as the Birmingham typhoon and the Boscastle floods – were certain evidence of climate change.

They singled out for criticism a report last month by the American Association for the Advancement of Science, which said intensification of droughts, heatwaves, floods, wildfires and storms were 'early warning signs of even more devastating damage to come'.

'It's certainly a very strong statement,' said Collier. 'To make the blanket assumption that all extreme weather events are increasing is a bit too early yet.'

Reporting of the recent report by the United Nations International Panel on Climate Change by the media was also criticised, especially the use of words not in the report such as 'catastrophic', 'shocking', 'terrifying' and 'devastating'.

'Campaigners, media and some scientists seem to be appealing to fear in order to generate a sense of urgency' said Professor Mike Hulme, director of the Tyndall Centre for Climate Change Research at the University of East Anglia and a contributor to yesterday's report. 'If they want to engage the public in responding to climate change, this is unreliable at best and counter-productive at worst.'

The report by Hardaker, Collier and other climate experts, 'Making Sense of the Weather and Climate', was launched at a conference in Oxford organised by the charity Sense About Science.

The authors said they firmly believe global warming is happening and man-made emissions of greenhouse gases are partly to blame.

Some scientists also acknowledged that dramatic warnings about climate change had helped generate public debate and support for action to reduce the threat. But Hardaker warned that exaggeration of the problems made the public confused and made it easier for sceptics to argue that the scientists were wrong.

An example of a low probability event given too much weight was the risk of the Gulf Stream, which keeps the North Atlantic relatively warm, 'switching off' and plunging the region into an ice age – the scenario dramatised by the Hollywood film *The Day after Tomorrow*, which also came in for criticism for exaggerating that problem.

As a result scientists had to be more honest about the uncertainties surrounding climate change prediction to avoid losing public trust, said Hardaker.

'Once you begin to exaggerate the science in either direction the debate gets out of control,' he said.

Their comments were backed today by other leading figures in the debate. Dr Peter Scott, manager of understanding and attributing climate change at the Hadley Centre for Climate Change, said he believed scientists have to make it clear there is a long way to go until we know how bad climate change will be.

He said: 'There is a lot more research to do to understand about exactly what effects it's going to have in the future.'

He said that while he welcomed a growing public awareness about the dangers brought about by films and deadlines, informed debate was vital.

'I think it is important that having said there is a problem, it would be unfortunate if people got the impression that there's nothing we can do about it because there is a lot we can do to change the future of climate change,' he said.

Al Gore, who has been praised for his Oscar-winning environmental film *An Inconvenient Truth* has also attracted criticism from scientists. 'I don't want to pick on Al Gore,' Don J Easterbrook, an emeritus professor of geology at Western Washington University, told hundreds of experts at the annual meeting of the Geological Society of America. 'But there are a lot of inaccuracies in the statements we are seeing, and we have to

Above, a tornado and the Boscastle flood. Left, disaster movie The Day After Tomorrow. Right, Oscar winner Al Gore. Getty

temper that with real data.'

Gore, in an email exchange about the critics, said his work made 'the most important and salient points' about climate change, if not 'some nuances and distinctions'. 'The degree of scientific consensus on global warming has never been stronger,' he said, adding. 'I am trying to communicate the essence of it in the lay language that I understand.'

Category E—Advertising

9. *"While advertisements convey messages about particular products, services or brands, they also convey messages about society, gender, lifestyle and values."*

   How far do you agree?

   In your answer to Question 9, you may refer to the advertisements provided for Question 10, but your answer **must** also include references to **other** advertisements or advertising campaigns.

10. For this question, you are provided with two advertisements—published in *The Times* and *The Sunday Times* in May 2005.

    NB These advertisements are provided separately as colour inserts.

    Make a detailed analysis of these two advertisements, examining carefully:

    • the construction of the image in each advertisement
    • the cultural codes which establish the representation of the adults and the children
    • the written codes—caption and copy
    • the gender stereotyping
    • the implied values.

[END OF QUESTION PAPER]

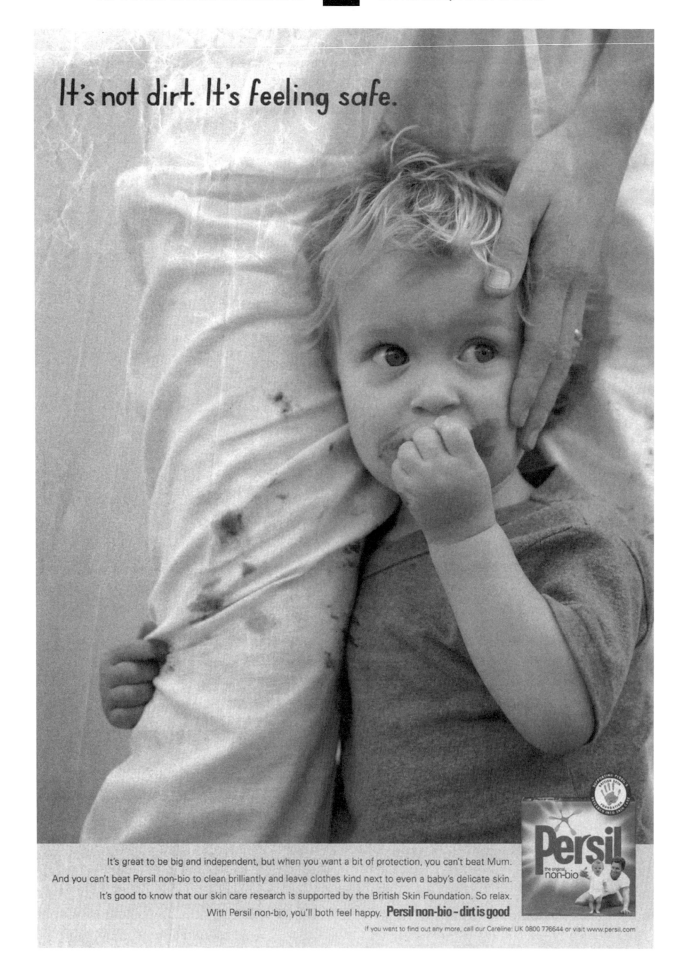

ADVANCED HIGHER

2010

[BLANK PAGE]

X115/701

NATIONAL QUALIFICATIONS 2010	WEDNESDAY, 12 MAY 1.00 PM – 4.00 PM	ENGLISH ADVANCED HIGHER

There are four sections in this paper.

Section 1—Literary Study	pages	**2 – 12**
Section 2—Language Study	pages	**13 – 19**
Section 3—Textual Analysis	pages	**20 – 41**
Section 4—Reading the Media	pages	**42 – 43 (plus Insert)**

Depending on the options you have chosen, you must answer **one** or **two** questions.

If you have submitted a Creative Writing folio, you must answer only **one** question.

Otherwise, you must answer **two** questions.

If you are required to answer only **one question**

- it must be taken from **Section 1—Literary Study**
- you must leave the examination room **after 1 hour 30 minutes**.

If you are required to answer **two questions**

- your first must be taken from **Section 1—Literary Study**
- your second must be taken from **a different section**
- each answer must be written in **a separate answer booklet**
- the maximum time allowed for any question is **1 hour 30 minutes**.

You must identify each question you attempt by indicating clearly

- **the title of the section** from which the question has been taken
- **the number of the question** within that section.

You must also write inside the front cover of your Literary Study answer booklet

- **the topic** of your Specialist Study (Dissertation)
- **the texts** used in your Specialist Study (Dissertation).

Section 1—Literary Study

This section is **mandatory** for all candidates.

You must answer **one question only** in this section.

Unless otherwise indicated, your answer must take the form of a **critical essay** appropriately structured to meet the demands of your selected question.

DRAMA

1. Beckett

Discuss the importance of setting in *Waiting for Godot* **and** in *Endgame*.

2. Byrne

Discuss the role of Hector in *The Slab Boys Trilogy*.

3. Chekhov

How effective in your view is the ending of *Uncle Vanya* **and** the ending of *The Cherry Orchard*?

4. Friel

Discuss Friel's dramatic treatment of fear—fear of change, of abandonment, of the future—in *Translations* **and** in *Dancing at Lughnasa*.

5. Lindsay

Discuss the importance of the character of Diligence in *Ane Satyre of the Thrie Estaitis*.

6. Lochhead

Discuss Lochhead's dramatic treatment of power in *Mary Queen of Scots Got Her Head Chopped Off* **and** in *Dracula*.

7. Pinter

How effective in your view is Pinter's dramatic treatment of political tyranny in *One for the Road* **and** in *Mountain Language*?

8. **Shakespeare**

   EITHER

   (*a*)   ***Othello* and *Antony and Cleopatra***

   Make a detailed analysis of the characterisation and role **either** of Desdemona in *Othello* **or** of Cleopatra in *Antony and Cleopatra*.

   OR

   (*b*)   ***The Winter's Tale* and *The Tempest***

   Discuss Shakespeare's use of the supernatural in *The Winter's Tale* **and** in *The Tempest*.

9. **Stoppard**

   "*ROSENCRANTZ: Whatever became of the moment when one first knew about death? When it first occurred to you that you don't go on forever. It must have been shattering—stamped into one's memory. And yet I don't remember it.*"

   (*Rosencrantz and Guildenstern are Dead*, Act 2)

   "*SEPTIMUS: The procession is very long and life is very short. We die on the march.*"

   (*Arcadia*, Act 1)

   Keeping these two quotations in mind, make a comparative study of the importance of death as a theme in *Rosencrantz and Guildenstern are Dead* **and** in *Arcadia*.

10. **Wilde**

    "*The dandy is Wilde's trademark as a dramatist: cool, hard-edged, self-absorbed, the arbiter and exemplar of elegance and wit.*"

    Discuss the role of the "dandies"—Lord Darlington, Lord Goring and Algernon Moncrieff—in *Lady Windermere's Fan*, *An Ideal Husband* and *The Importance of Being Earnest*.

11. **Williams**

    Discuss what you consider to be the principal features of Williams's characterisation of Chance **and** his characterisation of Princess in *Sweet Bird of Youth*.

[Turn over

POETRY

12. Burns

Read the following poem carefully and then answer questions (a) **and** *(b) that follow it (Page five).*

THE DEATH AND DYING WORDS OF POOR MAILIE, THE AUTHOR'S ONLY PET YOWE

As Mailie, an' her lambs thegither,
Was ae day nibbling on the tether,
Upon her cloot she coost a hitch,
An' owre she warsled in the ditch;

5   There, groaning, dying, she did lie,
When Hughoc he cam doytin by.
    Wi glowrin' een, an lifted han's,
Poor Hughoc like a statue stan's;
He saw her days were near-hand ended,

10   But, wae's my heart! he could na mend it!
He gapèd wide, but naething spak;
At length poor Mailie silence brak:—

    "O thou, whase lamentable face
Appears to mourn my woefu' case!

15   My dying words attentive hear,
An' bear them to my Master dear.
    "Tell him, if e'er again he keep
As muckle gear as buy a sheep,—
O bid him never tie them mair

20   Wi' wicked strings o' hemp or hair!
But ca' them out to park or hill,
An' let them wander at their will;
So may his flock increase, an' grow
To scores o' lambs an' packs o' woo'!

25   "Tell him he was a Master kin',
An' aye was guid to me an' mine;
An' now my dying charge I gie him,
My helpless lambs, I trust them wi' him.
    "O bid him save their harmless lives

30   Frae dogs, an' tods, an' butchers' knives!
But gie them guid cow-milk their fill,
Till they be fit to fend themsel:
An' tent them duly, e'en an' morn,
Wi' teats o' hay an' ripps o' corn.

35   "An' may they never learn the gates
Of ither vile wanrestfu' pets—
To slink thro' slaps, an' reave an' steal,
At stacks o' pease, or stocks o' kale.
So may they, like their great forbears,

40   For mony a year come thro' the shears;
     So wives will gie them bits o' bread,
     An' bairns greet for them when they're dead
      "My poor tup-lamb, my son an' heir,
     O bid him breed up him wi' care!
45   An', if he live to be a beast,
     To pit some havins in his breast!
     An' warn him, what I winna name,
     To stay content wi' yowes at hame;
     An' no to rin an' wear his cloots,
50   Like ither menseless graceless brutes.
      "An' neist my yowie, silly thing,
     Gude keep thee frae a tether string!
     O may thou ne'er forgather up
     Wi' ony blastit moorland tup;
55   But ay keep mind to moop an' mell,
     Wi' sheep o' credit like thysel!
      "And now, my bairns, wi' my last breath
     I lea'e my blessin wi' you baith;
     An' when you think upo' your mither,
60   Mind to be kind to ane anither.
      "Now, honest Hughoc, dinna fail
     To tell my master a' my tale;
     An' bid him burn this cursed tether;
     An', for thy pains, thou'se get my blether."

65   This said, poor Mailie turn'd her head,
     An' closed her een amang the dead!

(a) Discuss Burns's use of humour in this poem.

AND

(b) Go on to discuss Burns's use of humour in **one** other poem.

13. Chaucer

In *The Nun's Priest's Prologue*, the Host calls on the Nun's Priest to "*telle us swich thyng as may oure hertes glade*".

How effectively does Chaucer make *The Nun's Priest's Tale* one that "*may oure hertes glade*"?

14. Donne

Make a detailed analysis of Donne's treatment of spiritual experience in the following three poems:

 "*Death be not proud . . .*"
 Good Friday, 1613. Riding Westward
 Hymne to God my God in my sicknesse.

15. **Duffy**

Read the following poem carefully and then answer questions (a) **and** *(b) that follow it.*

MOMENTS OF GRACE

I dream through a wordless, familiar place.
The small boat of the day sails into morning,
past the postman with his modest haul, the full trees
which sound like the sea, leaving my hands free
5   to remember. Moments of grace. *Like this.*

Shaken by first love and kissing a wall. *Of course.*
The dried ink on the palms then ran suddenly wet,
a glistening blue name in each fist. I sit now
in a kind of sly trance, hoping I will not feel me
10   breathing too close across time. A face to the name. *Gone.*

The chimes of mothers calling in children
at dusk. *Yes.* It seems we live in those staggering years
only to haunt them; the vanishing scents
and colours of infinite hours like a melting balloon
15   in earlier hands. The boredom since.

Memory's caged bird won't fly. These days
we are adjectives, nouns. In moments of grace
we were verbs, the secret of poems, talented.
A thin skin lies on the language. We stare
20   deep in the eyes of strangers, look for the doing words.

Now I smell you peeling an orange in the other room.
Now I take off my watch, let a minute unravel
in my hands, listen and look as I do so,
and mild loss opens my lips like *No.*
25   Passing, you kiss the back of my neck. A blessing.

(a)   Make a detailed analysis of Duffy's treatment of love in this poem.

AND

(b)   Go on to discuss Duffy's treatment of love in **two** other poems.

16. **Heaney**

Discuss the uses Heaney makes of the land and the natural world in the following three poems:

    Personal Helicon
    Exposure
    The Harvest Bow.

17. Henryson

EITHER

(a)   Discuss the importance of the role of the narrator in *The Testament of Cresseid*.

OR

(b)   "*In **The Morall Fabillis**, Henryson is a master of easy colloquial dialogue, dramatic irony, wit and word play.*"

Discuss **some** or **all** of these features of Henryson's style in **two** or **three** of *The Morall Fabillis*.

18. Keats

Make a detailed analysis of form and imagery in the following three sonnets:

> *On first looking into Chapman's Homer*
> "*When I have fears that I may cease to be . . .*"
> "*Bright star, would I were steadfast as thou art . . .*"

19. MacDiarmid

"*What is striking about MacDiarmid's poetry is its fusion of lyrical grace and intellectual force.*"

Discuss **either** with reference to *A Drunk Man Looks at the Thistle* **or** with reference to the other specified poems.

20. Muir

*Read the following poem carefully and then answer questions (a) **and** (b) that follow it (Page eight).*

SCOTLAND'S WINTER

Now the ice lays its smooth claws on the sill,
The sun looks from the hill
Helmed in his winter casket,
And sweeps his arctic sword across the sky.
5   The water at the mill
Sounds more hoarse and dull.
The miller's daughter walking by
With frozen fingers soldered to her basket
Seems to be knocking
10   Upon a hundred leagues of floor
With her light heels, and mocking
Percy and Douglas dead,
And Bruce on his burial bed,

```
       Where he lies white as may
15     With wars and leprosy,
       And all the kings before
       This land was kingless,
       And all singers before
       This land was songless,
20     This land that with its dead and living waits the Judgement Day.
       But they, the powerless dead,
       Listening can hear no more
       Than a hard tapping on the sounding floor
       A little overhead
25     Of common heels that do not know
       Whence they come or where they go
       And are content
       With their poor frozen life and shallow banishment.
```

(*a*)   Make a detailed analysis of the themes and techniques of this poem.

AND

(*b*)   How far are the themes and techniques of this poem characteristic of the themes and techniques of other poems by Muir?

21. Plath

Read the following poem carefully and then answer questions (a) **and** *(b) that follow it (Page nine).*

BLACKBERRYING

```
       Nobody in the lane, and nothing, nothing but blackberries
       Blackberries on either side, though on the right mainly,
       A blackberry alley, going down in hooks, and a sea
       Somewhere at the end of it, heaving.  Blackberries
5      Big as the ball of my thumb, and dumb as eyes
       Ebon in the hedges, fat
       With blue-red juices.  These they squander on my fingers.
       I had not asked for such a blood sisterhood; they must love me.
       They accommodate themselves to my milkbottle, flattening their sides.

10     Overhead go the choughs in black, cacophonous flocks—
       Bits of burnt paper wheeling in a blown sky.
       Theirs is the only voice, protesting, protesting.
       I do not think the sea will appear at all.
       The high, green meadows are glowing, as if lit from within.
15     I come to one bush of berries so ripe it is a bush of flies,
       Hanging their bluegreen bellies and their wing panes in a Chinese screen.
       The honey-feast of the berries has stunned them; they believe in heaven.
       One more hook, and then the berries and bushes end.
```

20   The only thing to come now is the sea.
        From between two hills a sudden wind funnels at me,
        Slapping its phantom laundry in my face.
        These hills are too green and sweet to have tasted salt.
        I follow the sheep path between them. A last hook brings me
        To the hills' northern face, and the face is orange rock
25   That looks out on nothing, nothing but a great space
        Of white and pewter lights, and a din like silversmiths
        Beating and beating at an intractable metal.

(*a*)   How effectively in your view does Plath create a sense of menace in this poem?

AND

(*b*)   Go on to discuss the means by which Plath creates a sense of menace in **one** or **two** other poems.

22. Yeats

Discuss Yeats's use of symbolism in **three** or **four** poems.

PROSE FICTION

23. Atwood

"*In* **Cat's Eye** *and in* **Alias Grace***, Atwood's presentation of women is characterised by patterns of doubleness and ambiguity.*"

Discuss.

24. Austen

Make a comparative study of Austen's treatment of marriage in *Pride and Prejudice* **and** in *Persuasion*.

25. Dickens

Discuss Dickens's treatment of childhood experience and education in *Hard Times* **or** in *Great Expectations* **or** in both novels.

26. Fitzgerald

Discuss Fitzgerald's treatment of illusion and reality in *The Beautiful and Damned* **and** in *Tender is the Night*.

[Turn over

27. Galloway

Read carefully the following extract from **The Trick is to Keep Breathing** *and then answer questions (a)* ***and*** *(b) that follow it (Page eleven).*

I used to sew a lot. It occupied me. During the day I went to school and in the evenings I cut cloth. I cut cloth into shapes from paper and then sewed it together again. Needles punctured pincushions into my finger ends and left little scratches on my wrists alongside the bruises from shifting furniture, sears from the oven and tears
5 in my nails from cleaning. Domestic wounds. I sewed at the table from when I came back from work to when I thought bed-time should be. At intervals, according to the clock, I would prepare something to eat: maybe a can of soup, a sandwich. Functional food. One evening, I was so intent on a hem, I forgot. When I did look at my watch, it was well after the usual meal-time. Hunger hadn't interrupted. I sat and thought
10 about this for a while

There was a can of vegetable soup in the cupboard: individual size. I found the opener and dug it into the top, lifting it higher with each turn of the handle. Some of the stuff inside smeared on my knuckle. It felt slimy, unpleasant. Inside the can the surface was a kind of flattened jelly, dark red with bits of green and yellow poking
15 through. Watery stuff like plasma started seeping up the sides of the viscous block. It didn't look like food at all. I slid one finger into it to the depth of a nail. The top creased and some of the pink fluid slopped up and over the jagged lip of the can. It was sickening but pleasantly so. Like a little kid playing with mud. The next thing I knew, I'd pushed my hand right inside the can. The semi-solid mush seethed and
20 slumped over the sides and on to the worktop as my nails tipped the bottom and the torn rim scored the skin. I had to withdraw carefully. Soup stung into the cuts so I used my other hand and scooped up as much of the mess as I could and cradled it across the room, red soup and blood dripping onto the lino. There, my cupped hands over the sink, I split my fingers and let the puree slither, spattering unevenly onto the
25 white porcelain. I was learning something as I stared at what I was doing; the most obvious thing yet it had never dawned on me till I stood here, bug-eyed at the sink, congealing soup up to my wrists. I didn't need to eat.
I didn't need to eat.

The first four days were the worst. After that, it found its own level. I occasionally
30 still cut cloth in the evenings, now without interruption. Not tonight. I'm too tired to force myself to stay in one place. Only the phone is left. I can't face the phone tonight either.

Perfect Pasta in minutes
No-nonsense looks for the Working Mum
35 The Lie that Tells the Truth

Nothing better get in your way this month, cos you mean
business! Something that's been irritating you for a while
finally gets its chance to see the light of day. Meanwhile,
those around you are in for a rough ride: be careful or
40 you'll say something you might regret later. Especially if
it's to someone close. Your love life is on an upturn –
maybe all that drive is packing you with

Last month's. No good.
But then it's all no good.

8

(a) Galloway has commented that she often adopts "*a physical, visceral style that enables the reader to touch, taste and feel what a character is experiencing*".

Show how in this extract Galloway enables the reader to "*touch, taste and feel*" what Joy is experiencing.

AND

(b) Go on to discuss Galloway's use of this "*physical, visceral style*" elsewhere in *The Trick is to Keep Breathing* **and** in *Foreign Parts*.

28. Gray

"*A full appreciation of an Alasdair Gray novel depends upon the reader's readiness to unravel its intricate complexities, to solve its puzzles, to reshuffle its elements until a final resolution emerges.*"

How far do you agree?

You should support your answer to this question with detailed evidence from *Lanark* **or** from *Poor Things* **or** from both novels.

29. Hardy

"*In **The Return of the Native** and **Tess of the D'Urbervilles** the failure of Clym Yeobright and Angel Clare to understand the women with whom they fall in love is central to the tragedy.*"

Discuss.

30. Hogg

Discuss Hogg's use of irony in *The Private Memoirs and Confessions of a Justified Sinner* **and** in **one** or **two** of the specified short stories.

31. Joyce

"*Escape! She must escape! Frank would save her. He would give her life, perhaps love too. But she wanted to live.*"

(from *Eveline* in *Dubliners*)

By referring to *Eveline* and to **one** other story from *Dubliners* **and** to *A Portrait of the Artist as a Young Man*, discuss Joyce's presentation of the need to escape.

32. Stevenson

"*Here is a tale which extends over many years and travels into many countries.*"
(Robert Louis Stevenson, in the prefatory letter to *The Master of Ballantrae*)

Discuss the importance of setting—in time **and** in place—in *The Master of Ballantrae*.

[Turn over

33. Waugh

"*One of the principal fictional techniques employed by Waugh is the juxtaposition of the comic and the serious.*"

Discuss with reference to *A Handful of Dust* **and** to *Brideshead Revisited*.

PROSE NON-FICTION

34. How effectively in your view is the experience of discovery **and** of self-discovery conveyed in any **one** of the specified texts?

35. "*Place is more than just the physical facts of topography and environment; the idea of place inevitably incorporates our own presence in it.*"

How effectively in your view is "*the idea of place*" conveyed in any **two** of the specified texts?

Section 2—Language Study

You must answer **one question only** in this section.

Unless otherwise indicated, your answer must take the form of an **essay/analytical report** appropriately structured to meet the demands of your selected questions.

Topic A—Varieties of English or Scots

1. Discuss some of the major phonological, lexical and syntactic features of a particular variety of English **or** Scots you have studied.

2. Show how you have employed some of the basic principles of dialectology in your study of a particular variety of English **or** Scots.

Topic B—The historical development of English or Scots

3. From your study of the historical development of English **or** Scots, describe and account for some of the ways in which words have changed in form and in meaning.

4. What do you consider to be the principal factors that have influenced the development of a standard language in England **or** in Scotland?

Topic C—Multilingualism in contemporary Scotland

5. Describe some of the principal structural and functional patterns associated with codeswitching by multilingual speakers in contemporary Scotland.

6. *"Language shift does not take place in a social, political or educational vacuum."*

   Discuss the importance of context—social, political or educational—in the process of language shift in contemporary Scotland.

   You should support your answer with evidence drawn from your own study of multilingualism in the community **and** of language policies relevant to contemporary Scotland.

[Turn over

Topic D—The use of Scots in contemporary literature

For this topic you are provided with two examples of the use of Scots in contemporary literature:

- an extract from *Nice to be Nice*, a short story by James Kelman
- an extract from *In Love*, a play by Iain Mills.

Read the extracts carefully and then answer **either** Question 7 **or** Question 8 (*Page fifteen*).

Extract from *Nice to be Nice*

Big Moira came doon oan Tuesday mornin wi a letter sayin she'd definitely hiv tae be oot the hoose by the thertieth ir else they'd take "immediate action". She wis in a helluva state in so wis her maw kis she couldny take thim, wi her only hivvin a single-end. A offered, bit a room in kitchen isny much better even though A've goat an

5 inside toilet. Still A sippose it id dae it a pinch. Anywey A wint roon is minny factors is A could tae try in git her a hoose bit nae luck. Nothin! Nothin at aw. Ach A didny ixpect nothin anywey – A mean a singil wummin wi four weans, ye kiddin? Naw it wis hopeless so A telt her maw A'd go up tae Clyde Hoose in see if they'd offer alternit accomidation, in no tae worry kis they'd never throw thim inty the street. Singil

10 wummin in four weans? Naw the coarpiration widny chance it. A'd ixplain the situation aw right. Imagine ixpectin her tae pey a fiver a week anywey! It's beyond a joke. In she says the rooms ir damp tae, in whin she cawed in the sanitry they telt her tae open the windaes in let in the err. Open the windaes and let in the err? November? Aye in is soon is she turns her back aw the villains ir in screwin the metres in whit no.

15 A wis ragin in whin A left the hoose in Wedinsday mornin A wis still helliva angry. Moira waantit tae come up wi me bit A telt her naw.

So A wint up tae Clyde Hoose in queued up tae see the manajir bit he wisny available so A saw the same wan Moira saw, a young filla cawed Mr Frederick. A done ma best tae ixplain bit he wisny botherin much in afore A'd finished he butts in sayin

20 that in the furst place he'd ixplained evry thin tae Mrs Donnelly (Moira) in the department hid sent her two letters – in the second place it wis nane i ma business.

Extract from *In Love*

SCENE THREE Low wall Moonlight

CRAIGIE: (*Speaking to camera, and still holding the flowers*) Ye ken aw yon stuff aboot "love is blind" an aw that crap? It's true an aw. Ah could hear whit Jaz wis telling us an it aw made sense, sorta, but Ah kent Ah'd nae intention a takin his advice. Aw Ah could think of wis goin up

5   ther tae see her again. Look, see when Ah'm tellin ye aw this . . . (*Leans forward and lowers voice*) . . . Ah'm gonnae miss oot a lot a the details, aw the kissin bits an stuff, an me an Ellen up the park an that . . . well, its kinna embarrassin . . . An it's sorta . . . personal, like. Yiz widnae be interestit onyway, so Ah'll spare ye aw they bits. But we

10   got oan real guid, me an Ellen. This wis aw new tae me. A lotta the time we jist talked aboot ordnary hings, like. Ah mind one time . . . innocent, like, askin her if she'd ony brers an sisters. "Aye" she goes, "Ah've twa big brers, James an Alastair", giein them ther Sunday names, like. Ah near says "Whit wan's Cleaver and whit wan's

15   Banjo?", but Ah stoapt masel in time. Ah goes "Whit are they like?"
       an she goes "Aw, ther great. See if sumdy messed us aboot like . . .",
       an she's lookin at us kinna funny, an Ah feels this cauld shiver runnin
       up ma back, ken whit Ah mean? But Ah jist shrugs it aff an we . . .
       (*Raising hands in "stop" gesture*) Naw . . . Ah says Ah wisnae gonnae
20   tell yiz the personal bits. But how wis Jaz takin aw this?

SCENE FOUR Secondary school playground at break time

       JAZ and CRAIGIE are talking in a corner of the school playground.
       JAZ is very serious.

JAZ: Ah wis talking tae big Tam Melville aboot they McGills. Ah'm
       telling ye Craigie, ther bad news.

25 CRAIGIE: Right Jaz, yiv tellt us that a hunner times, so ye huv.

JAZ: Naw, listen . . . ther no' jist usin aw sorta stuff, ther dealin an aw. You
       name it Craigie . . . the McGills'll sell ye it. An see ye owe them an
       cannae pay . . . Tam says he kens a boy Banjo took a sword tae, whit a
       mess he wis Craigie . . .

30 CRAIGIE: Bit whit's that goat tae dae wi me, Jaz. It's no' Banjo Ah'm seein, is
       it?

JAZ: See that Ellen, Craigie? Ye want tae watch her. Ah mean, she kin
       seem nice an that, but . . .

CRAIGIE: (*Becoming angry*) Whit is it wi you, Jaz? *Ah* don' go oan an oan when
35   *you're* seein a lassie, dae Ah? Ah mean . . . it's nane a your business, is it?

JAZ: Course it is Craigie . . . Ah mean, *sumdy's* goat tae look efter you if
       yiv no' the sense tae look efter yersel!

CRAIGIE: (*Pointing finger angrily towards JAZ's chest*) Who dae ye think ye ur,
       talking tae *me* like that? Ye think yer that cool . . . Naebidy's
40   supposed tae know onythin apart fae you. Sometimes Ah don' think
       yer hauf as smart as evrybidy thinks ye ur. Ah think yer jist . . .

JAZ: (*Interrupting by turning his back and starting to walk away, shouting*
       back at CRAIGIE as he does so) Onyway . . . yer no' gaun tae be much
       use tae the fitba team wi an airm hingin aff or yer kneecaps done in,
45   ur ye!

7. Compare and contrast the authors' use of Scots in the two extracts.

In your answer you should consider **some** or **all** of the following:

- spelling
- vocabulary
- idiom
- grammar
- any other feature you consider relevant.

8. Discuss the effectiveness of using Scots to explore aspects of life in contemporary
Scotland.

You should base your answer on your reading of these extracts **and** on your reading of
other texts in Scots.

Topic E—Language and social context

9. From your exploration of attitudes to language variation, in English **or** in Scots, what evidence have you found to support or to refute the claim that a "correct" variety of the language exists?

10. Discuss the relationship between the social characteristics of a speaker—class, gender, ethnicity, age—and his or her use of English **or** of Scots.

Topic F—The linguistic characteristics of informal conversation

11. Discuss some of the ways in which, in informal conversation, *"communicators actively collaborate to ensure that understanding takes place"*.

(Sanna-Kaisa Tanskanen)

12. For this question, you are provided with a transcript of part of a conversation between two women, followed by a transcription key.

Read the transcript carefully and then answer the following question.

Make a detailed analysis of the linguistic features of the transcript which characterise it as informal conversation.

Transcript

```
1    Lottie hello
2    Emma are you answering the pho::ne
3    (0.2)
4    Lottie hah .hh I was just gonna call you ehh
5    [huh huh
6    Emma [I just got he:re
7    (0.5)
8    Lottie reall[y
9    Emma [oh it's been so foggy we didn't come do:wn oh it's
10   so foggy Lottie all our way (off/all) our way it's terrible
11   (0.4)
12   Lottie no kidding
13   Emma yeah we came down Rosemea:d real slo:w
14   (0.8)
15   Emma .hh oh [yeah they w]arned you to stay away
16   Lottie [ (mm::) ]
17   Emma from them (0.4) five ten miles on the freeways last
18   night you know so
19   (0.2)
20   Lottie yeah I know it but you know it wasn't (b)e- it wasn't
21   bad here it a:ll
22   Emma that's what Gladys just tells me but it's bad inland
23   it's terrible you only have about a block visibility
24   it's just (.) awful:
25   (0.7)
26   Lottie yeah
```

Transcription Key

```
:       marks a sustention of sound; the more colons, the longer the sound
(0.2)   marks a pause of 0.2 seconds; (0.4) marks a pause of 0.4 seconds, and so on
.hh     marks audible breathing
(.)     marks a pause of less than one tenth of a second
[       marks the beginning of an overlapping turn
]       marks the end of an overlapping turn
```

Words or letters in brackets, such as (off/all) in line 10, indicate the transcriber's best guess at the word or sound.

Topic G—The linguistic characteristics of political communication

13. Discuss some of the linguistic and rhetorical techniques that politicians use to make their communications persuasive in **at least two** of the following:

- party political broadcasts
- debates in parliament
- political advertising
- political interviews.

14. For this question, you are provided with an extract from the Scottish National Party's manifesto for the Scottish Parliamentary elections in 2007, as published on the party's website (http://www.snp.org/policies).

Read the extract carefully and then answer the following question.

Make a detailed analysis of the linguistic and rhetorical features of the extract which characterise it as political communication.

Our Vision for Government

Fresh thinking and a new approach

The SNP has clear ambitions for Scotland. We have no doubt Scotland can be more successful.

Healthier

5   Our nation can be healthier. The SNP will keep vital health services local and reverse the decision to close Ayr and Monklands A&E. With an SNP government there will be a presumption against centralisation of core hospital services to protect local access to healthcare.

Wealthier

10   Families in Scotland can be wealthier. An SNP government will remove the burden of business rates from 120,000 small businesses, freeing them to grow and create more and better paid jobs. Small businesses sit at the heart of local economies and with the right support they will flourish.

Safer

15   Local communities can be safer. An SNP government will put more police on our streets to detect and deter crime. And we will come down hard on those who sell alcohol to underage Scots and fuel anti-social behaviour.

Fairer

Local taxes can be fairer. The SNP will scrap the Council tax and introduce a fairer
20   system based on ability to pay. Families and individuals on low and middle incomes will on average be between £260 and £350 a year better off. Nine out of ten pensioners will pay less local tax.

Easier

Life should be easier for young families. The SNP will increase by 50% the amount of
25 free nursery education available for 3 and 4 year olds.

Greener

Scotland can be greener. An SNP government will not give the go ahead for new
nuclear power stations. We will invest instead in developing Scotland's extensive
renewable energy potential.

30 ### Smarter

Scotland can be smarter. It's time for more opportunities for young Scots with smaller
class sizes and it's time to dump student debt.

A more successful Scotland

The SNP cares about success for families in Scotland. That is why we are passionate
35 about independence and equality for our nation.

The 300-year old Union is no longer fit for purpose. It was never designed for the
21st century world. It is well past its sell by date and is holding Scotland back.

The SNP believe Scotland and England should be equal nations – friends and
partners – both free to make our own choices.

40 ### Success for Scotland

Scotland can be more successful. Looking around at home and at our near
neighbours abroad, more and more Scots believe this too. Independence is the
natural state for nations like our own.

Scotland has the people, the talent and potential to become one of the big success
45 stories of the 21st century. We can match the success of independent Norway –
according to the UN the best place in the world to live. We can do as well as
independent Ireland, now the fourth most prosperous nation on the planet.

With independence Scotland will be free to flourish and grow. We can give our nation
a competitive edge.

50 ### Peace and Prosperity

Together we can build a more prosperous nation, a Scotland that is a force for good, a
voice for peace in our world.

Free to bring Scottish troops home from Iraq.

Free to remove nuclear weapons from Scotland's shores.

55 Free to invest our oil wealth in a fund for future generations.

Peace and prosperity – equality and opportunity.

These are some of the best reasons for independence and why the SNP trust the
people of Scotland to decide on independence in a referendum.

The choice will rest with you – that is the fair and democratic way.

[Turn over

Section 3—Textual Analysis

You must answer **one question only** in this section.

Unless otherwise indicated, your answer must take the form of a **critical analysis** appropriately structured to meet the demands of your selected question.

1. **Prose fiction [*Pages twenty to twenty-four*]**

   *The following extract is from Chapter 2 of **Vanity Fair** (1848) by William Makepeace Thackeray.*

   Rebecca (Becky) Sharp and Amelia Sedley are leaving Chiswick Mall, a school for young ladies kept by Miss Pinkerton (Minerva) and her sister, Miss Jemima. Amelia has been educated there and is returning to her family. Rebecca has been there as an "articled pupil" repaying her tuition by giving French lessons to the younger pupils. She is to spend a few days with Amelia's family before becoming a governess.

   In the previous chapter, Rebecca has been given a copy of Johnson's Dictionary ("the Dixonary") and has thrown it from the carriage as she is driven away.

   Read the extract carefully and then answer the question that follows it. (*Page twenty-four*)

   When Miss Sharp had performed the heroical act mentioned in the last chapter, and had seen the Dixonary flying over the pavement of the little garden, fall at length at the feet of the astonished Miss Jemima, the young lady's countenance, which had before worn an almost livid look of hatred, assumed a smile that perhaps was scarcely more
5 agreeable, and she sank back in the carriage in an easy frame of mind, saying, "So much for the Dixonary; and, thank God, I'm out of Chiswick."

   Miss Sedley was almost as flurried at the act of defiance as Miss Jemima had been; for, consider, it was but one minute that she had left school, and the impressions of six years are not got over in that space of time. Nay, with some persons those awes and terrors of youth last for ever and ever. I know, for instance, an old gentleman of sixty-
10 eight, who said to me one morning at breakfast, with a very agitated countenance, "I dreamed last night that I was flogged by Dr. Raine." Fancy had carried him back five-and-fifty years in the course of that evening. Dr. Raine and his rod were just as awful to him in his heart, then, at sixty-eight, as they had been at thirteen. If the Doctor, with a large birch, had appeared bodily to him, even at the age of three score and eight,
15 and had said in awful voice, "Boy, take down your pant—"? Well, well, Miss Sedley was exceedingly alarmed at this act of insubordination.
   "How could you do so, Rebecca?" at last she said, after a pause.
   "Why, do you think Miss Pinkerton will come out and order me back to the
20 black-hole?" said Rebecca, laughing.
   "No: but—"
   "I hate the whole house," continued Miss Sharp, in a fury. "I hope I may never set eyes on it again. I wish it were in the bottom of the Thames, I do; and if Miss Pinkerton were there, I wouldn't pick her out, that I wouldn't. Oh how I should like to
25 see her floating in the water yonder, turban and all, with her train streaming after her, and her nose like the beak of a wherry."
   "Hush!" cried Miss Sedley.
   "Why, will the black footman tell tales?" cried Miss Rebecca, laughing. "He may go back and tell Miss Pinkerton that I hate her with all my soul; and I wish he would; and
30 I wish I had a means of proving it, too. For two years I have only had insults and outrage from her. I have been treated worse than any servant in the kitchen. I have

never had a friend or a kind word, except from you. I have been made to tend the little girls in the lower school-room, and to talk French to the misses until I grew sick of my mother-tongue. But that talking French to Miss Pinkerton was capital fun, wasn't it?
35 She doesn't know a word of French, and was too proud to confess it. I believe it was that which made her part with me; and so thank Heaven for French. *Vive la France! Vive l'Empereur! Vive Bonaparte!*"

"O Rebecca, Rebecca, for shame!" cried Miss Sedley; for this was the greatest blasphemy Rebecca had as yet uttered; and in those days, in England, to say "Long live
40 Bonaparte!" was as much as to say "Long Live Lucifer!"
"How can you—how dare you say such wicked, revengeful thoughts?"
"Revenge may be wicked, but it's natural," answered Miss Rebecca. "I'm no angel." And, to say the truth, she certainly was not.

For it may be remarked in the course of this little conversation (which took place as
45 the coach rolled along lazily by the riverside) that though Miss Rebecca Sharp has twice had occasion to thank Heaven, it has been, in the first place, for ridding her of some person whom she hated, and secondly, for enabling her to bring her enemies to some sort of perplexity of confusion; neither of which are very amiable motives for religious gratitude, or such as would be put forward by persons of a kind and placable
50 disposition. Miss Rebecca was not, then, in the least kind or placable. All the world used her ill, said this young misanthropist, and we may be pretty certain that persons whom all the world treats ill, deserve entirely the treatment they get. The world is a looking-glass, and gives back to every man the reflection of his own face. Frown at it, and it will in turn look sourly upon you; laugh at it and with it, and it is a
55 jolly kind companion; and so let all young persons take their choice. This is certain, that if the world neglected Miss Sharp, she never was known to have done a good action in behalf of anybody; nor can it be expected that twenty-four young ladies should all be as amiable as the heroine of this work, Miss Sedley (whom we have selected for the very reason that she was the best-natured of all, otherwise what on
60 earth was to have prevented us from putting up Miss Swartz, or Miss Crump, or Miss Hopkins, as heroine in her place?)—it could not be expected that every one should be of the humble and gentle temper of Miss Amelia Sedley; should take every opportunity to vanquish Rebecca's hard-heartedness and ill-humour; and, by a thousand kind words and offices, overcome, for once at least, her hostility to her kind.

65 Miss Sharp's father was an artist, and in that quality had given lessons of drawing at Miss Pinkerton's school. He was a clever man; a pleasant companion; a careless student; with a great propensity for running into debt, and a partiality for the tavern. When he was drunk, he used to beat his wife and daughter; and the next morning, with a headache, he would rail at the world for its neglect of his genius, and abuse, with a
70 good deal of cleverness, and sometimes with perfect reason, the fools, his brother painters. As it was with the utmost difficulty that he could keep himself, and as he owed money for a mile round Soho, where he lived, he thought to better his circumstances by marrying a young woman of the French nation, who was by profession an opera-girl. The humble calling of her female parent, Miss Sharp never
75 alluded to, but used to state subsequently that the Entrechats were a noble family of Gascony, and took great pride in her descent from them. And curious it is, that as she advanced in life this young lady's ancestors increased in rank and splendour.

Rebecca's mother had had some education somewhere, and her daughter spoke French with purity and a Parisian accent. It was in those days rather a rare
80 accomplishment, and led to her engagement with the orthodox Miss Pinkerton. For her mother being dead, her father, finding himself not likely to recover, after his third

attack of *delirium tremens*, wrote a manly and pathetic letter to Miss Pinkerton, recommending the orphan child to her protection, and so descended to the grave, after two bailiffs had quarrelled over his corpse. Rebecca was seventeen when she came to
85 Chiswick, and was bound over as an articled pupil; her duties being to talk French, as we have seen; and her privileges to live cost free, and, with a few guineas a year, to gather scraps of knowledge from the professors who attended the school.

She was small and slight in person; pale, sandy-haired and with eyes habitually cast down: when they looked up they were very large, odd, and attractive; so attractive, that
90 the Reverend Mr. Crisp, fresh from Oxford, and curate to the Vicar of Chiswick, the Reverend Mr. Flowerdew, fell in love with Miss Sharp; being shot dead by a glance of her eyes, which was fired all the way across Chiswick Church from the school-pew to the reading-desk. This infatuated young man used sometimes to take tea with Miss Pinkerton, to whom he had been presented by his mamma, and actually proposed
95 something like marriage in an intercepted note, which the one-eyed applewoman was charged to deliver. Mrs. Crisp was summoned from Buxton, and abruptly carried off her darling boy; but the idea, even, of such an eagle in the Chiswick dovecot caused a great flutter in the breast of Miss Pinkerton, who would have sent away Miss Sharp, but that she was bound to her under a forfeit, and who never could thoroughly believe
100 the young lady's protestations that she had never exchanged a single word with Mr. Crisp, except under her own eyes on the two occasions when she had met him at tea.

By the side of many tall and bouncing young ladies in the establishment, Rebecca Sharp looked like a child. But she had the dismal precocity of poverty. Many a dun* had she talked to, and turned away from her father's door; many a tradesman had she
105 coaxed and wheedled into good humour, and into the granting of one meal more. She sat commonly with her father, who was very proud of her wit, and heard the talk of many of his wild companions—often but ill-suited for a girl to hear. But she never had been a girl, she said; she had been a woman since she was eight years old. Oh, why did Miss Pinkerton let such a dangerous bird into her cage?

110 The fact is, the old lady believed Rebecca to be the meekest creature in the world, so admirably, on the occasions when her father brought her to Chiswick, used Rebecca to perform the part of the *ingénue*, and only a year before the arrangement by which Rebecca had been admitted into her house, and when Rebecca was sixteen years old, Miss Pinkerton majestically, and with a little speech, made her a present of a
115 doll—which was, by the way, the confiscated property of Miss Swindle, discovered surreptitiously nursing it in school hours. How the father and daughter laughed as they trudged home together after the evening party (it was on the occasion of the speeches, when all the professors were invited), and how Miss Pinkerton would have raged had she seen the caricature of herself which the little mimic, Rebecca, managed
120 to make out of her doll. Becky used to go through dialogues with it; it formed the delight of Newman Street, Gerrard Street, and the artists' quarter; and the young painters, when they came to take their gin-and-water with their lazy, dissolute, clever, jovial senior, used regularly to ask Rebecca if Miss Pinkerton was at home: she was well known to them, poor soul! as Mr. Lawrence or President West. Once she had the
125 honour to pass a few days at Chiswick; after which she brought back Jemima, and erected another doll as Miss Jemmy; for though that honest creature had made and given her jelly and cake enough for three children, and a seven-shilling piece at parting, the girl's sense of ridicule was far stronger than her gratitude, and she sacrificed Miss Jemmy quite as pitilessly as her sister.

130 The catastrophe came, and she was brought to the Mall as to her home. The rigid formality of the place suffocated her: the prayers and the meals, the lessons and the

*dun—a debt collector

walks, which were arranged with a conventual regularity, oppressed her almost beyond endurance; and she looked back to the freedom and the beggary of the old studio in Soho with so much regret, that everybody, herself included, fancied she was consumed
135 with grief for her father. She had a little room in the garret, where the maids heard her walking and sobbing at night; but it was with rage, and not with grief. She had not been much of a dissembler, until now her loneliness taught her to feign. She had never mingled in the society of women: her father, reprobate as he was, was a man of talent; his conversation was a thousand times more agreeable to her than the talk of such of
140 her own sex as she now encountered. The pompous vanity of the old schoolmistress, the foolish good humour of her sister, the silly chat and scandal of the elder girls, and the frigid correctness of the governesses equally annoyed her; and she had no soft maternal heart, this unlucky girl, otherwise the prattle and talk of the younger children, with whose care she was chiefly entrusted, might have soothed and interested
145 her; but she lived among them two years, and not one was sorry that she went away. The gentle tender-hearted Amelia Sedley was the only person to whom she could attach herself in the least; and who could help attaching herself to Amelia?

The happiness—the superior advantages of the young women round about her, gave Rebecca inexpressible pangs of envy. "What airs that girl gives herself, because she is
150 an earl's granddaughter." she said of one. "How they cringe and bow to that Creole, because of her hundred thousand pounds! I am a thousand times cleverer and more charming than that creature, for all her wealth. I am as well-bred as the earl's granddaughter, for all her fine pedigree; and yet every one passes me by here. And yet, when I was at my father's, did not the men give up their gayest balls and parties in
155 order to pass the evening with me?" She determined at any rate to get free from the prison in which she found herself, and now began to act for herself, and for the first time to make connected plans for the future.

She took advantage, therefore, of the means of study the place offered her; and as she was already a musician and a good linguist, she speedily went through the little
160 course of study which was considered necessary for ladies in those days. Her music she practised incessantly, and one day, when the girls were out, and she had remained at home, she was overheard to play a piece so well, that Minerva thought wisely, she could spare herself the expense of a master for the juniors, and intimated to Miss Sharp that she was to instruct them in music for the future.

165 The girl refused; and for the first time, and to the astonishment of the majestic mistress of the school. "I am here to speak French with the children," Rebecca said abruptly, "not to teach them music, and save money for you. Give me money, and I will teach them."

Minerva was obliged to yield, and, of course, disliked her from that day. "For five-
170 and-thirty years," she said, and with great justice, "I never have seen the individual who has dared in my own house to question my authority. I have nourished a viper in my bosom."

"A viper—a fiddlestick," said Miss Sharp to the old lady, almost fainting with astonishment. "You took me because I was useful. There is no question of gratitude
175 between us. I hate this place, and want to leave it. I will do nothing here but what I am obliged to do."

It was in vain that the old lady asked her if she was aware she was speaking to Miss Pinkerton? Rebecca laughed in her face, with a horrid sarcastic demoniacal laughter, that almost sent the schoolmistress into fits. "Give me a sum of money," said the girl,
180 "and get rid of me—or, if you like better, get me a good place as governess in a

nobleman's family—you can do so if you please." And in their further disputes she always returned to this point, "Get me a situation—we hate each other, and I am ready to go."

Question

Discuss the principal means by which Thackeray presents the character of Rebecca in this extract.

2. **Prose non-fiction [*Pages twenty-four to twenty-seven*]**

    The following essay, **The Secret Life of James Thurber**, *by the American humorist, James Thurber, was written in 1944.*

    Read the essay carefully and then answer the question that follows it (Page twenty-seven).

The Secret Life of James Thurber

I have only dipped here and there into Salvador Dali's *The Secret Life of Salvador Dali** (with paintings by Salvador Dali and photographs of Salvador Dali), because anyone afflicted with what my grandmother's sister Abigail called "the permanent jump" should do no more than skitter through such an autobiography, particularly in
5 these melancholy times.

One does not have to skitter far before one comes upon some vignette which gives the full shape and flavour of the book: the youthful dreamer of dreams biting a sick bat or kissing a dead horse, the slender stripling going into man's estate with the high hope and fond desire of one day eating a live but roasted turkey, the sighing lover covering
10 himself with goat dung and aspic that he might give off the true and noble odor of the ram. In my flying trip through Dali I caught other glimpses of the great man: Salvador adoring a seed ball fallen from a plane tree, Salvador kicking a tiny playmate off a bridge, Salvador caressing a crutch, Salvador breaking the old family doctor's glasses with a leather-thonged mattress-beater. There would appear to be only two
15 things in the world that revolt him (and I don't mean a long-dead hedgehog). He is squeamish about skeletons and grasshoppers. Oh, well, we all have our idiosyncrasies.

Señor Dali's memoirs have set me to thinking. I find myself muttering as I shave, and on two occasions I have swung my crutch at a little neighbor girl on my way to the post office. Señor Dali's book sells for six dollars. My own published personal history
20 (Harper & Brothers, 1933) sold for $1.75. At the time I complained briefly about this unusual figure, principally on the ground that it represented only fifty cents more than the price asked for a book called *The Adventures of Horace the Hedgehog*, published the same month. The publishers explained that the price was a closely approximated vertical, prefigured on the basis of profitable ceiling, which in turn was arrived at by
25 taking into consideration the effect on diminishing returns of the horizontal factor.

In those days all heads of business firms adopted a guarded kind of double talk, commonly expressed in low, muffled tones, because nobody knew what was going to happen and nobody understood what had. Big business had been frightened by a sequence of economic phenomena which had clearly demonstrated that our civilisation
30 was in greater danger of being turned off than of gradually crumbling away. The upshot of it all was that I accepted the price of $1.75. In so doing, I accepted the state

* The autobiography of the Spanish surrealist artist, Salvador Dali, had recently been published in the United States.

of the world as a proper standard by which the price of books should be fixed. And now, with the world in ten times as serious a condition as it was in 1933, Dali's publishers set a price of six dollars on his life story. This brings me to the inescapable
35 conclusion that the price-fixing principle, in the field of literature, is not global but personal. The trouble, quite simply, is that I told too much about what went on in the house I lived in and not enough about what went on inside myself.

Let me be the first to admit that the naked truth about me is to the naked truth about Salvador Dali as an old ukelele in the attic is to a piano in a tree, and I mean a
40 piano with breasts. Señor Dali has the jump on me from the beginning. He remembers and describes in detail what it was like in the womb. My own earliest memory is of accompanying my father to a polling booth in Columbus, Ohio, where he voted for William McKinley.
It was a drab and somewhat battered tin shed on wheels, and it was filled with
45 guffawing men and cigar smoke; all in all, as far removed from the paradisiacal placenta of Salvador Dali's first recollection as could well be imagined. A fat, jolly man dandled me on his knee and said that I would soon be old enough to vote against William Jennings Bryan. I thought he meant that I could push a folded piece of paper into the slot of the padlocked box as soon as my father was finished. When this turned
50 out not to be true, I had to be carried out of the place kicking and screaming. In my struggles I knocked my father's derby off several times. The derby was not a monstrously exciting love object to me, as practically everything Salvador encountered was to him, and I doubt, if I had that day to live over again, that I could bring myself, even in the light of exotic dedication as I now know it, to conceive an intense and
55 perverse affection for the derby. It remains obstinately in my memory as a rather funny hat, a little too large in the crown, which gave my father the appearance of a tired, sensitive gentleman who had been persuaded against his will to take part in a game of charades.
We lived on Champion Avenue at the time, and the voting booth was on Mound
60 Street. As I set down these names, I begin to perceive an essential and important difference between the infant Salvador and the infant me. This difference can be stated in terms of environment. Salvador was brought up in Spain, a country colored by the legends of Hannibal, El Greco, and Cervantes. I was brought up in Ohio, a region steeped in the tradition of Coxey's Army, the Anti-Saloon League, and William
65 Howard Taft. It is only natural that the weather in little Salvador's soul should have been stirred by stranger winds and enveloped in more fantastic mists than the weather in my own soul. But enough of mewling apology for my lack-lustre early years. Let us get back to my secret life, such as it was, stopping just long enough to have another brief look at Señor Dali on our way.

70 Salvador Dali's mind goes back to a childhood half imagined and half real, in which the edges of actuality were sometimes less sharp than the edges of dream. He seems somehow to have got the idea that this sets him off from Harry Spencer, Charlie Doakes, I. Feinberg, J. J. McNaboe, Willie Faulkner, Herbie Hoover, and me. What Salvie had that the rest of us kids didn't was the perfect scenery, characters, and
75 costumes for his desperate little rebellion against the clean, the conventional, and the comfortable. He put perfume on his hair (which would have cost him his life in, say, Bayonne, N. J., or Youngstown, Ohio), he owned a lizard with two tails, he wore silver buttons on his shoes, and he knew, or imagined he knew, little girls named Galuchka and Dullita. Thus he was born halfway along the road to paranoia, the soft Poictesme*
80 of his prayers, the melting Oz** of his oblations, the capital, to put it so that you can

* Poictesme—a fictional land   **Oz—another fictional land

see what I am trying to say, of his heart's desire. Or so, anyway, it must seem to a native of Columbus, Ohio, who, as a youngster, bought his twelve-dollar suits at the F. & R. Lazarus Co., had his hair washed out with Ivory soap, owned a bull terrier with only one tail, and played (nicely and a bit diffidently) with little girls named Irma and
85 Betty and Ruby.

Another advantage that the young Dali had over me, from the standpoint of impetus toward paranoia, lay in the nature of the adults who peopled his real world. There was, in Dali's home town of Figueras, a family of artists named Pitchot (musicians, painters, and poets), all of whom adored the ground that the *enfant terrible*
90 walked on. If one of them came upon him throwing himself from a high rock – a favorite relaxation of our hero – or hanging by his feet with his head immersed in a pail of water, the wild news was spread about the town that greatness and genius had come to Figueras. There was a woman who put on a look of maternal interest when Salvador threw rocks at her. The mayor of the town fell dead one day at the boy's feet. A doctor
95 in the community (not the one he had horsewhipped) was seized of a fit and attempted to beat him up. (The contention that the doctor was out of his senses at the time of the assault is Dali's, not mine.)

The adults around me when I was in short pants were neither so glamorous nor so attentive. They consisted mainly of eleven maternal great-aunts, all Methodists, who
100 were staunch believers in physic, mustard plasters, and Scripture, and it was part of their dogma that artistic tendencies should be treated the same way as hiccups or hysterics. None of them was an artist, unless you can count Aunt Lou, who wrote sixteen-stress verse, with hit-and-miss rhymes, in celebration of people's birthdays or on the occasion of great national disaster. It never occurred to me to bite a bat in my
105 aunts' presence or to throw stones at them. There was one escape, though: my secret world of idiom.

Two years ago my wife and I, looking for a house to buy, called on a firm of real-estate agents in New Milford. One of the members of the firm, scrabbling through a metal box containing many keys, looked up to say, "The key to the Roxbury
110 house isn't here." His partner replied, "It's a common lock. A skeleton will let you in." I was suddenly once again five years old, with wide eyes and open mouth. I pictured the Roxbury house as I would have pictured it as a small boy, a house of such dark and nameless horrors as have never crossed the mind of our little bat-biter.

It was of sentences like that, nonchalantly tossed off by real-estate dealers,
115 great-aunts, clergymen, and other such prosaic persons, that the enchanted private world of my early boyhood was made. In this world, businessmen who phoned their wives to say they were tied up at the office sat roped to their swivel chairs, and probably gagged, unable to move or speak, except somehow, miraculously, to telephone; hundreds of thousands of businessmen tied to their chairs in hundreds of
120 thousands of offices in every city in my fantastic cosmos. An especially fine note about the binding of all the businessmen in all the cities was that whoever did it always did it around five o'clock in the afternoon.

Then there was the man who left town under a cloud. Sometimes I saw him all wrapped up in the cloud, and invisible, like a cat in a burlap sack. At other times it
125 floated, about the size of a sofa, three or four feet above his head, following him wherever he went. One could think about the man under the cloud before going to sleep; the image of him wandering around from town to town was a sure soporific.

Not so the mental picture of a certain Mrs Huston, who had been terribly cut up when her daughter died on the operating table. I could see the doctors too vividly, just
130 before they set upon Mrs Huston with their knives, and I could hear them. "Now Mrs Huston, will we get up on the table like a good girl, or will we have to be put there?" I

could usually fight off Mrs Huston before I went to sleep, but she frequently got into my dreams, and sometimes she still does.

135 I remember the grotesque creature that came to haunt my meditations when one evening my father said to my mother, "What did Mrs Johnson say when you told her about Betty?" and my mother replied, "Oh, she was all ears." There were many other wonderful figures in the secret, surrealist landscapes of my youth: the old lady who was always up in the air, the husband who did not seem to be able to put his foot down, the man who lost his head during a fire but was still able to run out of the house
140 yelling, the young lady who was, in reality, a soiled dove. It was a world that, of necessity, one had to keep to oneself and brood over in silence, because it would fall to pieces at the touch of words. If you brought it out into the light of actual day and put it to the test of questions, your parents would try to laugh the miracles away, or they would take your temperature and put you to bed. (Since I always ran a temperature,
145 whenever it was taken, I was put to bed and left there all alone with Mrs Huston.)

Such a world as the world of my childhood is, alas, not year-proof. It is a ghost that, to use Henley's words, gleams, flickers, vanishes away. I think it must have been the time my little Cousin Frances came to visit us that it began surely and forever to dissolve. I came into the house one rainy dusk and asked where Frances was. "She
150 is," said our cook, "up in the front room crying her heart out." The fact that a person could cry so hard that his heart would come out of his body, as perfectly shaped and glossy as a red velvet pincushion, was news to me. For some reason I had never heard the expression, so common in American families whose hopes and dreams run so often counter to attainment. I went upstairs and opened the door of the front room.
155 Frances, who was three years older than I, jumped up off the bed and ran past me sobbing, and down the stairs.

My search for her heart took some fifteen minutes. I tore the bed apart and kicked up the rugs and even looked in the bureau drawers. It was no good. I looked out the window at the rain and the darkening sky. My cherished mental image of the man
160 under the cloud began to grow dim and fade away. I discovered that, all alone in a room, I could face the thought of Mrs Huston with cold equanimity. Downstairs, in the living room, Frances was still crying. I began to laugh.

Ah there, Salvador!

Question

How effective in your view is *The Secret Life of James Thurber* as a humorous essay?

Your answer should be based on detailed analysis of those aspects of the content, structure and tone of the essay that you consider to be important.

[**Turn over**

3. **Poetry (*Page twenty-eight to twenty-nine*)**

Read carefully the poem **The Year's Afternoon** *(1997) by Douglas Dunn and then answer the question that follows it (Page twenty-nine).*

The Year's Afternoon

As the moment of leisure grows deeper
I feel myself sink like a slow root
Into the herbaceous lordship of my place.
This is my time, my possessive, opulent
5 Freedom in free-fall from salaried routines,
Intrusions, the boundaryless tedium.
This is my liberty among trees and grass
When silence is the mind's imperfect ore
And a thought turns and dallies in its space
10 Unhindered by desire or transactions.
For three hours without history or thirst
Time is my own unpurchased and intimate
Republic of the cool wind and blue sea.
For three hours I shall be my own tutor
15 In the coastal hedge-school of grass furniture.
Imaginary books fly to my hand
From library trees. They are all I need.
Birdsong is a chirp of meditative silence
Rendered in fluttered boughs, and I am still,
20 Very still, in philosophical light.
I am all ears in my waterside aviary.
My breath is poised for truth to whisper from
Inner invisibilities and the holiness
Venturesome little birds live with always
25 In their instinctive comforts. I am shedding
The appetites of small poetry and open to
Whatever visits me. I am all eyes
When light moves on water and the leaves shake.
I am very still, a hedge-hidden sniper
30 In whose sights clarified infinity sits
Smiling at me, and my skin is alive
To thousands of brushed touches, very light
Delicate kisses of time, thought kisses,
Touches which have come out of hiding shyly
35 Then go back again into the far away
Surrender they came from and where they live.
Perfecting my afternoon, I am alert to
Archival fragrances that float to me
Unexplained over the world's distances.
40 This is my time. I am making it real.
I am getting rid of myself. This is my time.
I am free to do whatever I wish
In these hours, and I have chosen this
Liberty, which is an evanishment

45 To the edges of breath, a momentary
   Loss of the dutiful, a destitute
   Perchance, a slipping away from life's
   Indignities and works into my freedom
   Which is beyond all others and is me.

50 I am free to do as I like, and do this;
   I sink like a slow root in the name of life
   And in the name of what it is I do.
   These are my hours of 1993.
   Ears, eyes, nose, skin and taste have gone.

55 For a little while I shall be nothing and good.
   Then other time will come back, and history.
   I shall get up and leave my hiding place,
   My instinctive, field-sized republic.
   I shall go home, and be that other man.

60 I shall go to my office. I shall live
   Another year longing for my hours
   In the complete afternoon of sun and salt.
   My empty shoes at the bedside will say to me,
   "When are we taking you back? Why be patient?

65 You have much more, so much more, to lose."

Question

Write a critical evaluation of this poem.

Your evaluation should be based on detailed analysis of those aspects of the content, structure and language of the poem that you find interesting and significant.

[Turn over

4.   **Drama (*Pages thirty to forty-one*)**

Mother Figure is the first of a sequence of loosely linked plays that together make up *Confusions* (1974) by Alan Ayckbourn.

Read **Mother Figure** carefully and then answer the question that follows it (*Page forty-one*).

Mother Figure

Lucy's sitting-room

It is a suburban room, fairly untidy, with evidence of small children.   There are two doors—one to the kitchen and back door, one to the bedrooms and front door

Lucy hurries in from the bedrooms on her way to the kitchen.   She is untidy, unmade-up, in
5   *dressing-gown and slippers*

Lucy (*calling behind her*) Nicholas! Stay in your own bed and leave Sarah alone.
The telephone rings

Lucy goes out to the kitchen, returning at once with a glass of water

All right, Jamie, darling.   Mummy's coming with a dinkie . . . (*As she passes the*
10   *telephone, she lifts the receiver off the rest and almost immediately replaces it*) Mummy's coming, Jamie, Mummy's coming.

Lucy goes off to the bedroom with the glass

The front door chimes sound.   A pause, then they sound again

Lucy returns from the bedrooms

15   Sarah!   You're a naughty, naughty girl.   I told you not to play with Jamie's syrup.   That's for Jamie's toothipegs . . .

The door chimes sound again

Lucy ignores these and goes off to the kitchen.   She returns almost at once with a toilet roll, hauling off handfuls of it as she goes to perform some giant mopping-up operation

20   Nicholas, if you're not in your bed by the time I come up, I shall smack your botty.
There are two rings on the back doorbell

Lucy goes off to the bedroom

A pause

Rosemary, a rather frail, mousey-looking woman, comes in from the kitchen

25 **Rosemary** (*calling timidly*) Woo-hoo!

Lucy returns from the bedroom

Lucy (*calling as before*) Now go to sleep.   At once. (*Seeing Rosemary*) Oh.

Rosemary Hallo.   I thought you must be in.

Lucy (*puzzled*) Hallo?

30 **Rosemary** I thought you were in.

Lucy Yes.

Rosemary You are.

Lucy Yes.

Rosemary Hallo.

35 **Lucy** Hallo. (*A slight pause*) Who are you?

Rosemary Next door.

Lucy What?

Rosemary From next door. Mrs Oates. Rosemary. Do you remember?

Lucy (*vaguely*) Oh, yes. Hallo.

40 **Rosemary** Hallo. I did ring both bells but nobody seemed . . .

Lucy No. I don't take much notice of bells.

Rosemary Oh.

Lucy I've rather got my hands full.

Rosemary Oh yes. With the children, you mean? How are they?

45 **Lucy** Fine.

Rosemary All well?

Lucy Yes.

Rosemary Good. It's three you've got, isn't it?

Lucy Yes.

50 **Rosemary** Still, I expect it's time well spent.

Lucy I haven't much option.

Rosemary No.

Lucy Well.

Rosemary Oh, don't let me—if you want to get on . . .

55 **Lucy** No.

Rosemary I mean, if you were going to bed.

Lucy Bed?

Rosemary (*indicating Lucy's attire*) Well . . .

Lucy Oh, no. I didn't get dressed today, that's all.

60 **Rosemary** Oh. Not ill?

Lucy No.

Rosemary Oh.

Lucy I just wasn't going anywhere.

Rosemary Oh, well . . .

65 **Lucy** I haven't been anywhere for weeks.

Rosemary That's a shame.

Lucy I don't think I've got dressed for weeks, either.

Rosemary Ah. No, well, I must say we haven't seen you. Not that we've been looking but we haven't seen you.

70 **Lucy** No. Do you want to sit down?

Rosemary Oh, thank you. Just for a minute

Lucy If you can find somewhere. (*She moves the odd toy*)

Rosemary (*sitting*) Yes, we were wondering if you were alright, actually. My husband and I—Terry, that's my husband—he was remarking that we hadn't seen you for a bit.

75 **Lucy** No.

Rosemary We heard the children, of course. Not to complain of, mind you, but we heard them but we didn't see you.

Lucy No. (*She picks up various toys during the following and puts them in the play-pen*)

Rosemary Or your husband.

80 **Lucy** No.

Rosemary But then I said to Terry, if they need us they've only to ask. They know where we are. If they want to keep themselves to themselves, that's all right by us. I mean, that's why they put up that great big fence so they could keep themselves to themselves. And that's all right by us.

85 **Lucy** Good.

Rosemary And then ten minutes ago, we got this phone call.

Lucy Phone call?

Rosemary Yes. Terry answered it—that's my husband—and they say will you accept a transfer charge from a public phone box in Middlesbrough and Terry says, hallo,
90 that's funny, he says, who do we know in Middlesbrough and I said, not a soul and he says, well, that's funny, Terry says, well who is it? How do we know we know him? If we don't know him, we don't want to waste money talking to him but if we do, it might be an emergency and we won't sleep a wink. And the operator says, well suit yourself, take it or leave it, its all the same to me. So we took it and it was your
95 husband.

Lucy Harry?

Rosemary Harry, yes. Mr Compton.

Lucy What did he want?

Rosemary Well—you. He was worried. He's been ringing you for days. He's had the
100 line checked but there's been no reply.

Lucy Oh.

Rosemary Has it not been ringing?

Lucy Possibly. I don't take much notice of bells. (*She goes to listen for the children*)

Rosemary Oh. Anyway, he sounded very worried. So I said I'd pop round and make
105 sure. I took his number in case you wanted to . . .

Lucy is clearly not listening

Are you alright?

Lucy Yes, I was listening for Nicholas.

Rosemary Oh. That's the baby?

110 **Lucy** No.

Rosemary (*warmly*) Ah.

Lucy I'm sorry. I'm being very rude. It's just I haven't—spoken to anyone for days. My husband isn't home much.

Rosemary Oh, I quite understand. Would you like his number?

115 **Lucy** What?

Rosemary Your husband's telephone number in Middlesbrough. Would you like it? He said he'd hang on. It's from a hotel.

Lucy No.

Rosemary Oh.

120 **Lucy** Whatever he has to say to me, he can say to my face or not at all.

Rosemary Ah. (*Laying a slip of paper gingerly on the coffee-table*) Well, it's there.

Lucy Would you care for a drink or something?

Rosemary A drink? Oh—well—what's the time? Well—I don't know if I should. Half past—oh yes, well—why not? Yes, please. Why not? A little one.

125 **Lucy** Orange or lemon?

Rosemary I beg your pardon?

Lucy Orange juice or lemon juice? Or you can have milk.

Rosemary Oh, I see. I thought you meant . . .

Lucy Come on. Orange or lemon? I'm waiting.

130 **Rosemary** Is there a possibility of some coffee?

Lucy No.

Rosemary Oh.

Lucy It'll keep you awake. I'll get you an orange, it's better for you.

Rosemary Oh . . .

135 **Lucy** (*as she goes*) Sit still. Don't run around. I won't be a minute.

Lucy goes out into the kitchen

Rosemary sits nervously. She rises after a second, looks guiltily towards the kitchen and sits again. The door chimes sound. Rosemary looks towards the kitchen. There is no sign of Lucy. The door chimes sound again. Rosemary gets up hesitantly

140 **Rosemary** (*calling*) Mrs—er . . .

Lucy (*off, in the kitchen*) Wait, wait, wait! I'm coming . . .

The door chimes sound again

Rosemary runs off to the front door. Lucy returns from the kitchen with a glass of orange juice

145 Here we are, Rosemary, I . . . (*She looks round the empty room, annoyed. Calling*) Rosemary! It's on the table.

Lucy puts the orange juice on the coffee-table and goes out to the kitchen again. Rosemary returns from the hall with Terry, a rather pudgy man in shirt sleeves

Rosemary (*sotto voce*) Come in a minute.

150 **Terry** I'm watching the telly.

Rosemary Just for a minute.

Terry I wondered where you'd got to. I mean, all you had to do was give her the number . . .

Rosemary I want you to meet her. See what you think. I don't think she's well.

155 **Terry** How do you mean?

Rosemary She just seems . . .

Terry Is she ill?

Rosemary I don't know . . .

Terry Well, either she is or she isn't.

160 **Rosemary** Ssh.

Lucy returns from the kitchen with a plate of biscuits

Lucy Here we are now. (*Seeing Terry*) Oh.

Terry Evening.

Lucy Hallo.

165 **Rosemary** My husband.

Lucy Terry, isn't it?

Terry Yes.

Lucy That's a nice name, isn't it? (*Pointing to the sofa*) Sit down there then. Have you got your orange juice, Rosemary?

170 *Terry sits*

Rosemary Yes, thank you. (*She picks up the glass of orange juice and sits*)

Terry Orange juice?

Rosemary Yes.

Terry What are you doing drinking that?

175 **Rosemary** I like orange juice.

Lucy Now, here's some very special choccy bics but you musn't eat them all. I'm going to trust you. (*She starts tidying up again*)

Rosemary (*still humouring her*) Lovely. (*She mouths "say something" to Terry*)

Terry Yes. Well, how are you keeping then—er, sorry, I'm forgetting. Lesley, isn't it?

180 **Lucy** Mrs Compton.

Terry Yes. Mrs Compton. How are you?

Lucy I'm very well, thank you, Terry. Nice of you to ask.

Terry And what about Har—Mr Compton?

Lucy Very well. When I last saw him. Rosemary dear, try not to make all that noise
185 when you drink.

Rosemary Sorry.

Terry Yes, we were saying that your husband's job obviously takes him round and about a lot.

Lucy Yes. (*She starts folding nappies*)

190 **Terry** Doesn't get home as much as he'd like, I expect.

Lucy I've no idea.

Terry But then it takes all sorts. Take me, I'm home on the nose six o'clock every night. That's the way she wants it. Who am I . . .? (*Pause*) Yes I think I could quite envy your husband, sometimes. Getting about a bit. I mean, when you think about
195 it, it's more natural. For a man. His natural way of life. Right back to the primitive. Woman stays in the cave, man the hunter goes off roving at will. Mind you, I think the idea originally was he went off hunting for food. Different sort of game these days, eh?

Rosemary (*hissing*) Terry!

200 **Terry** Be after something quite different these days, eh? (*He nods and winks*)

Lucy Now don't get silly, Terry.

Terry What? Ah—beg your pardon.

A pause. Terry munches a biscuit. Rosemary sips her orange juice.

Rosemary Very pleasant orange juice.

205 **Lucy** Full of vitamin C.

Terry No, I didn't want to give you the wrong impression there. But seriously, I was saying to Rosie here, you can't put a man in a cage. You try to do that, you've lost him. See my point?

Lucy That can apply to women, too, surely?

210 **Rosemary** Yes, quite right.

Terry What do you mean, quite right?

Rosemary Well . . .

Terry You're happy enough at home, aren't you?

Rosemary Yes, but—yes—but . . .

215 **Terry** Well then, that's what I'm saying. You're the woman, you're happy enough at home looking after that. I'm the man, I have to be out and about.

Rosemary I don't know about that. You'd never go out at all unless I pushed you.

Terry What do you mean? I'm out all day.

Rosemary Only because you have to be. You wouldn't be if you didn't have to be.
220 When you don't, you come in, sit down, watch the television and go to bed.

Terry I have to relax.

Rosemary You're always relaxing.

Terry Don't deny me relaxing.

Rosemary I don't.

225 **Terry** Yes, you do, you just said . . .

Lucy Now, don't quarrel. I won't have any quarrelling.

Terry Eh?

Rosemary Sorry.

Lucy Would you like an orange drink as well, Terry? Is that what it is?

230 **Terry** Er . . . Oh no—I don't go in for that sort of drink much, if you know what I mean. (*He winks, then reaches for a biscuit*) I'll have another one of these though, if you don't mind?

Lucy Just a minute, how many have you had?

Terry This is my second. It's only my second.

235 **Lucy** Well, that's all. No more after that. I'll get you some milk. You better have something that's good for you.

Terry (*half rising*) Oh no—thank you, not milk, no.

Lucy (*going to the kitchen*) Wait there. (*Seeing Terry has half risen*) And don't jump about while you're eating, Terry.

240 *Lucy goes out to the kitchen*

Terry You're right. She's odd.

Rosemary I said she was.

Terry No wonder he's gone off.

Rosemary Perhaps that's why she's odd.

245 **Terry** Why?

Rosemary Because he's gone off.

Terry Rubbish. And we'll have less of that, too, if you don't mind.

Rosemary What?

Terry All this business about me never going out of the house.

250 **Rosemary** It's true.

Terry It's not true and it makes me out to be some bloody idle loafer.

Rosemary All I said . . .

Terry And even if it is true, you have no business saying it in front of other people.

Rosemary Oh, honestly, Terry, you're so touchy. I can't say a thing right these days,
255 can I?

Terry Very little. Now you come to mention it.

Rosemary Niggle, niggle, niggle. You keep on at me the whole time. I'm frightened to open my mouth these days. I don't know what's got into you lately. You're in a filthy mood from the moment you get up till you go to bed . . .

260 **Terry** What are you talking about?

Rosemary Grumbling and moaning . . .

Terry Oh, shut up.

Rosemary You're a misery to live with these days, you really are.

Terry I said, shut up.

265 **Rosemary** (*more quietly*) I wish to God you'd go off somewhere sometimes, I really do.

Terry Don't tempt me. I bloody feel like it occasionally, I can tell you.

Rosemary (*tearfully*) Oh, lovely . . .

Terry If you think I enjoy spending night after night sitting looking at you . . . (*He throws the biscuit down*) What am I eating these damn things for . . . you're mistaken.
270 (*Thirsty from the biscuits, he grabs her orange juice glass and drains it in one*)

Rosemary That's mine, do you mind. (*She rises and stamps her foot*)

Terry Come on. Let's go. (*He jumps up*)

Rosemary That was my orange juice when you've quite finished.

Lucy enters with a glass of milk

275 **Lucy** Now what are you doing jumping about?

Rosemary sits

Terry We've got to be going, I'm sorry.

Lucy Not till you've finished. Sit down.

Terry Listen, I'm sorry we . . .

280 **Lucy** (*seeing Rosemary's distraught state*) What's the matter with Rosemary?

Rosemary (*sniffing*) Nothing . . .

Lucy What have you been doing to her?

Terry Nothing.

Lucy Here's your milk.

285 **Terry** Thank you.

Lucy You don't deserve it.

Terry I don't want it.

Lucy Don't be tiresome.

Terry I hate the damned stuff.

290 **Lucy** I'm not going to waste my breath arguing with you, Terry. It's entirely up to you if you don't want to be big and strong.

Terry Now, look . . .

Lucy If you want to be a little weakling, that's up to you. Just don't come whining to me when all your nails and teeth fall out. Now then, Rosemary, let's see to you. (*She*
295 *puts down the milk and picks up the biscuits*) Would you like a choccy biccy?

Rosemary No, thank you.

Lucy Come on, they're lovely choccy, look. Milk choccy . . .

Rosemary No, honestly.

Terry Rosie, are you coming or not?

300 **Lucy** Well, have a drink, then. Blow your nose and have a drink, that's a good girl. (*Seeing the glass*) Oh, it's all gone. You've drunk that quickly, haven't you?

Rosemary I didn't drink it. He did.

Lucy What?

Rosemary He drank it.

305 **Lucy** Terry, did you drink her orange juice?

Terry Look, there's a programme I want to watch . . .

Lucy Did you drink Rosemary's orange juice?

Terry Look, good night . . .

Rosemary Yes, he did.

310 **Lucy** Well, I think that's really mean.

Rosemary He just takes anything he wants.

Lucy Really mean.

Rosemary Never thinks of asking.

Terry I'm going.

315 **Lucy** Not before you've apologized to Rosemary

Terry Good night.

Terry goes out

Lucy (*calling after him*) And don't you dare come back until you're ready to apologize. (*To Rosemary*) Never mind him. Let him go. He'll be back.

320 **Rosemary** That's the way to talk to him.

Lucy What?

Rosemary That's the way he ought to be talked to more often.

Lucy I'm sorry. I won't have that sort of behaviour. Not from anyone.

Rosemary He'll sulk now. For days.

325 **Lucy** Well, let him. It doesn't worry us, does it?

Rosemary No. It's just sometimes—things get on top of you—and then he comes back at night—and he starts on me and I . . . (*She cries*) Oh dear—I'm so sorry—I didn't mean to . . .

Lucy (*cooing*) Come on now. Come on . . .

330 **Rosemary** I've never done this. I'm sorry . . .

Lucy That's all right. There, there.

Rosemary I'm sorry. (*She continues to weep*)

Lucy Look who's watching you.

Rosemary Who?

335 **Lucy** (*picking up a doll*) Mr Poddle. Mr Poddle's watching you. (*She holds up the doll*) You don't want Mr Poddle to see you crying, do you? Do you?

Rosemary (*lamely*) No . . .

Lucy Do we, Mr Poddle? (*She shakes Mr Poddle's head*) No, he says, no. Stop crying, Rosie. (*She nods Mr Poddle's head*) Stop crying, Rosie. Yes—yes.

340 *Rosemary gives an embarrassed giggle*

That's better. Was that a little laugh, Mr Poddle? Was that a little laugh?

Lucy wiggles Mr Poddle about, bringing him close up to Rosmary's face and taking him away again

Was that a little laugh? Was that a little laugh? Was that a little laugh?

345 *Rosemary giggles uncontrollably*

Terry enters from the hall and stands amazed

Terry Er . . .

Lucy and Rosemary become aware of him

Er—I've locked myself out.

350 **Lucy** Have you come back to apologize?

Terry You got the key, Rosie?

Rosemary Yes.

Terry Let's have it then.

Lucy Not until you apologize.

355 **Terry** Look, I'm not apologizing to anyone. I just want the key. To get back into my own house, if you don't mind. Now, come on.

Rosemary (*producing the key from her bag*) Here.

Lucy Rosemary, don't you dare give it to him.

Terry Eh?

360 **Rosemary** What?

Lucy Not until he apologizes.

Terry Rosie, give me the key.

Lucy No, Rosemary. I'll take it. Give it to me.

Terry Rosie.

365 **Lucy** Rosemary.

Rosemary (*torn*) Er . . .

Lucy (*very fiercely*) Rosemary, will you give me that key at once.

Rosemary gives Lucy the key. Terry regards Lucy

Terry Would you mind most awfully giving me the key to my own front door.

370 **Lucy** Certainly.

Terry Thank you so much.

Lucy Just as soon as you've apologized to Rosemary.

Terry I've said, I'm not apologizing to anyone.

Lucy Then you're not having the key.

375 **Terry** Now listen, I've got a day's work to do tomorrow. I'm damned if I'm going to start playing games with some frustrated nutter . . .

Rosemary Terry . . .

Lucy Take no notice of him, Rosemary, he's just showing off.

Terry Are you going to give me that key or not?

380 **Lucy** Not until you apologize.

Terry All right. I'll have to come and take it off you, won't I.

Lucy You try. You just dare try, my boy.

Terry All right. (*He moves towards Lucy*)

Rosemary Terry . . .

385 **Lucy** Just you try and see what happens.

Terry (*halted by her tone; uncertainly*) I'm not joking.

Lucy Neither am I.

Terry Look, I don't want to . . . Just give me the key, there's a good . . .

Lucy Not until you apologize to Rosemary.

390 **Terry** Oh, for the love of . . . All right (*To Rosemary*) Sorry.

Lucy Say it nicely.

Terry I'm very sorry, Rosie. Now give us the key, for God's sake.

Lucy When you've drunk your milk. Sit down and drink your milk.

Terry Oh, blimey . . . (*He sits*)

395 **Lucy** That's better.

Terry I hate milk.

Lucy Drink it up.

Terry scowls and picks up the glass. Rosemary, unseen by Lucy, sticks her tongue out at him. Terry bangs down his glass and moves as if to hit her.

400   Terry!

Terry She stuck her tongue out at me.

Lucy Sit still.

Terry But she . . .

Lucy Sit!

405 *Terry sits scowling. Rosemary smirks at him smugly*

(*Seeing her*) And don't do that, Rosemary. If the wind changes, you'll get stuck like it. And sit up straight and don't slouch.

Rosemary does so

Terry (*taking a sip of the milk*) This is horrible.

410 *Silence. He takes another sip*

It's warm

Silence. Another sip

Terry There's a football international on television, you know.

Lucy Not until you've drunk that up, there isn't. Come on, Rosemary. Help Terry to
415   drink it. "Georgie Porgie Pudding and Pie, kissed the girls and . . .?

Rosemary "Made them cry."

Lucy Good.

Rosemary } "When the boys came out to play, Georgie Porgie   { (*Speaking*
Lucy   } ran away.   { *together*)

420 **Terry** (*finishing his glass with a giant swallow*) All gone. (*He wipes his mouth*)

Lucy Good boy.

Terry Can I have the key now, please?

Lucy Here you are.

Terry goes to take it

425 What do you say?

Terry Thank you.

Lucy All right. Off you go, both of you.

Rosemary (*kissing her on the cheek*) Night night.

Lucy Night night, dear. Night night, Terry.

430 **Terry** (*kissing Lucy likewise*) Night night.

Lucy Sleep tight.

Terry Hope the bugs don't bite.

Lucy Hold Rosemary's hand, Terry.

Rosemary and Terry hold hands

435 See her home safely.

Terry Night.

Rosemary Night.

Lucy Night night.

Terry and Rosemary go off hand in hand

440 *Lucy blows kisses*

(*With a sigh*) Blooming kids. Honestly.

The telephone rings. Lucy, as she passes it, picks it up and replaces it as before. As she does so, the Lights fade to a single spot in a call-box. Harry is there, with the receiver in his hand.

445 **Harry** Oh, blast, not again. Hallo—hallo—oh, damn and blast. (*He jiggles the receiver*) Operator? Operator? Hallo—hallo . . . Operator, there must be a fault on this line. . . The line I have been trying unsuccessfully to dial. . . . Yes—six-four-one-nine. I mean, this is quite unforgivable. This is the third time I have reported it and I am still quite unable to make contact with my wife. . . . Yes, well, thank you for your
450 sympathy. Let's try a little action, shall we? Because I'm going to take this to the top. . . . Yes, top. . . . What? . . . No—T for Toffee, O for Orange. . . . Oh, forget it. (*He rings off*) Give me strength.

Question

It has been said that "*Alan Ayckbourn is a dramatist whose work, characteristically, deals with the eccentricities, fears and neuroses of the suburban middle class*".

In what ways and how effectively does Ayckbourn dramatise "*the eccentricities, fears and neuroses of the suburban middle class*" in *Mother Figure*?

Section 4—Reading the Media

You must answer **one question only** in this section.

Unless otherwise indicated, your answer must take the form of a **critical essay** appropriately structured to meet the demands of your selected question.

Category A—Film

1. Make a detailed study of the cinematic techniques used in the opening sequences of **two** films by the **same** director.

2. Discuss the contribution of the sound track—speech, music, sound effects—to the effectiveness of **at least two** sequences from any **one** film.

Category B—Television

3. "*The domestic audience places considerable constraints on both the form and the content of television drama.*"

   Discuss with reference to any **one** television drama (soap, serial, series or single play).

4. In what ways does any news **or** current affairs **or** documentary programme (or series of programmes) both inform and entertain its audience?

Category C—Radio

5. "*The challenge that faces each radio channel today is how to keep its loyal audience while at the same time attracting new listeners.*"

   Discuss.

6. How does any news **or** current affairs **or** sports programme exploit the advantages of communicating in a non-visual medium?

Category D—Print journalism

7. Discuss the use of narrative **and** representation in any **one** newspaper's coverage of a major news event.

   NB You may not use the materials provided for question 8 in order to answer question 7.

8. For this question, you are provided with copies of some of *The Independent's* front page coverage in September 2007 of the demonstrations against the military regime in Burma (*pages 1–5 of the colour insert provided for this section*).

   Analyse the images and written text employed in these front pages and evaluate their effectiveness in conveying the narrative of a developing news story.

Category E—Advertising

9. *"Television advertisements often exploit other television genres—for example, sitcoms, game shows, sports programmes."*

Discuss the ways in which a range of television advertisements **or** a television advertising campaign exploits other television genres.

10. For this question, you are provided with two advertisements for Suzuki Swift published in *The Guardian Weekend* and *The Observer Magazine* in August 2007 (*pages 6 and 7 of the colour insert provided for this section*).

How effectively does each advertisement convey to its target audience the distinctive brand identity of the product?

[END OF QUESTION PAPER]

[BLANK PAGE]

Insert for Section 4 – Reading the Media Question 8

70p

Monday 24 September 2007
www.independent.co.uk
NUMBER 6313

THE INDEPENDENT

CHELSEA'S DAY OF PAIN
ALL THE PREMIER LEAGUE ACTION 24 PAGES OF SPORT

THE DEFIANCE OF A PEOPLE

Monks and nuns lead Burma's
biggest protests for 20 years

THE HOPE OF A NATION

Aung San Suu Kyi greets
protesters in her first public
appearance since May 2003

FULL REPORTS PAGE 2

IN EXTRA
Beech Life
Richard Mabey on Britain's forests

Cover story

FREE INSIDE
20-PAGE BOOKLET
The great composers
Today: Haydn

PLUS FREE DOWNLOADS
FOR EVERY READER,
SEE PAGE 31
classicsonline

Kirsty Wark

.media
16-page colour supplement

Insert for Section 4 – Reading the Media Question 8

Insert for Section 4 – Reading the Media Question 8

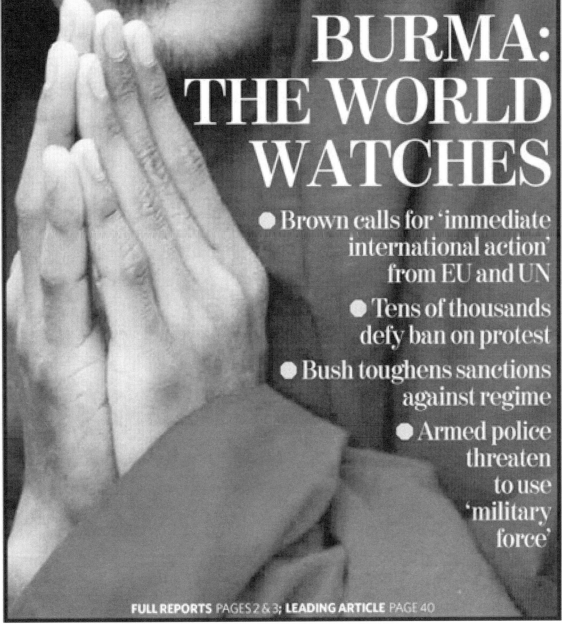

Insert for Section 4 – Reading the Media Question 8

THE INDEPENDENT

70p

Thursday 27 September 2007
www.independent.co.uk

SPRINGSTEEN
ANDY GILL ON THE ROCK COMEBACK OF THE YEAR IN EXTRA

'...Riot police and soldiers are beating monks... I saw a truck full of police with guns... They are using tear-gas bombs against the crowd... Buddhist monks are now chanting: "All humans be free from killing and torturing"... A monk was beaten to death while he was praying... The military has been ordered to shoot... About 200 people were hauled off on to the trucks and driven away... One patient died on arriving in hospital – four are still in a bad way... They are starting a crackdown... The junta is reducing the internet connection bandwidth... I think they will cut off communication... We are so afraid...'

INSIDE THE SAFFRON REVOLUTION
VOICES OF THE PROTESTERS PAGE 5; **REPORTS** PAGES 2&3; **GORDON BROWN** PAGE 2

Insert for Section 4 – Reading the Media Question 8

Saturday Edition

(Ireland, €1.80) £1.40

29 September 2007
www.independent.co.uk

50 BEST BIKE RIDES

FREE MAGAZINE TRACE YOUR FAMILY HISTORY
THE GUIDE TO FINDING YOUR ANCESTORS

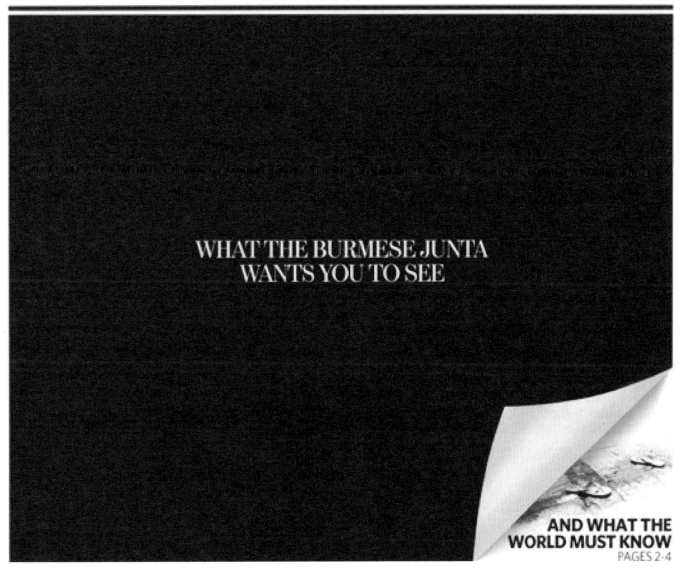

WHAT THE BURMESE JUNTA WANTS YOU TO SEE

AND WHAT THE WORLD MUST KNOW
PAGES 2-4

Insert for Section 4 – Reading the Media Question 10

Insert for Section 4 – Reading the Media Question 10

[BLANK PAGE]

ADVANCED HIGHER

2011

[BLANK PAGE]

X270/701

NATIONAL
QUALIFICATIONS
2011

FRIDAY, 13 MAY
1.00 PM – 4.00 PM

ENGLISH
ADVANCED HIGHER

There are four sections in this paper.

Section 1—Literary Study	pages	2 – 8
Section 2—Language Study	pages	9 – 16
Section 3—Textual Analysis	pages	17 – 40
Section 4—Reading the Media	pages	41 – 42 (plus Insert)

Depending on the options you have chosen, you must answer **one** or **two** questions.

If you have submitted a Creative Writing folio, you must answer only **one** question.

Otherwise, you must answer **two** questions.

If you are required to answer only **one question**

- it must be taken from **Section 1—Literary Study**
- you must leave the examination room **after 1 hour 30 minutes**.

If you are required to answer **two questions**

- your first must be taken from **Section 1—Literary Study**
- your second must be taken from **a different section**
- each answer must be written in **a separate answer booklet**
- the maximum time allowed for any question is **1 hour 30 minutes**.

You must identify each question you attempt by indicating clearly

- **the title of the section** from which the question has been taken
- **the number of the question** within that section.

You must also write inside the front cover of your Literary Study answer booklet

- **the topic** of your Specialist Study (Dissertation)
- **the texts** used in your Specialist Study (Dissertation).

Section 1—Literary Study

This section is **mandatory** for all candidates.

You must answer **one question only** in this section.

Unless otherwise indicated, your answer must take the form of a **critical essay** appropriately structured to meet the demands of your selected question.

DRAMA

1. **Beckett**

   *"In **Waiting for Godot** and in **Endgame**, Beckett has given a voice to men and women who are at the end of their tether, past pose or pretence, past claim of meaningful existence."*

   Discuss.

2. **Byrne**

   The slab room at A.F. Stobo & Co. Carpet Manufacturers . . . Paisley Town Hall in the 1950s . . . The Garden of Remembrance in a municipal cemetery.

   Discuss the contribution of setting to the effectiveness of each play in *The Slab Boys Trilogy*.

3. **Chekhov**

   One critic has asserted that, in *Uncle Vanya* **and** in *The Cherry Orchard*, "the principal targets of Checkov's comedy are those who have lost or who have given up their ideals".

   How far do you agree?

4. **Friel**

   In what ways and how effectively does Friel dramatise aspects of Irish identity in *Translations* **and** in *Dancing at Lughnasa?*

5. **Lindsay**

   "The dramatic turning point of the play is the entrance of Divyne Correctioun who, we are told, 'sall reforme into this land / Evin all the Thrie Estaits'."

   How far do you agree?

6. **Lochhead**

   How effective, in your view, are *Mary Queen of Scots Got Her Head Chopped Off* **and** *Dracula* as dramatic explorations of aspects of modern life?

7. **Pinter**

   Discuss the dramatic function of Ruth in *The Homecoming*, of Gila in *One for the Road* **and** of the two women in *Mountain Language.*

8. Shakespeare

EITHER

(a) *Othello* **and** *Antony and Cleopatra*

Discuss the contribution of the settings of Venice and Cyprus to the tragedy of *Othello* **or** of Rome and Egypt to the tragedy of *Antony and Cleopatra*.

OR

(b) *The Winter's Tale* **and** *The Tempest*

Make a detailed study of Shakespeare's dramatic treatment of power in *The Winter's Tale* **or** in *The Tempest*.

9. Stoppard

"Central to Stoppard's dramatic technique is juxtaposition—of scenes, characters, worlds . . ."

Discuss the effectiveness of Stoppard's use of juxtaposition in *Rosencrantz and Guildenstern Are Dead* **and** in *Arcadia*.

10. Wilde

"Ideals are dangerous things. Realities are better."
                                      (Mrs Erlynne to Lady Windermere in *Lady Windermere's Fan*)

"Women think that they are making ideals of men. What they are making of us are false idols merely."
                                      (Lord Chiltern to Lady Chiltern in *An Ideal Husband*)

Keeping these quotations in mind, discuss Wilde's dramatic treatment of *"ideals"* in *Lady Windermere's Fan* **and** in *An Ideal Husband*.

11. Williams

Discuss Williams's dramatic use of violence and the threat of violence in *A Streetcar Named Desire* **and** in *Sweet Bird of Youth*.

[Turn over

POETRY

12. **Burns**

With reference to *Holy Willie's Prayer* **and** *Address to the Unco Guid* **and** *The Holy Fair*, discuss some of the principal features of Burns's treatment of religious hypocrisy.

13. **Chaucer**

Compare and contrast Chaucer's use of narrative voice in *The Pardoner's Tale* with his use of narrative voice in *The Nun's Priest's Tale*.

14. **Donne**

Discuss Donne's treatment of love in *A Nocturnal upon St Lucie's Day* **and** in **two** of the other specified poems.

15. **Duffy**

Discuss some of the ways in which Duffy deals with the potential and the limitations of language in a range of her poems.

16. **Heaney**

Read carefully the following poem from the sequence *Clearances* and then answer questions (a) **and** (b) that follow it.

IV

Fear of affectation made her affect
Inadequacy whenever it came to
Pronouncing words "beyond her". *Bertold Brek*.
She'd manage something hampered and askew
5   Every time, as if she might betray
The hampered and inadequate by too
Well-adjusted a vocabulary.
With more challenge than pride, she'd tell me, "You
Know all them things." So I governed my tongue
10   In front of her, a genuinely well-
Adjusted adequate betrayal
Of what I knew better. I'd *naw* and *aye*
And decently relapse into the wrong
Grammar which kept us allied and at bay.

(a)   Make a detailed study of the ways in which Heaney presents recollections of his mother in this sonnet.

AND

(b)   Go on to discuss some of the ways in which he presents recollections of his mother in **two** or **three** other sonnets from *Clearances*.

17. Henryson

EITHER

(a) *"Henryson shows his heroine journeying from self-pity to the point where she says, 'Nane but my self as now I will accuse'."*

Discuss the principal techniques used by Henryson in *The Testament of Cresseid* to convey the progress of Cresseid's *"journeying"*.

OR

(b) *"And Clerkis sayis it is richt profitabill*
Amangis ernist to ming ane merie sport."

(The Prologue to the *Morall Fabillis*)

In what ways and how effectively, in your view, does Henryson combine serious and humorous elements in **two** or **three** of the *Morall Fabillis*?

18. Keats

Discuss in detail Keats's use of nature imagery in *Ode to a Nightingale* **and** in *To Autumn*.

19. MacDiarmid

"MacDiarmid's poems are characterised by comparison, contrast, juxtaposition, dizzying changes of mood and scale."

Discuss with reference **either** to *A Drunk Man Looks at the Thistle* **or** to **some** or **all** of the specified lyrics.

20. Muir

Discuss Muir's treatment of the idea of Eden in *One Foot in Eden* and in **two** or **three** other poems.

21. Plath

"In reading Plath's poems, what we are impressed by most of all is her honesty, her willingness to explore pain and fear without compromise."

Discuss some of the principal means Plath uses *"to explore pain and fear"* in **three** or **four** poems.

22. Yeats

Discuss the means by which Yeats explores the importance of art in *Byzantium* **and** in *Lapis Lazuli*.

[Turn over

PROSE FICTION

23. Atwood

Discuss Atwood's use of symbolism in *Cat's Eye* **and** in *Alias Grace*.

24. Austen

"*In her novels, Austen is particularly severe on those who try to influence the young.*"

How far do you agree?

You should support your answer with reference to Austen's presentation of Mr and Mrs Bennet in *Pride and Prejudice* **and** Sir Walter Elliot and Lady Russell in *Persuasion*.

25. Dickens

"'*Father,*' said Louisa, '*Do you think I love Mr Bounderby?*' Mr Gradgrind was extremely discomfited by this unexpected question. '*Well, my child,*' he returned, '*I—really—cannot take it upon myself to say.*'"

(*Hard Times*)

"'*Hear me, Pip! I adopted her to be loved. I bred her and educated her, to be loved. I developed her into what she is, that she might be loved. Love her!*'"

(*Great Expectations*)

Keeping these two quotations in mind, discuss the importance of love in *Hard Times* **and** in *Great Expectations*.

26. Fitzgerald

Discuss the thematic and structural significance of violence in *The Beautiful and Damned* **and** in *Tender is the Night*.

27. Galloway

Discuss some of the principal techniques used to present relationships between women in *The Trick is to Keep Breathing* **and** in *Foreign Parts*.

28. Gray

Discuss in detail the uses Gray makes of fantasy in *Lanark* **or** in *Poor Things*.

29. Hardy

"*Tess is at one with the natural world; Eustacia is in perpetual, frustrated opposition to it.*"

Taking these assertions into account, discuss the importance of "*the natural world*" in Hardy's presentation of Tess and Eustacia.

30. Hogg

Discuss the significance of the following extract in the structural and thematic development of *The Private Memoirs and Confessions of a Justified Sinner*.

I wept for joy to be thus assured of my freedom from all sin, and of the impossibility of my ever again falling away from my new state. I bounded away into the fields and the woods, to pour out my spirit in prayer before the Almighty for his kindness to me: my whole frame seemed to be renewed; every nerve was buoyant with new life; I felt as if I
5 could have flown in the air, or leaped over the tops of the trees. An exaltation of spirit lifted me, as it were, far above the earth, and the sinful creatures crawling on its surface; and I deemed myself as an eagle among the children of men, soaring on high, and looking down with pity and contempt on the grovelling creatures below.

As I thus wended my way, I beheld a young man of a mysterious appearance coming
10 towards me. I tried to shun him, being bent on my own contemplations; but he cast himself in my way, so that I could not well avoid him; and more than that, I felt a sort of invisible power that drew me towards him, something like the force of enchantment, which I could not resist. As we approached each other, our eyes met, and I can never describe the strange sensations that thrilled through my whole frame at that impressive
15 moment; a moment to me fraught with the most tremendous consequences; the beginning of a series of adventures which has puzzled myself, and will puzzle the world when I am no more in it. That time will now soon arrive, sooner than any one can devise who knows not the tumult of my thoughts, and the labour of my spirit; and when it hath come and passed over,—when my flesh and my bones are decayed, and my
20 soul has passed to its everlasting home, then shall the sons of men ponder on the events of my life; wonder and tremble, and tremble and wonder how such things should be.

That stranger youth and I approached each other in silence, and slowly, with our eyes fixed on each other's eyes. We approached till not more than a yard intervened between us, and then stood still and gazed, measuring each other from head to foot.
25 What was my astonishment, on perceiving that he was the same being as myself! The clothes were the same to the smallest item. The form was the same; the apparent age; the colour of the hair; the eyes; and, as far as recollection could serve me from viewing my own features in a glass, the features too were the very same. I conceived at first, that I saw a vision, and that my guardian angel had appeared to me at this important
30 era of my life; but this singular being read my thoughts in my looks, anticipating the very words that I was going to utter.

"You think I am your brother," said he; "or that I am your second self. I am indeed your brother, not according to the flesh, but in my belief of the same truths, and my assurance in the same mode of redemption, than which, I hold nothing so great or so
35 glorious on earth."

"Then you are an associate well adapted to my present state," said I. "For this time is a time of great rejoicing in spirit to me. I am on my way to return thanks to the Most High for my redemption from the bonds of sin and misery. If you will join with me heart and hand in youthful thanksgiving, then shall we two go and worship together;
40 but if not, go your way, and I shall go mine."

"Ah, you little know with how much pleasure I will accompany you, and join with you in your elevated devotions," said he fervently. "Your state is a state to be envied indeed; but I have been advised of it, and am come to be a humble disciple of yours; to be initiated into the true way of salvation by conversing with you, and perhaps by
45 being assisted by your prayers."

31. Joyce

Discuss in detail the techniques employed by Joyce to present the developing consciousness of Stephen Dedalus in *A Portrait of the Artist as a Young Man*.

32. Stevenson

Discuss Stevenson's use of pairs of contrasting or complementary characters in *The Master of Ballantrae* **and** in **one** of the specified short stories.

33. Waugh

Discuss the significance of Tony Last's journey to the Amazon in *A Handful of Dust* **and** of Charles Ryder's journey to and from South America in *Brideshead Revisited*.

PROSE NON-FICTION

34. Discuss the principal literary means by which any **two** of the specified texts engaged your interest in the cultures of particular places and times.

35. Discuss the principal means by which any **two** of the specified writers effectively shape their narratives.

Section 2—Language Study

You must answer **one question only** in this section.

Unless otherwise indicated, your answer must take the form of an **essay/analytical report** appropriately structured to meet the demands of your selected question.

Topic A—Varieties of English or Scots

1. What, in your view, are the distinctive linguistic features of a particular variety of contemporary English **or** Scots?

2. Describe and account for the distinctive lexical features of a particular variety of contemporary English **or** Scots.

Topic B—The historical development of English or Scots

3. Describe, with examples, some of the ways in which English **or** Scots has changed over time.

4. Discuss some of the ways in which the orthography and the lexis of **either** English **or** Scots have been influenced by developments in electronic media.

Topic C—Multilingualism in contemporary Scotland

5. To what extent do the media support the use of minority languages in Scotland?

6. Describe, with examples, ways in which some speakers in contemporary Scotland mix different languages in conversation.

[Turn over

Topic D—The use of Scots in contemporary literature

For this topic, you are provided with the first scene from the play *Silver Bullet* by Janet Paisley.

Read the scene carefully and then answer **either** Question 7 **or** Question 8 that follow it (*Page twelve*).

SCENE ONE: Living room Day

MEG sits in a chair reading a paper. ALEX enters.

	ALEX:	Whaur's that laddie? He kens I waant a haun sortin his bike!
	MEG:	Ehh?
	ALEX:	Oor Wattie. I'm hingin aboot oot there like a drip waitin tae faw.
5	MEG:	How, is it rainin?
	ALEX:	Naw, it's no rainin! Fur ony sake, Meg, git yer nose oot that book, an pey heed.
	MEG:	He's in his room.
	ALEX:	So ye've no went deef.
10	MEG:	I just waantit tae get tae the end. It's aboot this beast whit creeps aboot the hills at nicht, howlin at the moon an teerin folks thrapples oot.
	ALEX:	An nae doot, it'll meet a wheen o folk waantin thur throats ripped oot up oan the hills in the deid o nicht.
	MEG:	Och, I dinnae think they waant it tae happen.
15	ALEX:	So whit wey are they no in thur beds?
	MEG:	That's richt, take the mick.
	ALEX:	Weel, horror stories! Dae ye no think we've got enough tae worry aboot wi oor ain horror story up that stair?
	MEG:	Wha, Wattie? He's sixteen. He's jist growin up.
20	ALEX:	If he wis growin up, he'd be ootside helpin me sort his bike. I dinnae ken whit he's turnin intae.
		A blood curdling howl from offstage.
	MEG:	(*A beat*) He's practisin.
	ALEX:	Practisin? Whit fur?
25	MEG:	I dinnae ken.
		A blood curdling howl from offstage again.
	ALEX:	Weel, he waants practise. Cry that music? Its got neither words nor tune. No like in oor day, eh? (*Sings*) Be bop a lula, she's ma baby. Be bop a lula, don't mean maybe. Be bop a lula, she's ma baby now, ma baby now, ma baby now. (*Stops singing*) Guid stuff, eh?
30		
	MEG:	Aye, weel, it was guid, yince.
		WATTIE comes in. His voice is breaking and variable.
	WATTIE:	Wis that you singin, Da?

	ALEX:	Noo we ken hoo tae get you oot that room.
35	MEG:	Cries it singin ony road.
	ALEX:	(*To Wattie*) Right you, yer bike.
	WATTIE:	Gies a meenut. (*Down*) Mam, kin I talk tae ye?
	MEG:	Course, son. Whit aboot?
	WATTIE:	No the noo. Efter. Aboot (*Hesitates*) stuff.
40	ALEX:	Stuff! Ye dinnae talk tae yer mither aboot stuff. If ye waant tae talk aboot stuff, ye talk tae me.
	WATTIE:	You'll no like it.
	ALEX:	I'm no supposed tae like it. I'm yer faither. I'm supposed tae say if ye kin or if ye cannae.
45	MEG:	Whit is it ye waant tae ken, son?
	WATTIE:	He'll jist say no.
	ALEX:	No, I'll no. I'll think aboot it furst. Then I'll say no.
		He laughs uproariously at own joke.
	MEG:	Shut up, Alex. Whit is it, Wattie?
50	WATTIE:	Kin I git a nose ring?
	ALEX:	Nae chance.
	WATTIE:	Ye said ye'd think aboot it.
	ALEX:	I think quick. Pigs huv rings in thur noses. Bulls huv rings in thur noses. Folk dinnae.
55	WATTIE:	Weel, a stud then? That'd be cool.
	ALEX:	Is there somethin wrang wi yer lugs?
	WATTIE:	If an earring's aw richt, whey no a nose stud?
	ALEX:	Wi yer hearin! Somethin wrang wi yer hearin'. I said no.
	WATTIE:	(*Leaving*) Aw, furget it.
60		*Door slams*
	MEG:	Thanks fur lettin me answer him.
	ALEX:	(*Calls*) Hey, whit aboot this bike?
	MEG:	Every time. Ye dae it every time.
	ALEX:	Whit dae I dae?
65	MEG:	Git his back up.
	ALEX:	He never yaised tae huv a back tae git up. Yaised tae be a cheery wee boy, ay wantin his da, ay unner ma feet. Yaised tae like fitba an gaun his bike! Noo it's nose rings an a racket like he'd a fermyaird up thon stair. We never see him.
70	MEG:	He'll stey up there aw day noo.
	ALEX:	Weel, you tell me, whit is he turnin intae?
		Loud wolf howl from offstage.

7.   Make a detailed study of the ways in which Scots is used in this scene.

8.   Compare and contrast the Scots used by Janet Paisley in this scene with the Scots used by **one** other contemporary writer you have studied.

Topic E—Language and social context

9.   How does audience affect the way we speak?

   In your answer, you may wish to consider **some** or **all** of the following:

   *   the social characteristics of speaker and addressee(s)
   *   the relationship between speaker and addressee(s)
   *   the function and the context of the discourse.

10.   Describe some of the ways in which patterns of linguistic variation correlate with the different social contexts in which language is used.

Topic F—The linguistic characteristics of informal conversation

For this topic, you are provided with a transcript of an informal conversation in a group of four men and with details of the transcription conventions used.

Read the transcript and the transcription conventions carefully and then answer **either** Question 11 **or** Question 12 that follow them (*Page fourteen*).

Transcript

1   Alan: it nearly had him out/<LAUGHS> he come out all white/
    Chris: <LAUGHS>
    Kevin: <LAUGHS>
    John:

2   Alan:
    Chris: <LAUGHS>
    Kevin: I bet that could be dangerous ⌈couldn't it/
    John: ((⌊hurt himself/))

3   Alan:
    Chris:
    Kevin: if it fell ⌈on your head))   it's quite-
    John: ⌊he-   you know/ -

4   Alan:
    Chris: <LAUGHS> ⌈can I have some
    Kevin: ⌈it's quite big/
    John: ⌊he crapped himself/   he ⌊crapped himself/

5   Alan:
    Chris: pot noodles please Kevin <SILLY VOICE>
    Kevin: <LAUGHS> ⌈no/
    John: ⌊did he have to sit down

6   Alan: he- he- well . he was quite frightened ⌈actually/
    Chris:
    Kevin:
    John: and stuff? .   ⌊I know/

7   Alan: cos- cos-   ⌈well yeah/
    Chris: was it for you as well ⌊mate?
    Kevin:
    John: I must admit-

8   Alan: ((well I still-))
    Chris: did you go a bit white as well then did you?
    Kevin:
    John: god/

9   Alan:
     Chris: <u>don't get</u>
     Kevin:
     John: he was thinking 'god please don't wreck it'/

---

10 Alan:
     Chris: <u>any blood on it</u>/ <SARCASTIC>
     Kevin: is that the one with all the loa-
     John:

---

11 Kevin: lots of different things on it?

Transcription conventions

A hyphen indicates an incomplete word or utterance, e.g. all the loa-

Short pauses (less than 0.5 seconds) are indicated by a full stop with space on either side, e.g. well . he was quite frightened

Angled brackets give additional information, e.g. <LAUGHS>

Angled brackets also add clarificatory information about underlined words, e.g. <u>can I have some pot noodles please Kevin</u> <SILLY VOICE>

Double round parentheses indicate that there is doubt about the accuracy of the transcription, e.g. ((hurt himself/))

A question mark indicates the end of a chunk of talk which the transcriber has analysed as a question, e.g. did he have to sit down and stuff?

A slash (/) indicates the end of a tone group or chunk of talk, e.g. it nearly had him out/

The lines of text enclosed by the broken lines are to be read simultaneously, e.g.

Alan: it nearly had him out/<LAUGHS> he come out all white/
Chris: <LAUGHS>
Kevin: <LAUGHS>

An extended square bracket indicates the start of overlap between utterances, e.g.

Kevin: I bet that could be dangerous ⌈couldn't it/
John: ((⌊hurt himself/))

11. In what ways do you consider the linguistic features of the discourse recorded in the transcript to be characteristic of informal conversation?

12. Using the transcript, the transcription conventions and any data you may have from your own reading and research, describe some of the issues involved in the accurate transcription of naturally occurring informal conversation.

Topic G—The linguistic characteristics of political communication

13. "*There are certain common features that characterise all political communication, no matter what form it takes.*"

How far do you agree?

14. For this question, you are provided with an extract from a speech made by Barack Obama during the 2008 United States presidential election campaign.

Read the extract carefully and then answer the question that follows it (*Page sixteen*).

Extract from a speech made by Barack Obama

Ohio, I have just two words for you: two days.

After decades of broken politics in Washington, eight years of failed policies from George Bush, and twenty-one months of a campaign that has taken us from the rocky coast of Maine to the sunshine of California, we are two days away from change in
5   America.

In two days, you can turn the page on policies that have put the greed and irresponsibility of Wall Street before the hard work and sacrifice of folks on Main Street.

In two days, you can choose policies that invest in our middle-class, create new jobs,
10 and grow this economy so that everyone has a chance to succeed; from the CEO to the secretary and the janitor; from the factory owner to the men and women who work on its floor.

In two days, you can put an end to the politics that would divide a nation just to win an election; that tries to pit region against region, city against town, Republican
15 against Democrat, that asks us to fear at a time which we need hope.

In two days, at this defining moment in history, you can give this country the change we need.

We began this journey in the depths of winter nearly two years ago, on the steps of the Old State Capitol in Springfield, Illinois. Back then, we didn't have much money
20 or many endorsements. We weren't given much of a chance by the polls or the pundits. We knew how steep our climb would be.

But I also knew this. I knew that the size of our challenges had outgrown the smallness of our politics. I believed that Democrats and Republicans and Americans of every political stripe were hungry for new ideas, new leadership, and a new kind of
25 politics – one that favours common sense over ideology; one that focuses on those values and ideals we hold in common as Americans.

Most of all, I knew the American people were a decent, generous people willing to work hard and sacrifice for future generations. I was convinced that when we come together, our voices are more powerful than the most entrenched lobbyists, or the
30 most vicious political attacks, or the full force of a status quo in Washington that wants to keep things just the way they are.

[Turn over

Twenty-one months later, my faith in the American people has been vindicated. That's how we've come so far and so close – because of you. That's how we'll change this country – with your help. And that's why we can't afford to slow down, sit back
35 or let up for one day, one minute, or one second in these last few days. Not now. Not when so much is at stake.

We are in the middle of the worst economic crisis since the Great Depression. 760,000 workers have lost their jobs this year. Businesses and families can't get credit. Home values are falling. Pensions are disappearing. It's gotten harder and harder to
40 make the mortgage, or fill up your gas tank, or even keep the electricity on at the end of the month.

At a moment like this, the last thing we can afford is four more years of the tired, old theory that says we should give more to billionaires and big corporations and hope that prosperity trickles down to everyone else. The last thing we can afford is four
45 more years where no one in Washington is watching anyone on Wall Street because politicians and lobbyists killed common-sense regulations. Those are the theories that got us into this mess. They haven't worked, and it's time for change. That's why I'm running for President of the United States.

Discuss some of the linguistic features that characterise the discourse recorded in this extract as political communication.

Section 3—Textual Analysis

You must answer **one question only** in this section.

Unless otherwise indicated, your answer must take the form of a **critical analysis** appropriately structured to meet the demands of your selected question.

1. **Prose fiction [*Pages seventeen to twenty-one*]**

   Read carefully the short story *Elizabeth Stock's One Story* (1898) by Kate Chopin and then answer the question that follows it (*Page twenty-one*).

Elizabeth Stock's One Story

Elizabeth Stock, an unmarried woman of thirty-eight, died of consumption during the past winter at the St. Louis City Hospital. There were no unusually pathetic features attending her death. The physicians say she showed hope of rallying till placed in the incurable ward, when all courage seemed to leave her, and she relapsed into a silence
5 that remained unbroken till the end.

In Stonelift, the village where Elizabeth Stock was born and raised, and where I happen to be sojourning this summer, they say she was much given over to scribbling. I was permitted to examine her desk, which was quite filled with scraps and bits of writing in bad prose and impossible verse. In the whole conglomerate mass, I
10 discovered but the following pages which bore any semblance to a connected or consecutive narration.

Since I was a girl I always felt as if I would like to write stories. I never had that ambition to shine or make a name; first place because I knew what time and labor it meant to acquire a literary style. Second place, because whenever I wanted to write a
15 story I never could think of a plot. Once I wrote about old Si Shepard that got lost in the woods and never came back, and when I showed it to Uncle William he said:

"Why, Elizabeth, I reckon you better stick to your dressmaking: this here ain't no story; everybody knows about old Si Shepard."

No, the trouble was with plots. Whenever I tried to think of one, it always turned
20 out to be something that some one else had thought about before me. But here back awhile, I heard of great inducements offered for an acceptable story, and I said to myself:

"Elizabeth Stock, this is your chance. Now or never!" And I laid awake most a whole week; and walked about days in a kind of dream, turning and twisting things in
25 my mind just like I often saw old ladies twisting quilt patches around to compose a design. I tried to think of a railroad story with a wreck, but couldn't. No more could I make a tale out of a murder, or money getting stolen, or even mistaken identity; for the story had to be original, entertaining, full of action and Goodness knows what all. It was no use. I gave it up. But now that I got my pen in my hand and sitting here kind
30 of quiet and peaceful at the south window, and the breeze so soft carrying the autumn leaves along, I feel as I'd like to tell how I lost my position, mostly through my own negligence, I'll admit that.

My name is Elizabeth Stock. I'm thirty-eight years old and unmarried, and not afraid or ashamed to say it. Up to a few months ago I been postmistress of this village
35 of Stonelift for six years, through one administration and a half—up to a few months ago.

Often seems like the village was most too small; so small that people were bound to look into each other's lives, just like you see folks in crowded tenements looking into each other's windows. But I was born here in Stonelift and I got no serious complaints.

40 I been pretty comfortable and contented most of my life. There aint more than a hundred houses all told, if that, counting stores, churches, postoffice, and even Nathan Brightman's palatial mansion up on the hill. Looks like Stonelift wouldn't be anything without that.

He's away a good part of the time, and his family; but he's done a lot for this
45 community, and they always appreciated it, too.

But I leave it to any one—to any woman especially, if it aint human nature in a little place where everybody knows every one else, for the postmistress to glance at a postal card once in a while. She could hardly help it. And besides, seems like if a person had anything very particular and private to tell, they'd put it under a sealed envelope.

50 Anyway, the train was late that day. It was the breaking up of winter, or the beginning of spring; kind of betwixt and between; along in March. It was most night when the mail came in that ought have been along at 5:15. The Brightman girls had been down with their pony-cart, but had got tired waiting and had been gone more than an hour.

55 It was chill and dismal in the office. I had let the stove go out for fear of fire. I was cold and hungry and anxious to get home to my supper. I gave out everybody's mail that was waiting; and for the thousandth time told Vance Wallace there was nothing for him. He'll come and ask as regular as clockwork. I got that mail assorted and put aside in a hurry. There was no dilly dallying with postal cards, and how I ever come to give a
60 second look at Nathan Brightman's postal, Heaven only knows!

It was from St. Louis, written with pencil in large characters and signed, "Collins," nothing else; just "Collins." It read:

"Dear Brightman:

Be on hand tomorrow, Tuesday at 10. A.M. promptly. Important meeting of
65 the board. Your own interest demands your presence. Whatever you do, don't fail.

In haste,
Collins."

I went to the door to see if there was anyone left standing around: but the night was so raw and chill, every last one of the loungers had disappeared. Vance Wallace would
70 of been willing enough to hang about to see me home; but that was a thing I'd broken him of long ago. I locked things up and went on home, just ashivering as I went, it was that black and penetrating—worse than a downright freeze, I thought.

After I had had my supper and got comfortably fixed front of the fire, and glanced over the St. Louis paper and was just starting to read my Seaside Library novel, I got
75 thinking, somehow, about that postal card of Nath Brightman's. To a person that knew B. from bull's foot, it was just as plain as day that if that card laid on there in the office, Mr. Brightman would miss that important meeting in St. Louis in the morning. It wasn't anything to me, of course, except it made me uncomfortable and I couldn't rest or get my mind fixed on the story I was reading. Along about nine o'clock, I flung
80 aside the book and says to myself:

"Elizabeth Stock, you a fool, and you know it." There aint much use telling how I put on my rubbers and waterproof, covered the fire with ashes, took my umbrella and left the house.

I carried along the postoffice key and went on down and got out that postal card—in
85 fact, all of the Brightman's mail—wasn't any use leaving part of it, and started for "the house on the hill" as we mostly call it. I don't believe anything could of induced me to go if I had known before hand what I was undertaking. It was drizzling and the rain

kind of turned to ice when it struck the ground. If it hadn't been for the rubbers, I'd
of taken more than one fall. As it was, I took one good and hard one on the footbridge.
90 The wind was sweeping down so swiftly from the Northwest, looked like it carried me
clean off my feet before I could clutch the handrail. I found out about that time that
the stitches had come out of my old rubbers that I'd sewed about a month before, and
letting the water in soaking my feet through and through. But I'd got more than good
and started and I wouldn't think of turning around.

95   Nathan Brightman has got kind of steps cut along the side of the hill, going zig-zag.
What you would call a gradual ascent, and making it easy like to climb. That is to say,
in good weather. But Lands! There wasn't anything easy that night, slipping back one
step for every two; clutching at the frozen twigs along the path; and having to use my
umbrella half the time for a walking stick; like a regular Alpine climber. And my heart
100 would most stand still at the way the cedar trees moaned and whistled like doleful
organ tones; and sometimes sighing deep and soft like dying souls in pain.

Then I was a fool for not putting on something warm underneath that mackintosh.
I could of put on my knitted wool jacket just as easy as not. But the day had been so
mild, it bamboozled us into thinking spring was here for good; especially when we were
105 all looking and longing for it; and the orchards ready to bud, too.

But I forgot all the worry and unpleasantness of the walk when I saw how Nath
Brightman took on over me bringing him that postal card. He made me sit down
longside the fire and dry my feet, and kept saying:

"Why, Miss Elizabeth, it was exceedingly obliging of you; on such a night, too.
110 Margaret, my dear"—that was his wife—"mix a good stiff toddy for Miss Elizabeth,
and see that she drinks it."

I never could stand the taste or smell of alcohol. Uncle William says if I'd of had
any sense and swallowed down that toddy like medicine, it might of saved the day.

Anyhow, Mr. Brightman had the girls scampering around getting his grip packed;
115 one bringing his big top coat, another his muffler and umbrella; and at the same time
here they were all three making up a list of a thousand and one things they wanted him
to bring down from St. Louis.

Seems like he was ready in a jiffy, and by that time I was feeling sort of thawed out
and I went along with him. It was a mighty big comfort to have him, too. He was as
120 polite as could be, and kept saying:

"Mind out, Miss Elizabeth! Be careful here; slow now. My! but it's cold!
Goodness knows what damage this won't do to the fruit trees." He walked to my very
door with me, helping me along. Then he went on to the station. When the midnight
express came tearing around the bend, rumbling like thunder and shaking the very
125 house, I'd got my clothes changed and was drinking a hot cup of tea side the fire I'd
started up. There was a lot of comfort knowing that Mr. Brightman had got aboard
that train. Well, we all more or less selfish creatures in this world! I don't believe I'd
of slept a wink that night if I'd of left that postal card lying in the office.

Uncle William will have it that this heavy cold all came of that walk; though he got
130 to admit with me that this family been noted for weak lungs as far back as I ever heard
of.

Anyway, I'd been sick on and off all spring; sometimes hardly able to stand on my
feet when I'd drag myself down to that postoffice. When one morning, just like
lightning out of a clear sky, here comes an official document from Washington,
135 discharging me from my position as postmistress of Stonelift. I shook all over when I
read it, just like I had a chill; and I felt sick at my stomach and my teeth chattered. No
one was in the office when I opened that document except Vance Wallace, and I made

him read it and I asked him what he made out it meant. Just like when you can't understand a thing because you don't want to. He says:

140   "You've lost your position, Lizabeth. That what it means; they've passed you up."

I took it away from him kind of dazed, and says:

"We got to see about it. We got to go see Uncle William; see what he says. Maybe it's a mistake."

"Uncle Sam don't make mistakes," said Vance. "We got to get up a petition in this
145   here community; that's what I reckon we better do, and send it on to the gover'ment."

Well, it don't seem like any use to dwell on this subject. The whole community was indignant, and pronounced it an outrage. They decided, in justice to me, I had to find out what I got that dismissal for. I kind of thought it was for my poor health, for I would of had to send in my resignation sooner or later, with these fevers and cough.
150   But we got information it was for incompetence and negligence in office, through certain accusations of me reading postal cards and permitting people to help themselves to their own mail. Though I don't know as that ever happened except with Nathan Brightman always reaching over and saying:

"Don't disturb yourself, Miss Elizabeth," when I'd be sorting out letters and he
155   could reach his mail in the box just as well as not.

But that's all over and done for. I been out of office two months now, on the 26th. There's a young man named Collins, got the position. He's the son of some wealthy, influential St. Louis man; a kind of delicate, poetical-natured young fellow that can't get along in business, and they used their influence to get him the position when it was
160   vacant. They think it's the very place for him. I reckon it is. I hope in my soul he'll prosper. He's a quiet, nice-mannered young man. Some of the community thought of boycotting him. It was Vance Wallace started the notion. I told them they must be demented, and I up and told Vance Wallace he was a fool.

"I know I'm a fool, Lisabeth Stock," he said. "I always been a fool for hanging
165   round you for the past twenty years."

The trouble with Vance is, he's got no intellect. I believe in my soul Uncle William's got more. Uncle William advised me to go up to St. Louis and get treated. I been up there. The doctor said, with this cough and short breath, if I know what's good for me I'll spend the winter in the South. But the truth is, I got no more money,
170   or so little it don't count. Putting Danny to school and other things here lately, hasn't left me much to brag of. But I oughtn't be blamed about Danny; he's the only one of sister Martha's boys that seemed to me capable. And full of ambition to study as he was! it would have felt sinful of me, not to. Of course, I've taken him out, now I've lost my position. But I got him in with Filmore Green to learn the grocery trade, and
175   maybe it's all for the best; who knows!

But indeed, indeed, I don't know what to do. Seems like I've come to the end of the rope. O! it's mighty pleasant here at this south window. The breeze is just as soft and warm as May, and the leaves look like birds flying. I'd like to sit right on here and forget every thing and go to sleep and never wake up. Maybe it's sinful to make that
180   wish. After all, what I got to do is to leave everything in the hands of Providence, and trust to luck.

Question

How effectively does Kate Chopin enable you to develop your understanding of the central concerns of this short story?

In answering this question, you should take into account:

- the introductory narration (lines 1–11)

- Elizabeth Stock's own introduction to her story (lines 12–32)

- the story that she then tells (33–181).

[Turn over

2. **Prose non-fiction [*Pages twenty-two to twenty-seven*]**

The following extract is the opening section of an article *Authority and American Usage* (2005) written by David Foster Wallace in which he reviews a book called *A Dictionary of Modern American Usage* by Bryan A. Garner.

Read the extract carefully and then answer the question that follows it (*Page twenty-seven*).

Authority and American Usage

Did you know that probing the seamy underbelly of US lexicography reveals ideological strife and controversy and intrigue and nastiness and fervor on a near-Lewinskian scale?

For instance, did you know that some modern dictionaries are notoriously liberal
5 and others notoriously conservative, and that certain conservative dictionaries were actually conceived and designed as corrective responses to the "corruption" and "permissiveness" of certain liberal dictionaries? That the oligarchic device of having a special "Distinguished Usage Panel . . . of outstanding professional speakers and writers" is some dictionaries' attempt at a compromise between the forces of
10 egalitarianism and traditionalism in English, but that most linguistic liberals dismiss the Usage Panel device as mere sham-populism, as in e.g. "Calling upon the opinions of the elite, it claims to be a democratic guide"?

Did you know that US lexicography even *had* a seamy underbelly?

The occasion for this article is Oxford University Press's recent release of Mr. Bryan
15 A. Garner's *A Dictionary of Modern American Usage*, a book that Oxford is marketing aggressively and that it is my assigned function to review. It turns out to be a complicated assignment. In today's US, a typical book review is driven by market logic and implicitly casts the reader in the role of consumer. Rhetorically, its whole project is informed by a question that's too crass ever to mention up front: "Should
20 you buy this book?" And because Bryan A. Garner's usage dictionary belongs to a particular subgenre of a reference genre that is itself highly specialized and particular, and because at least a dozen major usage guides have been published in the last couple years and some of them have been quite good indeed, the central unmentionable question here appends the prepositional comparative ". . . rather than *that* book?" to
25 the main clause and so entails a discussion of whether and how *ADMAU* is different from other recent speciality-products of its kind.

The fact of the matter is that Garner's dictionary is extremely good, certainly the most comprehensive usage guide since E. W. Gilman's *Webster's Dictionary Of English Usage*, now a decade out of date. But the really salient and ingenious features of *A*
30 *Dictionary of Modern American Usage* involve issues of rhetoric and ideology and style, and it is impossible to describe why these issues are important and why Garner's

management of them borders on genius without talking about the historical context[1] in
which *ADMAU* appears, and this context turns out to be a veritable hurricane of
controversies involving everything from technical linguistics and public education to
35 political ideology, and these controversies take a certain amount of time to unpack
before their relation to what makes Garner's dictionary so eminently worth your
hard-earned reference-book dollar can even be established; and in fact there's no way
even to begin the whole harrowing polymeric discussion without first taking a moment
to establish and define the highly colloquial term *SNOOT*.

40 From one perspective, a certain irony attends the publication of any good new book on
American usage. It is that the people who are going to be interested in such a book are
also the people who are least going to need it—i.e., that offering counsel on the finer
points of US English is preaching to the choir. The relevant choir here comprises that
small percentage of American citizens who actually care about the current status of
45 double modals and ergative verbs. The same sorts of people who watched *The Story of
English* on PBS (twice) and read Safire's column with their half-caff every Sunday.
The sorts of people who feel that special blend of wincing despair and sneering
superiority when they see EXPRESS LANE—10 ITEMS OR LESS or hear
dialogue used as a verb or realize that the founders of the Super 8 Motel chain must
50 surely have been ignorant of the meaning of *suppurate*. There are lots of epithets for
people like this—Grammar Nazis, Usage Nerds, Syntax Snobs, the Grammar
Battalion, the Language Police. The term I was raised with is *SNOOT*.[2] The word
might be slightly self-mocking, but those other terms are outright dysphemisms. A
SNOOT can be loosely defined as someone who knows what *dysphemism* means and
55 doesn't mind letting you know it.

I submit that we SNOOTs are just about the last remaining kind of truly elitist
nerd. There are, granted, plenty of nerd-species in today's America, and some of these
are elitist within their own nerdy purview (e.g., the skinny, carbuncular, semi-autistic
Computer Nerd moves instantly up on the totem pole of status when your screen
60 freezes and now you need his help, and the bland condescension with which he
performs the two occult keystrokes that unfreeze your screen is both elitist and
situationally valid). But the SNOOT's purview is interhuman life itself. You don't,
after all (despite withering cultural pressure), have to use a computer, but you can't
escape language: language is everything and everywhere; it's what lets us have anything
65 to do with one another; it's what separates us from animals; Genesis 11:7–10 and so on.
And we SNOOTs know when and how to hyphenate phrasal adjectives and to keep

[1] Sorry about this phrase; I hate this phrase, too. This happens to be one of those very rare times when
"historical context" is the phrase to use and there is no equivalent phrase that isn't even worse (I actually
tried "lexico-temporal backdrop" in one of the middle drafts, which I think you'll agree is not preferable).

INTERPOLATION

The above[1] is motivated by the fact that this reviewer nearly always sneers and/or winces when he sees a
phrase like "historical context" deployed in a piece of writing and thus hopes to head off any potential
sneers/winces from the reader here, especially in an article about felicitous usage. One of the little
personal lessons I've learned in working on this essay is that being chronically inclined to sneer/wince at
other people's usage tends to make me chronically anxious about other people's sneering/wincing at my
usage. It is, of course, possible that this bivalence is news to nobody but me; it may be just a
straight-forward instance of Matt. 7:1's thing about "Judge not lest ye be judged." In any case, the
anxiety seems worth acknowledging up front.

[2] SNOOT (n) (*highly colloq*) is this reviewer's nuclear family's nickname à clef for a really extreme usage
fanatic, the sort of person whose idea of Sunday fun is to hunt for mistakes in the very prose of Safire's
column. This reviewer's family is roughly 70 percent SNOOT, which term itself derives from an
acronym, with the big historical family joke being that whether S.N.O.O.T. stood for "Sprachgefühl
Necessitates Our Ongoing Tendance" or "Syntax Nudniks Of Our Time" depended on whether or not
you were one.

participles from dangling, and we know that we know, and we know how very few other Americans know this stuff or even care, and we judge them accordingly.

70   In ways that certain of us are uncomfortable with, SNOOTs' attitudes about contemporary usage resemble religious/political conservatives' attitudes about contemporary culture.[3] We combine a missionary zeal and a near-neural faith in our beliefs' importance with a curmudgeonly hell-in-a-handbasket despair at the way English is routinely defiled by supposedly literate adults. Plus a dash of the elitism of, say, Billy Zane in *Titanic*—a fellow SNOOT I know likes to say that listening to most

75   people's public English feels like watching somebody use a Stradivarius to pound nails. We[4] are the Few, the Proud, the More or Less Constantly Appalled at Everyone Else.

THESIS STATEMENT FOR WHOLE ARTICLE

Issues of tradition vs. egalitarianism in US English are at root political issues and can be effectively addressed only in what this article hereby terms a "Democratic Spirit".

80   A Democratic Spirit is one that combines rigor and humility, i.e., passionate conviction plus a sedulous respect for the convictions of others. As any American knows, this is a difficult spirit to cultivate and maintain, particularly when it comes to issues you feel strongly about.   Equally tough is a DS's criterion of 100 percent intellectual integrity—you have to be willing to look honestly at yourself and at your motives for

85   believing what you believe, and to do it more or less continually.

This kind of stuff is advanced US citizenship. A true Democratic Spirit is up there with religious faith and emotional maturity and all those other top-of-the-Maslow-Pyramid-type qualities that people spend their whole lives working on. A Democratic Spirit's constituent rigor and humility and self-honesty are, in fact, so hard to maintain

90   on certain issues that it's almost irresistibly tempting to fall in with some established dogmatic camp and to follow that camp's line on the issue and to let your position harden within the camp and become inflexible and to believe that the other camps are either evil or insane and to spend all your time and energy trying to shout over them.

[3]This is true in my own case, at any rate—plus also the "uncomfortable" part. I teach college English part-time. Mostly Lit, not Composition. But I am so pathologically obsessed with usage that every semester the same thing happens: once I've had to read my students' first set of papers, we immediately abandon the regular Lit syllabus and have a three-week Emergency Remedial Usage and Grammar Unit, during which my demeanor is basically that of someone teaching HIV prevention to intravenous-drug users. When it emerges (as it does, every term) that 95 percent of these intelligent upscale college students have never been taught, e.g. what a clause is or why a misplaced *only* can make a sentence confusing or why you don't just automatically stick in a comma after a long noun phrase, I all but pound my head on the blackboard; I get angry and self-righteous; I tell them they should sue their hometown school boards, and mean it. The kids end up scared, both of me and for me. Every August I vow silently to *chill about usage* this year, and then by Labor Day there's foam on my chin. I can't seem to help it. The truth is that I'm not even an especially good or dedicated teacher; I don't have this kind of fervor in class about anything else, and I know it's not a very productive fervor, nor a healthy one—it's got elements of fanaticism and rage to it, plus a snobbishness that I know I'd be mortified to display about anything else.

[4]Please note that the strategically repeated 1-P pronoun is meant to iterate and emphasise that this reviewer is very much one too, a SNOOT, plus to connote the nuclear family mentioned *supra*. SNOOTitude runs in families. In *ADMAU*'s preface, Bryan Garner mentions both his father and grandfather and actually uses the word *genetic*, and it's probably true: 90 percent of the SNOOTs I know have at least one parent who is, by profession or temperament or both, a SNOOT. In my own case, my mom is a Comp teacher and has written remedial usage books and is a SNOOT of the most rabid and intractable sort. At least part of the reason I am a SNOOT is that for years my mom brainwashed us in all sorts of subtle ways. Here's an example. Family suppers often involved a game: if one of us children made a usage error, Mom would pretend to have a coughing fit that would go on and on until the relevant child had identified the relevant error and corrected it. It was all very self-ironic and lighthearted; but still, looking back, it seems a bit excessive to pretend that your small child is actually *denying you oxygen* by speaking incorrectly. The really chilling thing, though, is that I now sometimes find myself playing this same "game" with my own students, complete with pretend pertussion.

I submit, then, that it is indisputably easier to be Dogmatic than Democratic,
95 especially about issues that are both vexed and highly charged. I submit further that
the issues surrounding "correctness" in contemporary American usage are both vexed
and highly charged, and that the fundamental questions they involve are ones whose
answers have to be literally *worked out* instead of merely found.

A distinctive feature of *ADMAU* is that its author is willing to acknowledge that a
100 usage dictionary is not a bible or even a textbook but rather just the record of one
bright person's attempts to work out answers to certain very difficult questions. This
willingness appears to me to be informed by a Democratic Spirit. The big question is
whether such a spirit compromises Bryan Garner's ability to present himself as a
genuine "authority" on issues of usage. Assessing Garner's book, then, requires us to
105 trace out the very weird and complicated relationship between Authority and
Democracy in what we as a culture have decided is English. That relationship is, as
many educated Americans would say, still in process at this time.

A Dictionary of Modern American Usage has no Editorial Staff or Distinguished Panel.
It's been conceived, researched, and written by Mr. Bryan A. Garner. This Garner is
110 an interesting guy. He's both a lawyer and a usage expert (which seems a bit like being
both a narcotics wholesaler and a DEA agent). His 1987 *A Dictionary of Modern Legal
Usage* is already a minor classic; and now, instead of practicing law anymore, he goes
around conducting writing seminars for JDs and doing prose-consulting for various
judicial bodies. Garner's also the the founder of something called the H. W. Fowler
115 Society, a worldwide group of usage Trekkies who like to send one another linguistic
boners clipped from different periodicals. You get the idea. This Garner is one serious
and very hard-core SNOOT.

The lucid, engaging, and extremely sneaky preface to *ADMAU* serves to confirm
Garner's SNOOTitude in fact while undercutting it in tone. For one thing, whereas
120 the traditional usage pundit cultivates a remote and imperial persona—the kind who
uses *one* or *we* to refer to himself—Garner gives us an almost Waltonishly endearing
sketch of his own background:

> I realised early—at the age of 15—that my primary intellectual interest was the use of the English
> language . . . It became an all-consuming passion . . . I read everything I could find on the subject.
125 > Then, on a wintry evening while visiting New Mexico at the age of 16, I discovered Eric Partridge's
> *Usage and Abusage*. I was enthralled. Never had I held a more exciting book . . . Suffice it to say
> that by the time I was 18, I had committed to memory most of Fowler, Partridge, and their
> successors.

Although this reviewer regrets the bio-sketch's failure to mention the rather
130 significant social costs of being an adolescent whose overriding passion is English
usage,[5] the critical hat is off to yet another personable preface-section, one that Garner
entitles "First Principles": "Before going any further, I should explain my approach.
That's an unusual thing for the author of a usage dictionary to do—unprecedented, as
far as I know. But a guide to good writing is only as good as the principles on which it's
135 based. And users should be naturally interested in those principles. So, in the
interests of full disclosure . . ."

The "unprecedented" and "full disclosure" here are actually good-natured digs at
Garner's Fowlerite predecessors, and a slight nod to one camp in the wars that have
raged in both lexicography and education ever since the notoriously liberal *Webster's*
140 *Third New International Dictionary* came out in 1961 and included terms like *heighth*
and *irregardless* without any monitory labels on them. You can think of *Webster's Third*
as sort of the Fort Sumter of the contemporary Usage Wars. These wars are both the

---

[5]From personal experience, I can assure you that any kid like this is going to be at best marginalized and
at worst savagely and repeatedly Wedgied.

context and the target of a very subtle rhetorical strategy in *A Dictionary of Modern American Usage*, and without talking about them it's impossible to explain why
145 Garner's book is both so good and so sneaky.

We regular citizens tend to go to The Dictionary for authoritative guidance. Rarely, however, do we ask ourselves who exactly decides what gets in The Dictionary or what words or spellings or pronunciations get deemed substandard or incorrect. Whence the authority of dictionary-makers to decide what's OK and what isn't? Nobody elected
150 them, after all. And simply appealing to precedent or tradition won't work, because what's considered correct changes over time. In the 1600s, for instance, the second-singular took a singular conjugation—"You is." Earlier still, the standard 2-S pronoun wasn't *you* but *thou*. Huge numbers of now-acceptable words like *clever, fun, banter* and *prestigious* entered English as what usage authorities considered errors or
155 egregious slang. And not just usage conventions but English itself changes over time; if it didn't, we'd all still be talking like Chaucer. Who's to say which changes are natural and good and which are corruptions? And when Bryan Garner or E. Ward Gilman do in fact presume to say, why should we believe them?

These sorts of questions are not new, but they do now have a certain urgency.
160 America is in the midst of a protracted Crisis of Authority in matters of language. In brief, the same sorts of political upheavals that produced everything from Kent State to Independent Counsels have produced an influential contra-SNOOT school for whom normative standards of English grammar and usage are functions of nothing but custom and the ovine docility of a populace that lets self-appointed language experts
165 boss them around. See for example MIT's Steven Pinker in a famous *New Republic* article—"Once introduced, a prescriptive rule is very hard to eradicate, no matter how ridiculous."

In *ADMAU*'s preface, Garner addresses the Authority question with a Trumanesque simplicity and candor that simultaneously disguise the author's cunning
170 and exemplify it:

> As you might already suspect, I don't shy away from making judgments. I can't imagine that most readers would want me to. Linguists don't like it, of course, because judgment involves subjectivity. It isn't scientific. But rhetoric and usage, in the view of most professional writers,[6] aren't scientific endeavors. You[7] don't want dispassionate descriptions; you want sound guidance. And that requires
175 > judgment.

[6]Notice, please, the subtle appeal here to the same "writing establishment" that Steven Pinker scorns. This isn't accidental; it's rhetorical.* What's crafty is that this is one of several places where Garner uses professional writers and editors as support for his claims, but in the preface he also treats these language pros as the primary *audience* for *ADMAU*, as in e.g. "The problem for professional writers and editors is that they can't wait idly to see what direction the language takes. Writers and editors, in fact, influence that direction: they must make decisions . . . That has traditionally been the job of the usage dictionary: to help writers and editors solve editorial predicaments."

This is the same basic rhetorical move that President R. W. Reagan perfected in his televised Going-Over-Congress's-Head-to-the-People addresses, one that smart politicians ever since have imitated. It consists in citing the very audience you're addressing as the source of support for your proposals: "I'm pleased to announce tonight that we are taking the first steps toward implementing the policies that you elected me to implement," etc. The tactic is crafty because it (1) flatters the audience, (2) disguises the fact that the rhetor's purpose here is actually to persuade and rally support, not to inform or celebrate, and (3) preempts charges from the loyal opposition that the actual policy proposed is in any way contrary to the interests of the audience. I'm not suggesting that Bryan Garner has any particular political agenda. I'm simply pointing out that *ADMAU*'s preface is fundamentally rhetorical in the same way that Reagan's little Chats With America were.

*(In case it's not totally obvious, be advised that this article is using the word *rhetoric* in its strict traditional sense, something like "the persuasive use of language to influence the thoughts and actions of an audience.")

[7]See?

Whole monographs could be written just on the masterful rhetoric of this passage. Besides the FN 6 stuff, note for example the ingenious equivocation of *judgment*, which in "I don't shy away from making judgments" means actual rulings (and thus invites questions about Authority), but in "And that requires judgment" refers instead to
180 perspicacity, discernment, reason. As the body of *ADMAU* makes clear, part of Garner's overall strategy is to collapse these two different senses of *judgment*, or rather to use the second sense as a justification for the first. The big things to recognise here are (1) that Garner wouldn't be doing any of this if he weren't *keenly* aware of the Authority Crisis in modern usage, and (2) that his response to this crisis is—in the best
185 Democratic Spirit—rhetorical.

Question

In this opening section of his article, how effectively does Foster Wallace engage the interest of the reader?

In answering this question, you should take into account:

- the language he uses

- the tone he adopts

- the ways in which he shapes and presents his observations (including his use of footnotes)

- any other linguistic or rhetorical features you think important.

[Turn over

3.   **Poetry (*Page twenty-eight to twenty-nine*)**

Read carefully the poem *At the Fishhouses* (1947) by Elizabeth Bishop and then answer the question that follows it (*Page twenty-nine*).

At the Fishhouses

<pre>
    Although it is a cold evening,
    down by one of the fishhouses
    an old man sits netting,
    his net, in the gloaming almost invisible,
 5 a dark purple-brown,
    and his shuttle worn and polished.
    The air smells so strong of codfish
    it makes one's nose run and one's eyes water.
    The five fishhouses have steeply peaked roofs
10 and narrow, cleated gangplanks slant up
    to storerooms in the gables
    for the wheelbarrows to be pushed up and down on.
    All is silver: the heavy surface of the sea,
    swelling slowly as if considering spilling over,
15 is opaque, but the silver of the benches,
    the lobster pots, and masts, scattered
    among the wild jagged rocks,
    is of an apparent translucence
    like the small old buildings with an emerald moss
20 growing on their shoreward walls.
    The big fish tubs are completely lined
    with layers of beautiful herring scales
    and the wheelbarrows are similarly plastered
    with creamy iridescent coats of mail,
25 with small iridescent flies crawling on them.
    Up on the little slope behind the houses,
    set in the sparse bright sprinkle of grass,
    is an ancient wooden capstan,
    cracked, with two long bleached handles
30 and some melancholy stains, like dried blood,
    where the ironwork has rusted.
    The old man accepts a Lucky Strike.
    He was a friend of my grandfather.
    We talk of the decline in the population
35 and of codfish and herring
    while he waits for a herring boat to come in.
    There are sequins on his vest and on his thumb.
    He has scraped the scales, the principal beauty,
    from unnumbered fish with that black old knife,
40 the blade of which is almost worn away.

    Down at the water's edge, at the place
    where they haul up the boats, up the long ramp
    descending into the water, thin silver
</pre>

tree trunks are laid horizontally
45 across the gray stones, down and down
at intervals of four or five feet.

Cold dark deep and absolutely clear,
element bearable to no mortal,
to fish and to seals . . . One seal particularly
50 I have seen here evening after evening.
He was curious about me. He was interested in music;
like me a believer in total immersion,
so I used to sing him Baptist hymns.
I also sang "A Mighty Fortress is our God."
55 He stood up in the water and regarded me
steadily, moving his head a little.
Then he would disappear, then suddenly emerge
almost in the same spot, with a sort of shrug
as if it were against his better judgment.
60 Cold dark deep and absolutely clear,
the clear gray icy waters . . . Back, behind us,
the dignified tall firs begin.
Bluish, associating with their shadows,
a million Christmas trees stand
65 waiting for Christmas. The water seems suspended
above the rounded gray and blue-gray stones.
I have seen it over and over, the same sea, the same,
slightly, indifferently swinging above the stones,
icily free above the stones,
70 above the stones and then the world.
If you should dip your hand in,
your wrist would ache immediately,
your bones would begin to ache and your hand would burn
as if the water were a transmutation of fire
75 that feeds on stones and burns with a dark gray flame.
If you tasted it, it would first taste bitter,
then briny, then surely burn your tongue.
It is like what we imagine knowledge to be:
dark, salt, clear, moving, utterly free,
80 drawn from the cold hard mouth
of the world, derived from the rocky breasts
forever, flowing and drawn, and since
our knowledge is historical, flowing, and flown.

Question

Write a critical analysis of this poem.

In your analysis of the poem, you should make clear what you find interesting and significant about word choice and imagery, structure and sound, mood and tone.

4.   **Drama (*Pages thirty to forty*)**

The following extract is a scene from Act II of the play *August: Osage County* (2007) by Tracy Letts.

The play is set in the Oklahoma home of the Weston family where they gather for the funeral of their father, Beverly Weston. This scene takes place in the dining room of the large house where the family has gathered for a meal after the funeral service.

The characters in this scene are:

VIOLET, Beverly's widow, 65

BARBARA, Beverly and Violet's daughter, 46
BILL, Barbara's husband, 49
JEAN, their daughter, 14

IVY, Beverly and Violet's daughter, 44

KAREN, Beverly and Violet's daughter, 40
STEVE, Karen's fiancé, 50

MATTIE FAE, Violet's sister, 57
CHARLIE, Mattie Fae's husband, 60
LITTLE CHARLES, their son, 37

JOHNNA, housekeeper, 26

Read the extract carefully and then answer the question that follows it (*Page forty*).

Extract from *August: Osage County*

(*Violet enters with the framed photograph of her and Beverly.*)

VIOLET: Barb . . . will you put this—?

BARBARA: Yeah, sure . . .

 (*Barbara takes the photograph, places it on the sideboard.*)

5   MATTIE FAE: That's nice.

KAREN: That's sweet.

STEVE: Very nice, yes.

IVY: The table's lovely.

BARBARA: Johnna did it all.

10 JEAN: Yayyy, Johnna—

VIOLET: I see you gentlemen have all stripped down to your shirt fronts. I thought we were having a funeral dinner, not a cockfight.

 (*An awkward moment. The men glumly put their suit coats back on.*)

 (*Taking her seat*) Someone should probably say grace.

15   (*All look to one another.*)

 Barbara? Will you . . . ?

BARBARA: No, I don't think so.

VIOLET: Oh now, it's no big—

BARBARA: Uncle Charlie should say grace. He's the patriarch around here now.

20 CHARLIE: I am? Oh, I guess I am.

VIOLET: By default.

CHARLIE: Okay. (*Clears his throat*) Dear Lord . . .

(*All bow their heads, clasp hands.*)

25 We ask that you watch over this family in this sad time, O Lord . . . that you bless this good woman and keep her in your, in your . . . grace.

(*A cell phone rings, playing the theme from Sanford and Son. Steve quickly digs through his pockets, finds the phone, checks the caller ID.*)

STEVE: I'm sorry, I have to take this.

(*Steve hustles out to talk on the phone.*)

30 CHARLIE: We ask that you watch over Beverly, too, as he, as he . . . as he, as he, as he makes his journey.

We thank thee, O Lord, that we are able to join together to pay tribute to this fine man, in his house, with his beautiful family, his three beautiful daughters. We are truly blessed in our, our fellowship, our togetherness, our . . .
35 our fellowship.

Thank thee for the food, O Lord, that we can share this food and replenish our bodies with . . . with nourishment. We ask that you help us . . . get better. Be better. Be better people.

(*Steve reenters, snapping his phone shut.*)

40 We recognize, now more than ever, the power, the, the . . . joy of family. And we ask that you bless and watch over this family. Amen.

MATTIE FAE: Amen.

STEVE: Amen. Sorry, folks.

BILL: Let's eat.

45 (*They begin to eat.*)

VIOLET: Barbara, you have any use for that sideboard?

BARBARA: Hm?

VIOLET: That sideboard there, you have any interest in that?

BARBARA: This? Well . . . no. I mean, why?

50 VIOLET: I'm getting rid of a lot of this stuff and I thought you might want that sideboard.

BARBARA: No, Mom, I . . . I   KAREN: Really pretty.
wouldn't have any way to
get that to Boulder.

55 VIOLET: Mm. Maybe Ivy'll take it.

IVY: No, I have something like that, remember, from the—

BARBARA: What are you getting rid of?

VIOLET: All of it, I'm clearing all this stuff out of here. I want to have a brand-new everything.

60 BARBARA: I. I guess I'm just sort of . . . not prepared to talk about your stuff.

VIOLET: Suit yourself.

STEVE: This food is just spectacular.

KAREN: It's so good—   LITTLE CHARLES: Yes, it is—

IVY: You like your food, Mom?

65 VIOLET: I haven't tried much of it, yet—

BARBARA: Johnna cooked this whole meal by herself.

VIOLET: Hm? What?

BARBARA: I say Johnna cooked this whole meal by—

VIOLET: 'Swhat she's paid for.

70   (*A silent moment.*)

You all did know she's getting paid, right?

CHARLIE: Jean, so I'm curious, when you say you don't eat meat . . .

JEAN: Yeah?

CHARLIE: You mean you don't eat meat of any kind?

75 JEAN: Right.   BARBARA: No, she, hm-mm . . .

CHARLIE: And is that for health reasons, or . . . ?

JEAN: When you eat meat, you ingest an animal's fear.

VIOLET: Ingest what? Its fur?

JEAN: Fear.

80 VIOLET (*Snickers*): I thought she said—

CHARLIE: Its fear. How do you do that? You can't eat fear.

JEAN: Sure you can. I mean even if you don't sort of think of it spiritually, what happens to *you*, when you feel afraid? Doesn't your body produce all sorts of chemical reactions?

85 CHARLIE: Does it?

LITTLE CHARLES: It does.

IVY: Yes.

LITTLE CHARLES: Adrenaline, and, and—

JEAN: Your body goes through this whole chemical process when it experiences fear—

90 LITTLE CHARLES: —yep, and cortisol—

JEAN: —particularly like strong mortal fear, you know when you sweat and your heart races—

LITTLE CHARLES: —*oh* yeah—

CHARLIE: Okay, sure.

95 JEAN: Do you think an animal experiences fear?

STEVE: You bet it does.

JEAN: So when you eat an animal, you're eating all that fear it felt when it was slaughtered to make food.

CHARLIE: Wow.

100 STEVE: Right, right, I used to work in a processing factory and there's a lot of fear flying around that place—

CHARLIE: God, you mean I've been eating fear, what, three times a day for sixty years?

MATTIE FAE: This one won't have a meal unless there's meat in it.

CHARLIE: I guess it was the way I was raised, but it just doesn't seem like a legitimate
105 meal unless it has some meat somewhere—

MATTIE FAE: If I make a pasta dish of some kind, he'll just be like, "Okay, that was good for an appetizer, now where's the meat?"

VIOLET: "Where's the meat?" Isn't that some TV commercial, the old lady say, "Where's the meat?"

110 KAREN: "Beef." "Where's the beef?"

VIOLET (*Screeching*): *"Where's the meat?!" "Where's the meat?!" "Where's the meat?!"*

(*Everyone freezes, a little stunned.*)

CHARLIE: I sure thought the services were lovely.

KAREN: Yes, weren't they?—

115 STEVE: Preacher did a fine job.

VIOLET: (*Sticking her hand out, flat, waggling it back and forth*):
Ehhhhh! I give it a . . . (*Repeats gesture*) Ehhhhh!

KAREN: Really? I thought it was—

BARBARA: Great, now we get some dramatic criticism—

120 VIOLET: I would've preferred an open casket.

BARBARA: That just wasn't possible, Mom.

VIOLET: That today's the send-off Bev should've got if he died around 1974. Lots of talk about poetry, teaching. Well, he hadn't written any poetry to speak of since '65 and he never liked teaching worth a damn. Nobody talked about the good
125 stuff. Man was a world-class alcoholic, more'n fifty years. Nobody told the story about that night he got wrangled into giving a talk at a TU alumni dinner . . . (*Laughs*) Drank a whole bottle of rum, Ron Bocoy White Rum—I don't know why I remember that—and got up to give this talk . . . and he fouled himself! Comes back to our table with this huge—

130 BARBARA: Yeah, I can't imagine why no one told *that* story.

VIOLET: He didn't get invited back to any more alumni dinners, I'll tell you that!

(*She cracks up.*)

STEVE: You know, I don't know much about poetry, but I thought his poems were extraordinary. (*To Bill*) And your reading was very fine.

135 BILL: Thank you.

VIOLET (*To Steve*): Who *are* you?

KAREN: Mom, this is my fiancé, Steve, I introduced you at the church.

STEVE: Steve Heidebrecht.

VIOLET: Hide-the-what?

140 STEVE: Heidebrecht.

VIOLET: Hide-a-burrr . . . German, you're a German.

STEVE: Well, German-Irish, really, I—

VIOLET: That's peculiar, Karen, to bring a date to your father's funeral. I know the poetry was good, but I wouldn't have really considered it date material—

145 BARBARA: Jesus.

KAREN: He's not a date, he's my fiancé. We're getting married on New Year's.

CHARLIE: Man, these potatoes are—

KAREN: In Miami, I hope you can make it.

VIOLET: I don't really see that happening, do you?

150 KAREN: I—

VIOLET: Steve. That right? *Steve?*

STEVE: Yes, ma'am?

VIOLET: You ever been married before?

KAREN: That's personal.

155 STEVE: I don't mind. Yes, ma'am, I have.

VIOLET: More'n once?

STEVE: Three times, actually, three times before this—

VIOLET: You should pretty much have it down by now, then.

STEVE (*Laughs*): Right, right—

160 VIOLET (*To Mattie Fae*): I had that one pegged, didn't I? I mean, look at him, you can tell he's been married—

KAREN: I took Steve out to show him the old fort and it's gone!

IVY: That's been gone for years.

KAREN: That made me so sad!

165 BILL: What is this now?

KAREN: Our old fort, where we used to play Cowboys and Indians.

IVY: Daddy said rats were getting in there—

VIOLET: Karen! Shame on you!

KAREN: Hm?

170 VIOLET: Don't you know not to say "Cowboys and Indians"? You played Cowboys and Native Americans. Right, Barb?

BARBARA: What'd you take?

VIOLET: Hm?

BARBARA: What did you take? What pills did you take?

175 VIOLET: Lemme alone—

(*Charlie drops his head, appears distressed.*)

CHARLIE: Uh-oh . . .

MATTIE FAE: What is it?

CHARLIE: UH-OH!

180 MATTIE FAE: What's the matter?

(*Rising panic . . .*)

LITTLE CHARLES: Dad—?   IVY: You okay, Uncle—?

CHARLIE: I just got a big bite of fear!

(*Everyone laughs.*)

185   I'm shakin' in my boots!

(*Laughter, ad-libs, etc. Charlie digs into his plate ravenously.*)

Fear never tasted so good.

(*He winks at Jean.*)

STEVE (*Laughing*): Right, right, it's pretty good once you get used to the taste.

190 BARBARA (*Teasing*): I catch her eating a cheeseburger every now and again.

JEAN: I do not!

BARBARA: Double cheeseburger with bacon, extra fear.

JEAN: Mom, you are such a liar!

(*More laughter.*)

195 VIOLET (*Staring intensely at Jean*): Y'know . . . if I ever called my mom a liar? She would've knocked my goddamn head off my shoulders.

(*Silence.*)

Bill, I see you've gone through much of Beverly's office.

BILL: Not all of it, but—

200 VIOLET: Find any hidden treasure?

BILL: Not exactly, but it appears he was working on some new poetry.

KAREN: Really?

BILL: I found a couple of notebooks that had—

VIOLET: You girls know there's a will.

205 BARBARA: Mom . . .

VIOLET: We took care of that some time back, but—

BARBARA: Mom, really, we don't want to talk about this now—

VIOLET: I want to talk about it. What about what I want to talk about, that count for anything?

210 BARBARA: It's just—

VIOLET: Bev made some good investments if you can believe it, and we had things covered for you girls, but he and I talked it over after some years passed and decided to change things, leave everything to me. We never got around to taking care of it legally, but you should know he meant to leave everything to me. Leave
215   the money to me.

BARBARA: Okay.

VIOLET: Okay? (*Checks in with Ivy, Karen*) Okay?

IVY: Okay.

VIOLET: Karen? Okay?

220   (*Uncertain, Karen looks to Steve, then Barbara.*)

BARBARA: Okay.

KAREN: Okay.

VIOLET: Okay. But now some of this furniture, some of this old shit you can just have. I don't want it, got no use for it. Maybe I should have an auction.

225   MATTIE FAE: Sure, an auction's a fine idea—

VIOLET: Some things, though, like the silver, that's worth a pretty penny. But if you like I'll sell it to you, cheaper'n I might get in an auction.

BARBARA: Or you might never get around to the auction and then we can just have it for free after you die.

230   IVY: Barbara . . .

(*Pause. Violet coolly studies Barbara.*)

VIOLET: You might at that.

LITTLE CHARLES: Excuse me, Bill? I'm wondering, this writing you found, these poems—?

235   VIOLET: Where are you living now, Bill? You want this old sideboard?

BILL: I beg your pardon.

VIOLET: You and Barbara are separated, right? Or you divorced already?

(*Another silence.*)

BILL: We're separated.

240   VIOLET (*To Barbara*): Thought you could slip that one by me, didn't you?

BARBARA: What is the matter with you?

VIOLET: Nobody slips anything by me. I know what's what. Your father thought he's slipping one by me, right? No way. I'm sorry you two're having trouble . . . maybe you can work it out. Bev'n I separated a couple of times, 'course, though
245   we didn't call it that—

BARBARA: Please, help us to benefit from an illustration of your storybook marriage—

VIOLET: Truth is, sweetheart, you can't compete with a younger woman, there's no way to compete. One of those unfair things in life. Is there a younger woman involved?

250   BARBARA: You've already said enough on this subject, I think—

BILL: Yes. There's a younger woman.

VIOLET: Ah . . . y'see? Odds're against you there, babe.

IVY: Mom believes women don't grow more attractive with age.

KAREN: Oh, I disagree, I—

255   VIOLET: I didn't say they "don't grow more attractive," I said they get ugly. And it's not really a matter of opinion, Karen dear. You've only just started to prove it yourself.

CHARLIE: You're in rare form today, Vi.

VIOLET: The day calls for it, doesn't it? What form would you have me in?

260 CHARLIE: I just don't understand why you're so adversarial.

VIOLET: I'm just truth-telling. (*Cutting her eyes to Barbara*)
Some people get antagonised by the truth.

CHARLIE: Everyone here loves you, dear.

VIOLET: You think you can *shame* me, Charlie? Blow it out your ass.

265 BARBARA: Three days ago . . . I had to identify my father's corpse. And now I sit here
and listen to you viciously attack each and every member of this family—

(*Violet rises, her voice booming.*)

VIOLET: "Attack my family"?! You ever been attacked in your sweet spoiled life?! Tell
her 'bout attacks, Mattie Fae, tell her what an attack looks like!

270 MATTIE FAE: Vi, please—

IVY: Settle down, Mom—

VIOLET: Stop telling me to settle down, goddamn it! I'm not a goddamn invalid! I
don't need to be abided, do I?! Am I already passed over?!

MATTIE FAE: Honey—

275 VIOLET:(*Points to Mattie Fae*): This woman came to my rescue when one of my dear
mother's many gentlemen friends was attacking me, with a claw hammer! This
woman has dents in her skull from hammer blows! You think you been
attacked?! What do you know about life on these Plains? What do you know
about hard times?

280 BARBARA: I know you had a rotten childhood, Mom. Who didn't?

VIOLET: You DON'T know! You do NOT know! None of you know, 'cept this
woman right here and that man we buried today! Sweet girl, sweet Barbara, my
heart breaks for every time you ever felt pain. I wish I coulda shielded you from
it. But if you think for a solitary second you can fathom the pain that man
285   endured in his natural life, you got another thing coming. Do you know where
your father lived from age four till about ten? Do you?

(*No one responds.*)

Do you?!

BARBARA: No.

290 IVY: No.

VIOLET: *In a Pontiac sedan.* With his mother, his father, in a car! Now what else do
you want to say about your rotten childhood? That's the crux of the biscuit: we
lived too hard, then rose too high. We sacrificed everything and we did it all for
you. Your father and I were the first in our families to finish high school and he
295   wound up an award-winning poet. You girls, given a college education, taken for
granted no doubt, and where'd *you* wind up? (*Jabs a finger at Karen*) Whadda
you do? (*Jabs a finger at Ivy*) Whadda *you* do? (*Jabs a finger at Barbara*) Who're
you? Jesus, you worked as hard as us, you'd all be president. You never had real
problems so you got to make all your problems yourselves.

300 BARBARA: Why are you screaming at us?

VIOLET: Just time we had some truths told 'round here's all.

Damn fine day, tell the truth.

CHARLIE: Well, the truth is . . . I'm getting full.

STEVE: Amen.

305 JOHNNA: There's dessert, too.

KAREN: I saw her making those pies. They looked so good.

(*Little Charles suddenly stands.*)

LITTLE CHARLES: I have a truth to tell.

VIOLET: It speaks.

310   (*Little Charles looks to Ivy.*)

IVY (*Softly pleading*): Nooo, nooo—

CHARLIE: What is it , son?

LITTLE CHARLES: I have a truth.

(*Silence.*)

315 MATTIE FAE: Little Charles . . . ?

LITTLE CHARLES: I . . .

IVY (*Almost to herself*): Charles, not like this, please . . .

LITTLE CHARLES: The truth is, I . . . I forgot to set the clock.

This morning. The power didn't go out, I just . . . forgot to set the clock. Sorry,
320   Mom. I'm sorry, everyone. Excuse me . . . I . . . I.

(*He leaves the dining room, exits the house . . . pauses on the porch, exits.*)

VIOLET: Scintillating.

(*Charlie turns to Mattie Fae, confused.*)

MATTIE FAE: I gave up a long time ago . . . Little Charles is your project.

325 IVY (*Near tears*): Charles. His name is Charles.

(*The family eats in silence. Violet pats Ivy's wrists.*)

VIOLET: Poor Ivy. Poor thing.

IVY: Please, Mom . . .

VIOLET: Poor baby.

330 IVY: Please . . .

VIOLET: She's always had a feeling for the underdog.

IVY: Don't be mean to me right now, okay?

VIOLET: Everyone's got this idea I'm mean, all of a sudden.

IVY: *Please*, Momma.

335 VIOLET: I told you, I'm just telling the—

BARBARA: You're a drug addict.

VIOLET: That is the truth! That's what I'm getting at! I, everybody listen . . . I am a drug addict. I am addicted to drugs, pills, 'specially downers. (*Pulls a bottle of pills from her pocket, holds them up*) Y'see these little blue babies? These are my best friends and they never let me down. Try to get 'em away from me and I'll eat you alive.

340

BARBARA: Gimme those goddamn pills—

VIOLET: I'll eat you alive, girl!

345

(*Barbara lunges at the bottle of pills. She and Violet wrestle with it. Bill and Ivy try to restrain Barbara. Mattie Fae tries to restrain Violet. Others rise, ad-lib.*)

STEVE: Holy shit—

IVY: Barbara, stop it!—

CHARLIE: Hey, now, c'mon!—

KAREN: Oh God—

350

(*Violet wins, wrests the pills away from Barbara. Bill pulls Barbara back into her seat. Violet shakes the pill bottle, taunting Barbara. Barbara snaps, screams, lunges again, grabs Violet by the hair, pulls her up, toppling chairs. They crash through the house, pursued by the family.*

Pandemonium. Screaming. Barbara strangles Violet. With great effort, Bill and Charlie pry the two women apart. Mattie Fae and Johnna rush to Violet, tend to her.)

355

VIOLET (*Crying*): Goddamn you . . . goddamn you, Barb . . .

BARBARA: SHUT UP!

(*To the others*) Okay. Pill raid. Johnna, help me in the kitchen. Bill, take Ivy and Jean upstairs. (*To Ivy*) You remember how to do this, right?

360

IVY: Yeah . . .

BARBARA (*To Jean*): Everything. Go through everything, every counter, every drawer, every shoe box. Nothing's too personal. Anything even looks suspicious, throw it in a box and we can sort it out later. You understand?

365 CHARLIE: What should we do?

BARBARA: Get Mom some black coffee and a wet towel and listen to her bullshit. Karen, call Dr Burke.

KAREN: What do you want me to say?

BARBARA: Tell him we got a sick woman here.

370 VIOLET: You can't do this! This is *my* house! This is *my* house!

BARBARA: You don't get it, do you? (*With a burst of adrenaline, she strides to Violet, towers over her*) I'M RUNNING THINGS NOW!

(*Blackout.*)

[Turn over

Question

Discuss the techniques Tracy Letts uses to create dramatic tension in this scene.

In your answer, you should consider the presentation of the character of Violet **and** of the developing conflicts within the family.

Section 4—Reading the Media

You must answer **one question only** in this section.

Unless otherwise indicated, your answer must take the form of a **critical essay** appropriately structured to meet the demands of your selected question.

Category A—Film

1. *"A film should have a beginning, a middle and an end—but not necessarily in that order."*

   (Jean-Luc Godard)

   Discuss with reference to the narrative structure of **one** or **more than one** film you have studied.

2. Discuss the function of setting in **one** or **more than one** film you have studied.

Category B—Television

3. How successfully does any television drama you have studied combine elements of different genres—science fiction, crime, romance, historical, medical, domestic . . . ?

4. *"Today, television's response to its public service obligation is skewed in favour of entertainment—news as entertainment, current affairs as entertainment, documentary as entertainment . . ."*

   Discuss with reference to any news, current affairs or documentary programme(s) you have studied.

Category C—Radio

5. Discuss the ways in which any **one** national radio channel seeks to satisfy its intended audience.

6. *"The primary role of local radio is to articulate community concerns, interests and passions by giving air space to material not covered by national channels."*

   How far do you agree?

[Turn over

Category D—Print journalism

7. "*In reporting any national or global event, newspapers prefer the personal over the general, the concrete over the abstract, the neat resolution over the unresolved reality.*"

   How far do you agree?

   In your answer, you should discuss the coverage of a national or global event by **one** or **more than one** newspaper.

   NB You may not use the materials provided for question 8 in order to answer question 7.

8. For this question, you are provided with a double page spread from the coverage by *The Independent* of the state visit to the UK of the President of France in March 2008, accompanied by his new wife Carla Bruni-Sarkozy (*see pages 222–223 for this article*).

   Discuss the news values demonstrated in this extract from the newspaper's coverage of the event.

   You should consider:

   - the selection, content and construction of the images
   - the content, style and tone of the written text
   - the representation of gender and nation.

Category E—Advertising

9. "*In the 21st century, advertising still relies on traditional stereotypes: of age, gender, class, nation . . .*"

   How far do you agree?

   You should support your answer with evidence drawn from a **range** of advertisements (including, if you wish, those provided for question 10).

10. Examine carefully the following **three** advertisements for PULSAR watches:
    Poise Collection—*Glamour Magazine* (August 2004) (*Page 224*)
    Performance Collection—*The Guardian Weekend Magazine* (November 2004) (*Page 225*)
    Prestige Collection—*The Guardian Weekend Magazine* (December 2004) (*Page 226*).
    How effectively does each advertisement convey the message "*it's all in the detail*" to its target audience?

    In your answer you should consider:

    - the construction of each image—camera angle and distance, composition, cropping and framing
    - the cultural codes which establish the representation of the subjects
    - the role of the written texts (content **and** typography)
    - the stereotyping of gender in establishing the brand identity of each product.

[END OF QUESTION PAPER]

[BLANK PAGE]

Insert for Section 4 – Reading the Media Question 8

Mme Bruni-Sarkozy listens to her husband speaking at the Palace of Westminster, top, and is escorted by Prince Philip as she arrives at Windsor Castle, above. She was wearing outfits and accessories by Christian Dior, the Parisian designer AP/PA/REUTERS/POOL

FRENCH DRESSING

Carla Bruni, the supermodel now married to France's President, cut a surprisingly demure and understated figure yesterday when she arrived in Britain.

By Carola Long

When Carla Bruni-Sarkozy came down the steps of the plane at Heathrow yesterday you could be forgiven for thinking one of three things. That she had swapped outfits with an air hostess on board, that she had spent weeks studying pictures of Jackie Kennedy and her classic pillbox, or she had renounced being the President's wife and taken holy orders. Or perhaps all three.

For the supermodel turned singer and serial rock-star girlfriend who has declared herself easily "bored with monogamy", it was an astonishingly demure, almost nun-like outfit– but then that was precisely the idea. With a bold, nude picture of her just released to the press, it's hardly surprising that Mme Bruni-Sarkozy

wanted to cover herself up chastely as possible and prese an image that was formal, de rous and appropriate – a wo away from the bling-bling pre dent label that has attached its to M. Sarkozy and his Ray-Ba

It was a chic, flattering sha and showed off her figure b the grey colour was so unde stated she almost blended in the asphalt. Or perhaps she h matched her clothes to what s had heard about the Briti weather. Strangely, she chang three times throughout the d but into variations on the sa demure grey theme.

But perhaps these anti-clim tic ensembles should not ha come as such a surprise. H dress sense is nowhere near

[X270/701]

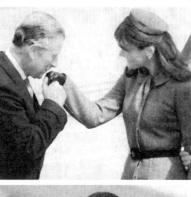

The muted tones matched the grey skies over Windsor

wild as her bohemian past and romantic trysts might lead you to expect. In fact, rather like An-

gelina Jolie, who has a reputation for being unconventional but wears the plainest and most classic of clothes, Mme Bruni-Sarkozy's recent outfits have been fairly understated.

At a recent dinner at the Elysée palace, her one-shouldered purple dress was upstaged by justice minister Rachida Dati's crystal-encrusted evening gown, and she often favours white shirts, plain black outfits or jeans and simple jumpers, almost always with flat shoes.

Yesterday's outfit was teamed with flat ballet pumps, while it was M.Sarkozy who sported shoes with a considerable heel to even out the height difference between him and his beloved.

Mme Bruni-Sarkozy has not

just toed the line with her tactful footwear and high neckline; her sober wool and jersey belted coat, bag and gloves were all made by Christian Dior, as were the two outfits she wore at Windsor Castle and Parliament.

By choosing a Parisian designer she has shown support for her country and one of its key industries – unlike Cécilia Sarkozy, who wore her rebellious streak on her sleeve when she wore a dress by Prada – an Italian label– at M. Sarkozy's inauguration.

M. Sarkozy might be the one branding himself as forward thinking, but it is his wife who has her eye on fashion's future. Her clothes – from Dior's autumn 2008 collection – will not be available in the shops for a couple of months.

Main picture, the Queen and the Duke of Edinburgh talk to M. Sarkozy and his wife Carla Bruni-Sarkozy as they wait to review the Guard of Honour at Windsor Castle. The Prince of Wales was also on hand to welcome the couple, top FAYRE,TERS/AFP/POOL

[END OF QUESTION PAPER]

Acknowledgements

Permission has been sought from all relevant copyright holders and Bright Red Publishing is grateful for the use of the following:

2008 SQP

An extract from 'Rosencrantz and Guildenstern are Dead' by Tom Stoppard (1967). Published by Faber & Faber Ltd (pp 3–5); The poem 'In Memoriam M.K.H., 1911–1984' by Seamus Heaney, taken from 'Opened Ground: Selected Poems, 1966–1996', published by Faber & Faber Ltd (p 6); The poem 'The Eemis Stane' by Hugh MacDiarmid, taken from 'Complete Poems' © Carcanet Press Ltd (p 7); An extract from 'Leddy-Bird, Leddy-Bird' by Sheena Blackhall. Reproduced with permission of Sheena Blackhall (pp 11–12); An extract from 'The Hamecomin' by Sheila Douglas. Taken from 'Scottish Short Stories' edited by Sheena Greco. Published by Harcourt Education (p 12); Extract from 'A Wee Tatty' by Alison Kermack, taken from 'A Tongue in Yer Heid' by James Robertson, published by Black & White Publishing © Black & White Publishing (p 13); A transcript from the Conservative Party Election Broadcast in 1997. Reproduced by permission of the Conservative Party Archive (pp 14–16); An extract from 'Wives and Daughters' by Elizabeth Gaskell (1866). Public Domain (pp 17–19); An extract from 'Moon Country' by Simon Armitage and Glyn Maxwell (1996). Published by Faber & Faber Ltd (pp 21–22); The poem 'At Marsden Bay' by Peter Reading, from 'Collected Poems 1: Poems 1970–1984' (Bloodaxe Books, 1995) (p 23).

2008 Paper

An extract from the play 'All My Sons' by Arthur Miller. Published by Penguin Classics (2000) © The Estate of Arthur Miller (pp 24–28); Two adverts for the Karen Hughes diamond and the Sarah Wesson Diamond © De Beers UK Limited (pp 30–31); An extract from 'Bhudda Da' by Anne Donovan, published by Canongate Books Ltd, 14 High Street, Edinburgh, EH1 1TE (p 7); The poem 'SOS SOS' taken from 'Blethertoun Braes' by Sheena Blackhall. Published by Black & White Publishing/Itchy Coo © Black & White Publishing (p 8); The poem 'A Manifesto for MSPs' taken from 'Voyage of Intent' by James Roberstson, published by Luath Press (p 8); The poem 'The Corrie Sailin' by John Law taken from Lallans. Published by Scots Language Society © John Law (p 9); A transcript taken from 'Crossing: Language and ethnicity among adolescents' by Ben Rampton © Ben Rampton (p 10); The short story 'Soldiers Home' taken from 'The Snows of Kilimanjaro and Other Stories' by Ernest Hemingway. Published by Jonathan Cape. Reprinted by permission of The Random House Group Ltd (pp 13–19); An extract from 'The Old Silk Route' taken from 'GRANTA #26' Spring 1989 by Colin Thubron © Granta (p 19–23); The poem 'Wind' taken from 'Hawk in the Rain' by Ted Hughes. Published by Faber & Faber Ltd (p 24); An extract from 'The Voysey Inheritance' (1905) by Harley Granville-Barker taken from 'Late Victorian Plays, 1890–1914, OWC no.614' by George Rowell 1968. By permission of Oxford University Press (pp 25–33); The article 'The Legend of the London Whale' by Cahal Milmo, taken from The Independent, Sunday 22 January 2006. Reproduced by permission of The Independent (pp 36–37).

2009 Paper

Extract from 'Arcadia' by Tom Stoppard, published by Faber & Faber Ltd (p 3); An extract from 'The Cotter's Saturday Night' by Robert Burns, 1796. Published by Penguin Popular Classics 1996. Public Domain (pp 4–5); Extract from 'The Poetry of Scotland, Gaelic, Scots and English' by Henryson and edited by Roderick Watson. Published by Edinburgh University Press (pp 6–7); Extract from 'The Steamie' by Tony Roper in 'Scot-Free: New Scottish Plays' selected by Alistair Cameron, copyright © 1990 Tony Roper, reproduced by permission of the publishers, Nick Hern Books Ltd: www.nickhernbooks.co.uk (pp 12–13); The poem 'Tae makk a Martyr' by Sheena Blackhall. Taken from 'The Wallace Muse', published by Luath Press © Sheena Blackhall (p 13); An extract taken from www.scottishcorpus.ac.uk © Scots Project (pp 14–15); A Scottish Parliament Official Record taken from: www.scottishparliament.uk. Parliamentary material is reproduced with the permission of the Controller of HMSO on behalf of Parliament (pp 16–17); An extract from from 'No Great Mischief' by Alistair MacLeod, published by Jonathan Cape. Reprinted by permission of the Random House Group Ltd (pp 18–21); The essay 'Where Does Writing Come From?' by Richard Ford, from 'GRANTA #62' (Spring 1998) © Richard Ford (pp 22–25); The poem 'The world is too much with us...' by William Wordsworth, published 1807. Public Domain (p 26); 'Walking Through Seaweed' from The Dancers Inherit the Party by Iain Hamilton Finlay is reproduced by permission of Polygon, an imprint of Birlinn Ltd. www.birlinn.co.uk (pp 27–36); Two articles from The Independent, Friday 16th March 2007, 'Collapse of Arctic Sea Ice has reached tipping point' by Steve Connor and 'Ocean heat blamed for mysterious disappearance of glaciers' by Steve Connor. Reproduced by permission of The Independent (p 38); A photograph by Jonathan Hayward, reproduced by permission of The Canadian Press (p 38);
The article 'Don't exaggerate climate dangers, scientists warn' by Juliette Jowit, 18 March 2007. Copyright Guardian News & Media Ltd 2007 (p 39); The article 'Weather Worries – Claims and Realities' taken from The Observer, 18 March 2007 © Sense About Science (p 39); Two adverts for Persil © Unilever Plc (insert).

2010 Paper

The poem `Moments of Grace' is taken from "Mean Time" by Carol Ann Duffy published by Anvil Press Poetry in 1993 (p 6); The poem 'Scotland's Winter' by Edwin Muir, taken from 'The Complete Poems of Edwin Muir. An Annotated Edition' edited by Peter Butter. Published by Faber & Faber Ltd (pp 7–8); The poem 'Blackberrying' by Sylvia Plath, taken from 'Crossing the Water' published by Faber & Faber Ltd, 1971 (pp 8–9); An extract from 'The Trick is to Keep Breathing' by Janice Galloway, published by Vintage 1991. Reprinted by permission of The Random House Group Ltd (p 10); An extract from 'Nice to be Nice' from 'The Old Pub Near the Angel' by James Kelman is reproduced by permission of Polygon, an imprint of Birlinn Ltd. www.birlinn.co.uk (p 14); An extract from 'In Love' by Iain Mills, published by Hodder Gibson 2007. Reproduced by permission of Hodder Gibson (pp 14–15); An extract from the Scottish National Party's manifesto for the Scottish Parliamentary elections in 2007, taken from http://www.snp.org/policies © SNP (pp 18–19); An extract from 'Vanity Fair' by William Makepeace Thackeray. Public domain (pp 20–24); The essay, 'The Secret Life of James Thurber' from The Thurber Carnival by James Thurber. Copyright ©1945 by Rosemary A.Thurber. Reprinted by arrangement with Rosemary A. Thurber and The Barbara Hogenson Agency. All rights

ADVANCED HIGHER | ANSWER SECTION

SQA ADVANCED HIGHER
ENGLISH 2008–2011

PRELIMINARY NOTE

1. The Student Notes

Following are guidance notes on the examination paper, the Specialist Study Dissertation and the Creative Writing Folio. These contain important information (based on or taken from the SQA's Arrangements document) and some useful pointers that should prove helpful to candidates. Please note that this answer section should only be used for guidance alongside everything that you have learned while taking the Advanced Higher English course. These notes are not meant to replace the advice you will receive from your teacher or lecturer.

2. The Marking Instructions

These sections contain extracts from the most relevant sections of the instructions which are presented to markers. They should give an idea of the standards that are required at this level, what will be expected of the best answers and some information about how the marker will assess answers. In addition to the material from the marking instructions for the actual examination papers, marking instructions for the Specialist Study Dissertation and for the Creative Writing Folio have also been included.

EXTERNAL EXAMINATION STUDENT NOTES

The Examination

1. Its Value

The examination paper is worth either 30% or 60% of your overall award – so it's important to take it very seriously.

2. How many questions should I answer?

At first glance, the Question Paper may seem daunting – around forty pages long, lots of detailed information to absorb on the opening page, a dozen or so pages and over forty questions in the mandatory Literary Study section alone.

But you needn't panic.

Only **one** or at most **two** questions have to be answered.

If Creative Writing is your chosen Option, you need only answer **one** question – which must, of course, be selected from the mandatory Literary Study section of the paper.

If you have chosen an Option other than Creative Writing, you will be required to answer **two** questions. Your first will be, as it is for all candidates, from the mandatory Literary Study section. Your second will be from the Language Study section **or** the Textual Analysis section **or** the Reading the Media section.

3. How much should I write?

Remember that you have one and a half hours in which to tackle each question. Of course, not all of that time should be spent writing. You should take as much time as you need to think about the question and to plan how you intend to respond to it. Then you should begin writing in as much detail as you think relevant and manageable in approximately one hour's worth of solid writing.

4. Will I have a choice of questions in each section of the paper?

For the mandatory Literary Study section, you should have studied the work of at least two authors (from different genres – Drama, Poetry, Prose). If you are properly prepared, therefore, for the examination, you should have a choice between the questions set on each of your chosen authors. There is similar choice in the Optional Sections of the paper: Language Study (for which two topics will have been studied), Textual Analysis (for which two genres will have been practised) and Reading the Media (for which two media categories will have been examined).

5. What if I can't remember my quotations accurately?

Because you don't have access to your texts during the examination, you will not be penalised for minor inaccuracies as you attempt to support your answer with relevant quotations and references. You should, however, be so familiar with the texts you have studied that quoting from them is instinctive and natural for you. Learning key quotations by heart is one way of ensuring that you have developed a firm grasp of the central concerns and features of the text.

6. What should I actually write?

The simple answer is that you should write directly in response to the terms of the question you are attempting. One of the main things examiners are looking for is evidence of your willingness to get involved, your ability to confront the terms of the question – to meet its implications head on and to deploy your knowledge of the text to provide convincing supporting evidence for the line of thought you are seeking to develop.

7. **The Standards Required**
The marking instructions which follow will help you to see clearly the difference between an answer that is acceptable and would pass and one that would earn top marks.

EXTERNAL EXAMINATION MARKING INSTRUCTIONS

Literary Study/Language Study/ Textual Analysis/Reading The Media

In relation to those components assessed by external examination, candidates will be subject to the following external assessment requirements:

Candidates will be allowed **1 hour 30 minutes** in which to answer one question in relation to each of the units they have studied.

No access to text(s) will be permitted

Authors, texts and topics that are central to the work of candidates in one component of course assessment may not be used in any other component of course assessment.

Candidates will be required to record on each answer booklet their Specialist Study texts and topics.

The use of category descriptions as the principal means of assessing candidate performance is informed partly by the advantage of using a familiar system and partly by the considerations below, which demonstrate that this system:

- offers validity and reliability through assessment procedures of proven fairness and robustness

- requires holistic assessment that rewards the actual attainment of each candidate within each assessment component by allocating each response to the category that best describes its overall quality

- allows for refinement of assessment by requiring the placing of each response at a particular point within the limited range of marks available for each category

- contributes to consistency of assessment by requiring repeated application of familiar and agreed statements of differentiated standards.

The starting point for the construction of category descriptions is the information on performance criteria and indicators of excellence for the various assessment components for Advanced Higher English published in the Arrangements document.

In all components, there is clear consistency of statement in relation to both performance criteria and indicators of excellence.

The extracts presented below, in which key features of required performance are emboldened, illustrate this consistency. Virtually identical statements are made about characteristic performance criteria and indicators of excellence for each of the assessment components − although it should be noted that the criterion of Expression does not apply to the assessment of Textual Analysis.

GRADE C Performance Criteria	GRADE A Indicators of Excellence *At least 4 bullet points from at least two categories*
Understanding The response takes a **relevant** and **thoughtful** approach to the prescribed task and demonstrates **secure** understanding of key elements …	**Understanding** • A **thorough exploration** is made of the implications of the prescribed task. • **Sustained insight** is revealed into key elements …
Analysis The response makes **relevant** and **thoughtful** … comment and demonstrates **secure** handling …	**Analysis** • A **full** and **satisfying** range of … comment is offered. • Literary/linguistic techniques … are handled with **skill** and **precision.**
Evaluation Judgements made are **relevant, thoughtful** and **securely based** on detailed evidence …	**Evaluation** • **Perceptive** and **incisive** judgements are made. • Deployment of evidence … is **skilful** and **precise.**
Expression Structure, style and language, including the use of appropriate critical/analytical terminology, are consistently **accurate** and **effective** in developing a **relevant** argument.	**Expression** • Structure, style and language, including the use of appropriate critical/analytical terminology, are **skilfully deployed** to develop a **pertinent** and **sharply focused** argument.

The words that best strike the note that is characteristic of competence of performance (equivalent to Grade C) at the level of Advanced Higher are:

- relevant
- thoughtful
- secure
- consistent
- accurate
- effective

At this level, excellence (equivalent to Grade A) is indicated by words such as:

- thorough
- sustained
- insight
- full
- satisfying
- perceptive
- incisive
- skilful
- precise
- pertinent
- sharply focused.

It may be relatively straightforward to find qualitative words that will differentiate – for each criterion – between candidate work that is competent (Grade C) and candidate work that is excellent (Grade A). It is clearly more difficult to find qualitative words to describe the range of performance (Grade B) that may lie between these two well-defined points.

The Arrangements document recognises this difficulty by noting: "Where the overall quality of a piece of work goes beyond the performance criteria for Grade C, but falls short of Grade A, it will attain Grade B. In this case, it may show only **one or two** of the A characteristics or it may show **three or more** of the indicators of excellence without reaching A quality for any."

In response to this flexibility, the following external assessment framework of four "pass" categories and two "fail" categories has been adopted for the grading of candidate performance in each of the Advanced Higher English assessment components:

Category 1 **Excellent** – well aligned with a significant number of the published indicators of excellence.

Category 2 **Still signs of excellence** – but not quite so well aligned with (or aligned with fewer of) the published indicators of excellence.

Category 3 **More than competent** – in some significant ways beyond some of the published performance criteria.

Category 4 **Competent** – in overall quality firmly anchored to the published performance criteria.

Category 5 **Less than competent** – in some significant ways not quite achieving all of the published performance criteria.

Category 6 **Incompetent** – well below Advanced Higher level as required by the published performance criteria.

A 30-point scale (corresponding to a weighting of 30% in the final award) has been adopted for the assessment of the six components that are assessed by external examination. It applies to these six categories as follows:

Category 1   Marks: 27–30

Excellent – well aligned with a significant number of the published indicators of excellence.

Understanding

- A thorough exploration is made of the implications of the prescribed task.

- Sustained insight is revealed into key elements, central concerns and significant details of the texts or of the linguistic or media field of study.

Analysis

- A full and satisfying range of critical/analytical comment is offered.

- Literary, linguistic or media concepts, techniques, forms, usages are handled with skill and precision.

Evaluation

- Perceptive and incisive judgements are made.

- Deployment of evidence from texts, sources or contexts is skilful and precise.

Expression

- Structure, style and language, including the use of appropriate critical/analytical terminology, are skilfully deployed to develop a pertinent and sharply focused argument.

Category 2   Marks: 23–26

Still signs of excellence – but not quite so well aligned with (or aligned with fewer of) the published indicators of excellence.

Understanding
As for Category 1, but

- the implications of the prescribed task are not quite so thoroughly explored

- insight is not quite so well sustained.

Analysis
As for Category 1, but

- the range of critical/analytical comment is not quite so full or satisfying

- relevant techniques, concepts, forms, usages are not handled with quite the same level of skill or precision.

Evaluation
As for Category 1, but

- judgements made are not quite so perceptive or incisive

- deployment of evidence is not quite so skilful or precise.

Expression
As for Category 1, but

- structure, style and language are not quite so skilfully deployed or argument quite so sharply focused.

Category 3   Marks: 19–22

More than competent – in some significant ways beyond some of the published performance criteria.

Understanding
As for Category 4, but

- with glimmers of – awareness of implications or thoroughness or insight.

Analysis
As for Category 4, but

- with glimmers of – fullness or skill or precision of critical/analytical comment.

Evaluation
As for Category 4, but

- with glimmers of – perceptiveness or incisiveness or skilful deployment of evidence.

Expression
As for Category 4, but

- with glimmers of – skilful deployment of language in the development of argument.

Category 4   Marks: 15–18

Competent – in overall quality firmly anchored to the published performance criteria.

Understanding

- The response takes a relevant and thoughtful approach to the prescribed task and demonstrates secure understanding of key elements, central concerns and significant details of the texts or of the linguistic or media field of study.

Analysis

- The response makes relevant and thoughtful critical/analytical comment and demonstrates secure handling of literary, linguistic or media concepts, techniques, forms, usages.

Evaluation

- Judgements made are relevant, thoughtful and securely based on detailed evidence drawn from texts, sources or contexts.

Expression

- Structure, style and language, including the use of appropriate critical/analytical terminology, are consistently accurate and effective in developing a relevant argument.

Category 5   Marks: 10–14

Less than competent – in some significant ways not quite achieving all of the published performance criteria.

Understanding
As for Category 4, but

- with some weakness in – relevance or thoughtfulness or security of understanding of key elements, central concerns, significant details.

Analysis
As for Category 4, but

- with some weakness in – relevance or thoughtfulness or accuracy or range of critical/analytical comment.

Evaluation
As for Category 4, but

- with some weakness in – relevance or thoughtfulness or substantiation of judgements made.

Expression
As for Category 4, but

- with some weakness in – accuracy and effectiveness of structure or style or language or critical/ analytical terminology in the development of argument.

Category 6   Marks: 00–09

Incompetent – well below Advanced Higher level as required by the published performance criteria.

Understanding

- The response is deficient in – relevance or thoughtfulness or security of understanding of key elements, central concerns, significant details.

Analysis

- The response is deficient in – relevance or thoughtfulness or accuracy or range of critical/analytical comment.

Evaluation

- The response is deficient in – relevance or thoughtfulness or substantiation of judgements made.

Expression

- The response is deficient in – accuracy and effectiveness of structure or style or language or critical/analytical terminology in the development of argument.

N.B. It should be noted that, in the category descriptions provided, where performance in one category is described as "significantly" different from performance in an adjacent category, this may be demonstrated by:

- marginally stronger or weaker performance **in a range of aspects**

or

- very much stronger or weaker performance **in one or two aspects.**

Several factors are taken into account before assigning each candidate response to a particular numerical mark within a particular category.

(*a*) Categories are not grades. Although derived from the performance criteria for Grade C and the indicators of excellence for Grade A, the six categories are designed primarily to assist with the placing of each candidate response at an appropriate point on a continuum of achievement. Assumptions about final grades or association of final grades with particular categories are not allowed to get in the way of objective assessment.

(*b*) The expectation is that the vast majority of candidates will already have demonstrated in unit assessment a level of competence that has merited achievement of the unit outcome. Markers begin, therefore, with the expectation that each response will meet, at least, the requirements of Category 4. While there may be some responses that for various reasons fail to demonstrate the level of competence required by Category 4, the likelihood is that they will prove characteristic of Category 5 – and it is expected that no response will be so incompetent as to require assignment to Category 6.

(*c*) For each category, a range of marks is available within which markers refine their assessments, for example within a mark or so at the upper end, the middle or the lower end of the category. The marks range within each category is sufficiently generous to allow markers scope for fair and justifiable discrimination. Markers are encouraged to make full use of the ranges of marks available to them.

(*d*) Mixed profiles of attainment will occur. Normally, these will represent variations within the range of performance that is characteristic of a particular category. In some instances, however, performance may be so uneven as to require markers to weigh up strengths and weaknesses of performance that extend across categories. Markers are reminded that their assessment should at all times be holistic – assigning each response to the category (and to the numerical point within that category) that best describes its overall achievement. In instances where there is genuine doubt as to whether a response should be placed at the lower end of a higher category or at the upper end of a lower category (and only in such instances), candidates should be given the benefit of the doubt, and their responses awarded the lowest mark in the higher category.

SPECIALIST STUDY DISSERTATION STUDENT NOTES

Specialist Study Dissertation

1. **Its Value**
   The dissertation is worth 40% of your overall award – so it's important to take it very seriously.

2. **Exclusions**
   Authors, texts and topics that are central to your work in one component of course assessment (for example, Literary Study) may not be used in any other component of course assessment (for example, your Specialist Study Dissertation). You will be required to record your Specialist Study Dissertation texts and topic on your answer booklet.

3. **What you have to do**
   You have to make an independent study of and produce a dissertation on an aspect or aspects of language or literature or media or some combination of these.

4. **Selecting Texts and Topic**
   The first stage in the process is the selection of texts or topics and the formulation of a brief descriptive statement of what you propose to study. This proposal must be approved by your teacher or lecturer in order to ensure that the materials are appropriate to an English course and worthy of study at this level and that the study itself is manageable. Your study should explore a limited area and examine it in detail with lots of appropriate supporting evidence.

   It should be noted that texts and topics:
   - must be personally selected by you (under the guidance of your teacher or lecturer)
   - must be accepted by your centre as suitable choices
   - must not be the subject of teaching in this unit
   - must not be the subject of teaching or assessment in other units of the Advanced Higher English course or in the units of other courses.

   You should select a topic that will enable you to offer a full exposition and discussion of a particular aspect of your chosen field of study. For example, a literary theme might be pursued through the works of a single author, or works of several authors, or over a historical period; a language topic might focus on language acquisition, the dialect of a specific locality, the language of specialist groups; a media topic might be related to the study of language or of literature.

   Studies of the works of a single author or single works by two or more authors should avoid a serial treatment in which each work is left isolated from the other(s). Studies that involve the collection and analysis of data and information should be presented in discursive form.

5. **The Production of the Dissertation**
   Clearly, production of the dissertation will vary from candidate to candidate and from centre to centre.

   In most cases, however, your teacher or lecturer will:
   - brief you on the nature of the task at the outset
   - illustrate the wide range of texts and topics available
   - discuss with you your relevant individual and personal interests
   - guide you towards consultation with librarians or other teachers/lecturers and towards use of databanks
   - give you practical help with final choice and location of texts and with the wording of topics and titles
   - provide regular opportunities for consultation and support
   - make clear to you the procedures that must apply in order to meet deadlines and evidence requirements

- record your progress at different stages in the production of the dissertation in order to ensure the authenticity of your work.

You should:

- write, type or word-process your dissertation on one side of A4 paper only
- use italics or underlining to indicate titles of texts
- set in from the margin all quotations of more than one line so that they are clearly distinguishable from the text of the dissertation
- use footnotes and page references where appropriate to identify quotations from and references to primary sources
- use footnotes and page references at all times to identify and acknowledge quotations from, references to and information/ideas gleaned from secondary sources
- provide an accurate bibliography
- give footnote and bibliography references in the following form:

    D. Gifford and D. McMillan, A History of Scottish Women's Writing, EUP, 1997.

6. Length

The dissertation you produce must be between 3500 and 4500 words in length, including quotations but excluding footnotes and bibliography. You should note that, in order to achieve consistency in this area, any dissertation that falls outwith these limits of length will not be accepted. You must indicate on the dissertation flyleaf the actual number of words used.

7. Plagiarism

While you should of course consult secondary sources, you must be careful not to rely on them excessively and you must never copy them without acknowledgement. Always remember that to plagiarise is to cheat – and that could lead to your disqualification from any award. Markers are instructed to report all instances where plagiarism is suspected for further investigation (so be warned!).

8. The Standards Required

The marking instructions which follow will help you to see clearly the difference between a dissertation that is acceptable and will pass and one that would earn you top marks.

SPECIALIST STUDY DISSERTATION MARKING INSTRUCTIONS

In relation to the Specialist Study Dissertation, candidates will be subject to the following external assessment requirements:

By **30 April,** candidates will be required to submit to SQA, as a mandatory component of course assessment, a dissertation on their nominated topic, authenticated as having been produced in a manner that satisfies the evidence requirements of the unit.

The chosen topic and the materials on which it is based must be deemed by the centre to be suitable for independent study (of appropriate quality, personally selected by candidates, not the subject of teaching in this unit or of teaching or assessment in other units of this course or other courses).

The dissertation must be between 3500 and 4500 words in length, including quotations but excluding mandatory footnotes and bibliography.

The dissertation must be unassisted and produced under a system of supervision that guarantees authenticity through a process requiring candidates to submit the following at appropriate stages:

- draft title and proposals
- outline plan
- first draft
- final submission.

Draft materials must be retained as evidence of authenticity.

The use of category descriptions as the principal means of assessing candidate performance is informed partly by the advantage of using a familiar system and partly by the considerations below, which demonstrate that this system:

- offers validity and reliability through assessment procedures of proven fairness and robustness
- requires holistic assessment that rewards the actual attainment of each candidate within each assessment component by allocating each response to the category that best describes its overall quality
- allows for refinement of assessment by requiring the placing of each response at a particular point within the limited range of marks available for each category
- contributes to consistency of assessment by requiring repeated application of familiar and agreed statements of differentiated standards.

The starting point for the construction of category descriptions is the information on performance criteria and indicators of excellence for the Specialist Study Dissertation published in the Arrangements document. Key features of required performance are emboldened in the table below.

GRADE C Performance Criteria	GRADE A Indicators of Excellence *At least 4 bullet points from at least two categories.*
Understanding The dissertation takes a **relevant** and **thoughtful** approach to the stated topic and demonstrates **secure** understanding of key elements …	**Understanding** • A **thorough exploration** is made of the implications of the stated topic. • **Sustained insight** is revealed into key elements …
Analysis The dissertation makes **relevant** and **thoughtful** … comment and demonstrates **secure** handling …	**Analysis** • A **full** and **satisfying** range of … comment is offered. • Literary/linguistic … techniques … are handled with **skill** and **precision.**
Evaluation Judgements made are **relevant, thoughtful** and **securely based** on detailed evidence …	**Evaluation** • **Perceptive** and **incisive** judgements are made. • Deployment of evidence … is **skilful** and **precise.**
Expression Structure, style and language, including the use of appropriate critical/analytical terminology, are consistently **accurate** and **effective** in developing a **relevant** argument.	**Expression** • Structure, style and language, including the use of appropriate critical/analytical terminology, are **skilfully deployed** to develop a **pertinent** and **sharply focused** argument.

The words that best strike the note that is characteristic of **competence** of performance (equivalent to Grade C) at the level of Advanced Higher are:

- relevant
- thoughtful
- secure
- consistent
- accurate
- effective.

At this level, **excellence** (equivalent to Grade A) is indicated by words such as:

- thorough
- sustained
- insight
- full
- satisfying
- perceptive
- incisive
- skilful
- precise
- pertinent
- sharply focused.

It may be relatively straightforward to find qualitative words that will differentiate – for each criterion – between candidate work that is competent (Grade C) and candidate work that is excellent (Grade A). It is clearly more difficult to find qualitative words to describe the range of performance (Grade B) that may lie between these two well-defined points.

The Arrangements document recognises this difficulty by noting: "Where the overall quality of a piece of work goes beyond the performance criteria for Grade C, but falls short of Grade A, it will attain Grade B. In this case, it may show only **one or two** of the A characteristics or it may show **three or more** of the indicators of excellence without reaching A quality for any".

In response to this flexibility, the following external assessment framework of four "pass" categories and two "fail" categories has been adopted for the grading of candidate performance in each of the Advanced Higher English assessment components:

Category 1 **Excellent** – well aligned with a significant number of the published indicators of excellence.

Category 2 **Still signs of excellence** – but not quite so well aligned with (or aligned with fewer of) the published indicators of excellence.

Category 3 **More than competent** – in some significant ways beyond some of the published performance criteria.

Category 4 **Competent** – in overall quality firmly anchored to the published performance criteria.

Category 5 **Less than competent** – in some significant ways not quite achieving all of the published performance criteria.

Category 6 **Incompetent** – well below Advanced Higher level as required by the published performance criteria.

A 40-point scale (corresponding to a weighting of 40% in the final award) has been adopted for the assessment of the dissertation. It applies to these six categories as follows:

Category 1   Marks: 35–40

Excellent – well aligned with a significant number of the published indicators of excellence.

Understanding

- A thorough exploration is made of the implications of the stated topic.

- Sustained insight is revealed into key elements, central concerns and significant details of the texts or of the linguistic or media field of study.

Analysis

- A full and satisfying range of critical/analytical comment is offered.

- Literary, linguistic or media concepts, techniques, forms, usages are handled with skill and precision.

Evaluation

- Perceptive and incisive judgements are made.

- Deployment of evidence from primary and, where appropriate, secondary sources is skilful and precise.

Expression

- Structure, style and language, including the use of appropriate critical/analytical terminology, are skilfully deployed to develop a pertinent and sharply focused argument.

Category 2   Marks: 30–34

Still signs of excellence – but not quite so well aligned with (or aligned with fewer of) the published indicators of excellence.

Understanding
As for Category 1, but

- the attempt made to explore the implications of the topic is not quite so thorough

- insight is not quite so well sustained.

Analysis
As for Category 1, but

- the range of critical/analytical comment is not quite so full or satisfying

- relevant techniques, concepts, forms, usages are not handled with quite the same level of skill and precision.

Evaluation
As for Category 1, but

- judgements made are not quite so perceptive or incisive

- deployment of evidence is not quite so skilful or precise.

Expression
As for Category 1, but

- expression is not quite so skilfully deployed or argument quite so sharply focused.

Category 3   Marks: 25–29

More than competent – in some significant ways beyond some of the published performance criteria.

Understanding
As for Category 4, but

- with glimmers of – awareness of implications or thoroughness or insight.

Analysis
As for Category 4, but

- with glimmers of – fullness or skill or precision of critical/analytical comment.

Evaluation
As for Category 4, but

- with glimmers of – perceptiveness or incisiveness or skilful deployment of evidence.

Expression
As for Category 4, but

- with glimmers of – skilful deployment of language in the development of argument.

Category 4   Marks: 20–24

Competent – in overall quality firmly anchored to the published performance criteria.

Understanding
The dissertation takes a relevant and thoughtful approach to the stated topic and demonstrates secure understanding of key elements, central concerns and significant details of the texts or of the linguistic or media field of study.

Analysis
The dissertation makes relevant and thoughtful critical/analytical comment and demonstrates secure handling of literary, linguistic or media concepts, techniques, forms, usages.

Evaluation
Judgements made are relevant, thoughtful and securely based on detailed evidence drawn from primary and, where appropriate, secondary sources.

Expression
Structure, style and language, including the use of appropriate critical/analytical terminology, are consistently accurate and effective in developing a relevant argument.

Category 5   Marks: 15–19

Less than competent – in some significant ways not quite achieving all of the published performance criteria.

Understanding
As for Category 4, but

- with some weakness in – relevance or thoughtfulness or security of understanding of key elements, central concerns, significant details.

Analysis
As for Category 4, but

- with some weakness in – relevance or thoughtfulness or accuracy or range of critical/analytical comment.

Evaluation
As for Category 4, but

- with some weakness in – relevance or thoughtfulness or substantiation of judgements made.

Expression
As for Category 4, but

- with some weakness in – accuracy or effectiveness of structure or style or language or critical/analytical terminology in the development of argument.

Category 6   Marks: 00–14

Incompetent – well below Advanced Higher level as required by the published performance criteria.

Understanding

- The dissertation is deficient in – relevance or thoughtfulness or security of understanding of key elements, central concerns, significant details.

Analysis

- The dissertation is deficient in – relevance or thoughtfulness or accuracy or range of critical/analytical comment.

Evaluation

- The dissertation is deficient in – relevance or thoughtfulness or substantiation of judgements made.

Expression

- The dissertation is deficient in – accuracy or effectiveness of structure or style or language or critical/analytical terminology in the development of argument.

N.B. It should be noted that, in the category descriptions provided, where performance in one category is described as "significantly" different from performance in an adjacent category, this may be demonstrated by:

- marginally stronger or weaker performance **in a range of aspects**

or

- very much stronger or weaker performance **in one or two aspects.**

Several factors are taken into account before assigning each candidate's dissertation to a particular numerical mark within a particular category.

(a) Categories are not grades. Although derived from the performance criteria for Grade C and the indicators of excellence for Grade A, the six categories are designed primarily to assist with the placing of each candidate response at an appropriate point on a continuum of achievement. Assumptions about final grades or association of final grades with particular categories are not allowed to get in the way of objective assessment.

(b) The expectation is that the vast majority of candidates will already have demonstrated in unit assessment a level of competence that has merited achievement of the unit outcome. Markers begin, therefore, with the expectation that the dissertation will meet, at least, the requirements of category 4. While there may be some dissertations that for various reasons fail to demonstrate the level of competence required by category 4, the likelihood is that they will prove characteristic of category 5 – and it is expected that no dissertation will be so incompetent as to require assignment to category 6.

(c) For each category, a range of marks is available within which markers refine their assessments, for example within a mark or two at the upper end, the middle or the lower end of the category. The marks range within each category is sufficiently generous to allow markers scope for fair and justifiable discrimination. Markers are encouraged to make full use of the ranges of marks available to them.

(d) Mixed profiles of attainment will occur. Normally, these will represent variations within the range of performance that is characteristic of a particular category. In some instances, however, performance may be so uneven as to require markers to weigh up strengths and weaknesses of performance that extend across categories. Markers are reminded that their assessment should at all times be **holistic** – assigning each dissertation to the category (and to the numerical point within that category) that best describes its overall achievement. In instances where there is genuine doubt as to whether a dissertation should be placed at the lower end of a higher category or at the upper end of a lower category (and only in such instances), candidates should be given the benefit of the doubt, and their dissertations awarded the lowest mark in the higher category.

CREATIVE WRITING FOLIO STUDENT NOTES

Creative Writing Folio

1. **Its Value**
   The Creative Writing Folio is worth 30% of your overall award – so it's important to take it very seriously.

2. **What you have to do**
   You must show that you can write creatively in more than one genre by submitting for assessment two pieces of creative writing. The genres from which you can choose are:
   - reflective essay
   - prose fiction
   - poetry
   - drama.

3. **Length**
   Other than poetry, where length should be appropriate to subject and form, each piece of creative writing should be at least 1000 words in length. You are required to indicate on the Creative Writing Folio Flyleaf the actual number of words used in each piece. You should also note that, although there is no prescribed maximum length, excessively lengthy pieces are usually self-penalising.

4. **Number of pieces you have to submit**
   There should really be no grounds for uncertainty or confusion about what is meant by "two pieces of creative writing". It should be noted, however, that in Advanced Higher it is no longer possible to submit a group of poems, thematically related or otherwise. The requirement is for the submission of a "poem". Whatever form the submission of poetry takes, therefore, it must display the constraining integrity of a single piece of work and be assessed accordingly. Similar restrictions apply to submissions in other genres: each submission, however constructed (a series of diary entries, an exchange of letters, different scenes in a play, a series of monologues) must represent a single "piece of creative writing".

5. **Plagiarism**
   Always remember that to plagiarise is to cheat – and that could lead to your disqualification from any award. Markers are instructed to report all instances where plagiarism is suspected for further investigation (so be warned!).

6. **Understanding the Potential of Each Genre**
   The distinctive characteristics of the four specified forms of creative writing require close attention.

   Reflective Essay
   The reflective essay will:
   - aim to interest or give pleasure, not, as a rule, information
   - concern itself with, usually, a single idea, insight, experience
   - be genuinely contemplative; its personal tone may be confidential, concerned, amused, indignant…
   - communicate to the reader a clear sense of the writer's personality
   - not merely offer the product of reflection, but engage the reader in the process of reflection.

   Although the form of writing within this genre is restricted to the essay, there is scope for a range of topics and a variety of treatments.

   The subject of reflection could, for example, be:
   - a person, a place, an object
   - a condition, a situation, a relationship
   - a mood, a memory, a feeling

- an image, an idea, an insight
- an issue, an activity, a theory, a belief.

Possible treatments could be:
- the impression of a mind exploring an idea
- an apparently random approach in the course of which insight is gained
- the development of an unobtrusive narrative framework as a convenient device through which issues and experiences are reflected upon.

Whatever the topic or the approach taken, the central feature of the reflective essay will be its reflective quality.

It follows from what has been said above that certain types of writing cannot be accepted as reflective essays; in particular
- writing that is mainly transactional or argumentative in effect
- writing that is clearly in some other imaginative writing form, such as fiction
- writing that is merely an account of personal history.

Prose Fiction

In prose fiction, the range of subject matter and themes open to the writer is limitless, and there is great scope here for different forms of writing. You may choose to produce, for example:
- a short story
- an extract, such as the opening, the conclusion or a key episode from an imaginary novel
- a focused piece of characterisation
- a monologue or dialogue
- a detailed description of an imaginary setting
- a series of diary entries
- an exchange of letters.

Whatever the subject matter or form chosen, you should note that the writing of fiction requires skill and control of the following features:
- a plot or clear narrative framework, centred on identifiable characters and leading to some kind of denouement
- a structure which shapes content and theme
- dialogue, imagery and symbolism
- a stance or tone, which, while not intrusive or obvious, demonstrates the writer's command of the material.

The choice of subject matter may include:
- a person, a place, an object
- an event, a situation, a relationship
- a discovery, a choice, a dilemma
- a prejudice, a delusion, an obsession
- a memory, an image, an insight
- an experience, an issue, an activity.

Fiction is primarily a means of aesthetic expression. It should be borne in mind, however, that it can serve many other functions and purposes, for example:
- to entertain, amuse
- to raise awareness of an issue
- to satirise
- to comment on the human condition.

Fiction writing allows you to choose from a wide variety of possible treatments, including the innovative and the experimental. The chosen treatment will depend to a large extent on your distinctive aim and imaginative grasp of theme and topic.

Poetry

Of all the genres, poetry allows the greatest freedom of subject matter and approach. It should be stressed, however, that it also calls for the greatest discipline and control.

Writing poetry involves much more than randomly chopping up prose into lines. Poetry should be recognisably different from prose in, for example:
- its choice and arrangement of words, lines and verses/stanzas
- the often surprising connections it makes between words
- its often condensed and heightened use of language
- its greater use of figurative language
- its deployment of sound and rhythm
- its often unconventional syntax and patterning of ideas and images.

When writing poetry, you should bear in mind the following considerations:
- a poem should present its topic in a striking and original way
- whatever the range and variety of its references and detail, the theme of a poem should be focused and unified through its imagery and structural control
- the poem should contain a clear sense of the writer's imaginative/emotional/intellectual involvement with the topic
- a poem should aim to engage the reader's imaginative/emotional/intellectual responses as fully as possible
- none of a poem's individual parts will seem unnecessary
- a poem's overall effect will be aesthetically pleasing.

For the writer of poetry, the choice of topic is limitless. For example, a poem may deal with:
- a person, a place, an object
- a condition, a situation, a relationship
- a mood, a memory, a feeling
- an image, an idea, an insight
- an experience, an issue, an activity.

Careful thought should be given to the appropriateness of stance and tone in the treatment of the topic; this will determine the entire structure of the poem.

Poetry offers great variety of layout and formal presentation. For example:
- a traditional metrical scheme
- a more modern rhythmic arrangement
- a regular verse/stanza form
- a recognised poetic form such as the sonnet
- a structured patterning that is determined by the poem's subject matter
- a visual shaping of text that is designed to be representative or symbolic as, for example, concrete poetry.

Drama

For writers of drama there is an equally wide range of choices – of topic, approach and form. In creating a dramatic script, however, you must be able to demonstrate your understanding of the nature and potential of the genre. In particular, you should be able to:
- create characters who are credible, interesting and capable of provoking in the reader an intellectual and/or emotional response
- make effective use of dialogue – and other modes of communication (including non-verbal modes such as gesture, body-language)
- establish a setting in which, and a situation out of which, the drama will arise
- develop and communicate a recognisable theme, a centre of interest that will give point to the script
- produce a particular effect, mood or atmosphere
- demonstrate familiarity with the requirements of script layout and presentation

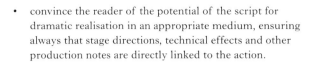

convince the reader of the potential of the script for dramatic realisation in an appropriate medium, ensuring always that stage directions, technical effects and other production notes are directly linked to the action.

A dramatic script may prove an effective vehicle for the treatment of a wide range of topics:
- an event, a situation, a relationship
- an argument, a conflict, a misunderstanding
- a discovery, a choice, a dilemma
- a prejudice, a delusion, an obsession
- a mood, a memory, a feeling.

Among the many possible approaches are:
- a dramatic monologue
- an opening scene of a play
- a complete one-act play
- a play for radio
- a television sit-com
- a storyboard, a shooting script, a film-script
- a documentary drama.

7. **The Standards Required**

The marking instructions which follow will help you to see clearly the difference between a piece of creative writing that is acceptable and will pass and one that would earn you top marks.

CREATIVE WRITING FOLIO MARKING INSTRUCTIONS

In relation to Creative Writing, candidates will be subject to the following external assessment requirements:

By the date of the examination, candidates will be required to submit a folio comprising two pieces of creative writing in different genres, authenticated as having been produced in a manner that satisfies the evidence requirements of the unit.

The genres from which candidates may select are:

- reflective essay
- prose fiction
- poetry
- drama.

Each piece of creative writing, poetry excepted, must be at least 1000 words in length. The length of a piece of poetry will depend on the chosen form, but should be sufficient to permit demonstration of all of the performance criteria.

Each piece of writing must be unassisted and produced under a system of supervision that guarantees authenticity through a process requiring candidates to submit the following at appropriate stages:

- draft title and proposals
- outline plan
- first draft
- final submission.

Draft materials must be retained as evidence of authenticity.

The use of category descriptions as the principal means of assessing candidate performance is informed partly by the advantage of using a familiar system and partly by the considerations below, which demonstrate that this system:

- offers validity and reliability through assessment procedures of proven fairness and robustness

- requires holistic assessment that rewards the actual attainment of each candidate within each assessment component by allocating each response to the category that best describes its overall quality

- allows for refinement of assessment by requiring the placing of each response at a particular point within the limited range of marks available for each category

- contributes to consistency of assessment by requiring repeated application of familiar and agreed statements of differentiated standards

The starting point for the construction of category descriptions is the information on performance criteria and indicators of excellence for Creative Writing published in the Arrangements document. Key features of required performance are emboldened in the table below.

GRADE C Performance Criteria	GRADE A Indicators of Excellence *At least 4 bullet points from at least two categories.*
Content The central thematic concern emerges in a way that reveals **thoughtfulness, insight, imagination.**	**Content** • The central thematic concern emerges in a way that reveals **a high degree of thoughtfulness, insight, imagination.**
Structure The structure of the chosen form is **exploited to achieve desired effects.**	**Structure** • **Skilful** shaping and sequencing contribute significantly to impact. • The potential of the chosen form is exploited with **a high degree of skill and imagination.**
Stance/tone/mood The stance adopted by the writer in relation to the reader and to the material is **clear** and **appropriate;** tone or mood is **controlled** and **deliberate.**	**Stance/tone/mood** • A **distinctive** authorial voice emerges. • Tone or mood is **skilfully created and sustained.**
Expression Style and language, including the use of techniques relevant to the genre, are **deployed to achieve desired effects.**	**Expression** • Techniques relevant to the genre are deployed with **resourcefulness** and **subtlety.** • Style and language are deployed with **skill** and **originality.**

The words that best strike the note that is characteristic of competence of performance (equivalent to Grade C) at the level of Advanced Higher are:

- thoughtfulness
- insight
- imagination
- clear
- appropriate
- controlled
- deliberate.

At this level, excellence (equivalent to Grade A) is indicated by words such as:

- skilful
- distinctive
- sustained
- resourcefulness
- subtlety
- originality.

It may be relatively straightforward to find qualitative words that will differentiate – for each criterion – between candidate work that is competent (Grade C) and candidate work that is excellent (Grade A). It is clearly more difficult to find qualitative words to describe the range of performance (Grade B) that may lie between these two well-defined points.

The Arrangements document recognises this difficulty by noting: "Where the overall quality of a piece of work goes beyond the performance criteria for Grade C, but falls short of Grade A, it will attain Grade B. In this case, it may show only **one or two** of the A characteristics or it may show **three or more** of the indicators of excellence without reaching A quality for any". In response to this flexibility, the following external assessment framework of four "pass" categories and two "fail" categories has been adopted for the grading of candidate performance in each of the Advanced Higher English assessment components:

Category 1   **Excellent** – well aligned with a significant number of the published indicators of excellence.

Category 2   **Still signs of excellence** – but not quite so well aligned with (or aligned with fewer of) the published indicators of excellence.

Category 3   **More than competent** – in some significant ways beyond some of the published performance criteria.

Category 4   **Competent** – in overall quality firmly anchored to the published performance criteria.

Category 5   **Less than competent** – in some significant ways not quite achieving all of the published performance criteria.

Category 6   **Incompetent** – well below Advanced Higher level as required by the published performance criteria.

A 30-point scale (corresponding to a weighting of 30% in the final award) has been adopted for the assessment of each of the two pieces of creative writing submitted for external assessment. It applies to these six categories as follows:

Category 1   Marks: 30–27

Excellent – well aligned with a significant number of the published indicators of excellence.

Content

- The central thematic concern emerges in a way that reveals a high degree of thoughtfulness, insight, imagination.

Structure

- Skilful shaping and sequencing contribute significantly to impact.
- The potential of the chosen form is exploited with a high degree of skill and imagination.

Stance/tone/mood

- A distinctive authorial voice emerges.
- Tone or mood is skilfully created and sustained.

Expression

- Techniques relevant to the genre are deployed with resourcefulness and subtlety.
- Style and language are deployed with skill and originality.

Category 2   Marks: 23–26

Still signs of excellence – but not quite so well aligned with (or aligned with fewer of) the published indicators of excellence.

Content

As for Category 1, but

- there may not be quite such a high degree of thoughtfulness or insight or imagination in the way in which the central thematic concern emerges.

Structure

As for Category 1, but

- shaping and sequencing may not be quite so skilful or contribute so significantly to impact

- there may not be quite such a high degree of skill or imagination in exploiting the potential of the chosen form.

Stance/tone/mood

As for Category 1, but

- the authorial voice that emerges may not be quite so distinctive

- tone or mood may not be quite so well created or sustained.

Expression

As for Category 1, but

- techniques relevant to the genre may not be deployed with quite the same resourcefulness or subtlety

- style and language may not be deployed with quite the same skill or originality.

Category 3   Marks: 19–22

More than competent – in some significant ways beyond some of the published performance criteria.

Content

As for Category 4, but

- with glimmers of – a high degree of thoughtfulness or insight or imagination in the way in which the central thematic concern emerges.

Structure

As for Category 4, but

- with glimmers of – skilful shaping or sequencing or skill or imagination in the handling of the chosen form.

Stance/tone/mood

As for Category 4, but

- with glimmers of – the emergence of a distinctive authorial voice or of tone or mood being skilfully created or sustained.

Expression

As for Category 4, but

- with glimmers of – resourcefulness or subtlety or skill or originality in the deployment of style or language or techniques relevant to the genre.

Category 4   Marks: 15–18

Competent – in overall quality firmly anchored to the published performance criteria.

Content

- The central thematic concern emerges in a way that reveals thoughtfulness, insight, imagination.

Structure

- The structure of the chosen form is exploited to achieve desired effects.

Stance/tone/mood

- The stance adopted by the writer in relation to the reader and to the material is clear and appropriate; tone or mood is controlled and deliberate.

Expression

- Style and language, including the use of techniques relevant to the genre, are deployed to achieve desired effects.

Category 5   Marks: 10–14

Less than competent – in some significant ways not quite achieving all of the published performance criteria.

Content

As for Category 4, but

- with some weakness in – thoughtfulness or insight or imagination.

Structure

As for Category 4, but

- with some weakness in – exploitation of the structure of the chosen form or achievement of desired effects.

Stance/tone/mood

As for Category 4, but

- with some weakness in – clarity or appropriateness of stance or control of tone or mood.

Expression

As for Category 4, but

- with some weakness in – style or language or use of techniques relevant to the genre.

Category 6   Marks: 00–09

Incompetent – well below Advanced Higher level as required by the published performance criteria.

Content

- The piece of creative writing is deficient in – thoughtfulness or insight or imagination.

Structure

- The piece of creative writing is deficient in – exploitation of the structure of the chosen form or achievement of desired effects.

Stance/tone/mood

- The piece of creative writing is deficient in – clarity or appropriateness of stance or control of tone or mood.

Expression

- The piece of creative writing is deficient in – style or language or techniques relevant to the genre.

N.B. It should be noted that, in the category descriptions provided, where performance in one category is described as "significantly" different from performance in an adjacent category, this may be demonstrated by:

- marginally stronger or weaker performance **in a range of aspects**

or

- very much stronger or weaker performance **in one or two aspects.**

Several factors are taken into account before assigning each piece of creative writing to a particular numerical mark within a particular category.

(a) Categories are not grades. Although derived from the performance criteria for Grade C and the indicators of excellence for Grade A, the six categories are designed primarily to assist with the placing of each candidate response at an appropriate point on a continuum of achievement. Assumptions about final grades or association of final grades with particular categories are not allowed to get in the way of objective assessment.

(b) The expectation is that the vast majority of candidates will already have demonstrated in unit assessment a level of competence that has merited achievement of the unit outcome. Markers begin, therefore, with the expectation that each piece of creative writing will meet, at least, the requirements of category 4. While there may be some pieces that for various reasons fail to demonstrate the level of competence required by category 4, the likelihood is that they will prove characteristic of category 5 – and it is expected that no piece of creative writing will be so incompetent as to require assignment to category 6.

(c) For each category, a range of marks is available within which markers may refine their assessments, for example within a mark or two at the upper end, the middle or the lower end of the category. The marks range within each category are sufficiently generous to allow markers scope for fair and justifiable discrimination. Markers are encouraged to make full use of the ranges of marks available to them.

(d) Mixed profiles of attainment will occur. Normally, these will represent variations within the range of performance that is characteristic of a particular category. In some instances, however, performance may be so uneven as to require markers to weigh up strengths and weaknesses of performance that extend across categories. Markers are reminded that their assessment should at all times be **holistic** – assigning each piece of creative writing to the category (and to the numerical point within that category) that best describes its overall achievement. In instances where there is genuine doubt as to whether a piece of writing should be placed at the lower end of a higher category or at the upper end of a lower category (and only in such instances), candidates should be given the benefit of the doubt, and their submission awarded the lowest mark in the higher category.

(e) Each piece of creative writing will be awarded a mark out of 30. The two marks are added together then divided by two. The resultant mark represents the total attainment of the candidate out of 30.

Hey! I've done it

Published by Bright Red Publishing Ltd, 6 Stafford Street, Edinburgh, EH3 7AU
Tel: 0131 220 5804, Fax: 0131 220 6710, enquiries: sales@brightredpublishing.co.uk,
www.brightredpublishing.co.uk

Official SQA answers to 978-1-84948-230-1
2008-2011